Isaac Asimov, world maest
Smolensk in 1920 and brou
years later. He grew up in F
and at the age of eight he gain
helped him to finish high sch
to Columbia University and
follow the medical career hi
in chemistry and after a shor
in 1949 and qualified as an instructor in biochemistry at Boston University School of Medicine where he became Associate Professor in 1955, doing research in nucleic acid. Increasingly, however, the pressures of chemical research conflicted with his aspirations in the literary field, and in 1958 he retired to full-time authorship while retaining his connection with the University.

Asimov's fantastic career as a science fiction writer began in 1939 with the appearance of a short story *Marooned Off Vesta* in *Amazing Stories*. Thereafter he became a regular contributor to the leading SF magazines of the day including *Astounding, Astonishing Stories, Super Science Stories* and *Galaxy*. He has won the Hugo Award three times and the Nebula Award once. With some three hundred books to his credit and several hundred articles, Asimov's output is prolific by any standards. Apart from his many world-famous science fiction works, Asimov had also written highly successful detective mystery stories, a four-volume *History of North America*, a two-volume *Guide to the Bible*, a biographical dictionary, encyclopaedias, textbooks and an impressive list of books on many aspects of science, as well as two volumes of autobiography.

To Alasdair

with best wishes

Andy Eyre

September 1989.

By the same author

The Foundation Saga
Foundation
Foundation and Empire
Second Foundation
Foundation's Edge
Foundation and Earth

Galactic Empire Novels
The Currents of Space
The Stars Like Dust
Pebble in the Sky

Earth is Room Enough
The Martian Way
The End of Eternity
The Winds of Change

Asimov's Mysteries
The Gods Themselves
Nightfall One
Nightfall Two
Buy Jupiter
The Bicentennial Man
Nine Tomorrows

Robot Stories and Novels
I, Robot
The Rest of the Robots
The Complete Robot
The Caves of Steel
The Naked Sun
The Robots of Dawn
Robots and Empire

The Early Asimov: Volume 1
The Early Asimov: Volume 2
The Early Asimov: Volume 3

Nebula Award Stories 8 (editor)
The Science Fictional Solar System
　(editor, with Martin Harry Greenberg and Charles G. Waugh)
The Stars in their Courses (non-fiction)
The Left-Hand of the Electron (non-fiction)
Asimov on Science Fiction (non-fiction)
The Sun Shines Bright (non-fiction)
Counting the Eons (non-fiction)

Tales of the Black Widowers (detection)
More Tales of the Black Widowers (detection)
Casebook of the Black Widowers (detection)
Authorised Murder (detection)
The Union Club Mysteries (detection)

OPUS

A SELECTION FROM THE
FIRST 200 BOOKS BY
ISAAC ASIMOV

GRAFTON BOOKS

A Division of the Collins Publishing Group

LONDON GLASGOW
TORONTO SYDNEY AUCKLAND

Grafton Books
A Division of the Collins Publishing Group
8 Grafton Street, London W1X 3LA

Published by Grafton Books 1982
Reprinted 1987

First published in Great Britain by
André Deutsch Limited 1980

ISBN 0-586-05128-7

Printed and bound in Great Britain by
Cox & Wyman Ltd, Reading

Set in Times

OPUS 100

DEDICATION

To Time and Circumstance
which have been kind to me.

Contents

Introduction

Frankly, I never planned it this way. I never planned anything at all in my writing career. I don't even have an agent to do my planning for me. I just worked along, from day to day, as the spirit moved me, rather like the cheerful idiot I seem to be, and everything broke right.

To begin with, I have never quite recovered from the rather incredulous relief I feel that people are willing to pay me for what I write. If they didn't pay me, I would still write, of course, for I wrote for years and years before it occurred to me to submit anything for publication. However, if I wrote for non-pay as an adult, my friends and family would view me as some kind of nut. (Come to think of it, they do, anyway.)

On October 21, 1938, when I was eighteen, I made my first professional sale – a 6,400-word short story, entitled 'Marooned Off Vesta', for which I received $64.00. The price of one cent a word was what I commanded in those days and sometimes I commanded even less. The story appeared in the March, 1939 issue of *Amazing Stories*, an issue which was on sale in January of that year, just a couple weeks after my nineteenth birthday.

I had the fugitive thought, even then, that I might succeed in writing and selling other science-fiction stories, but my expectations were rather moderate to begin with. After all, I had a college education to finish, a chemical career to launch, and a life to live. Writing was merely an amusement, and the most I could honestly hope for were a few dollars to help pay my college tuition.

For eleven years I continued to sell science-fiction stories to the magazines and to gain a certain minor fame among that very small (but infinitely wonderful) segment of the population known as 'science-fiction fandom'. And *it did* help me with my college tuition. Indeed, it helped me right through to my Ph.D. in chemistry which I received from Columbia University on June 1, 1948 (I was delayed by World War II).

Then, on January 19, 1950, my first book appeared – just two and a half weeks after my thirtieth birthday. It was *Pebble in the Sky* (Doubleday, 1950). I received some small reviews that were, for the most part, mildly favourable, and I felt much more like a professional writer than I had ever felt before.

But it was still only science fiction and I still reached only science-fiction fandom. Even a real hardbound opus, a regular *book*, couldn't make me think of myself as, primarily, a writer. After all, I had just begun a teaching career as Instructor in Biochemistry at Boston University School of Medicine (on June 1, 1949 – for those who must have exact statistics) and there was no question in my mind that my true calling lay in the classroom and the laboratory. Writing was only my avocation.

It was a curious avocation, though, since I was in no position to 'take it or leave it'. I had been writing ever since I was eleven – I would have started sooner, I think, if I could have laid my hands on a nickel copybook – whenever opportunities were in the least favourable. Even when I was in the army, I cajoled the post librarian (a most sympathetic lady) into letting me stay inside when it was closed so that I could write in peace. I not only managed to write a story under those conditions; I sold it.

And here I was in the early 1950s, attaining professorial status in 1951, and yet still scribbling away at all times, evenings and weekends. I was beginning to realize consciously what I must surely have known unconsciously all along. Let's face it: I was that serious distortion of the human condition – the compulsive writer.

My 'avocation' continued to grow and by the end of 1957, I could no longer kid myself into thinking I wrote 'on the side'. Writing was all I really wanted to do. What's more, by the close of 1957, I had published a total of twenty-four books, and six of them were *not* science fiction or, indeed, any kind of fiction. I was beginning to write books on science. ('Straight' science, I am forced to call it, so that it is clearly distinguished from science fiction.) I could scarcely consider twoscore books in eight years a mere sideline. Especially since my writing income was now two and one-half times my school income.

In 1958, then, I abandoned teaching altogether and began to devote myself entirely to writing. And if I needed anything to tell me that I had made the right decision, it was the feeling of absolute delight that washed over me as I did so.

With the thought that now I could bang, bang, bang away at my typewriter for ten hours at a time every day if I wished (and I bought an electric typewriter to lower the rate of approach of physical exhaustion), a little bug bit me. I was turning out books at an increasing rate (in 1957 five of them had been published) and, being very number conscious, I couldn't help but do a little figuring. Could I live long enough to publish a hundred books?

Somewhat wistfully, I mentioned the possibility to my wife, who promptly found herself out of sympathy with that as a tenable ambition. Being the wife of a compulsive writer is a fate worse than death anyway, since your husband is physically home and mentally absent most of the time, and that is the worst possible combination. The thought that I would set myself a hundred-book goal and get worse and worse as I strove to reach it was too much for her.

She said to me, 'Someday, Isaac, when you feel your life drawing to a close, you'll think back on how you spent it at the typewriter and you'll feel sorry you missed all the pleasures you might have experienced. You'll regret all the years you wasted just so that you could write a hundred books, and it will be too late!'

I'm afraid I was not impressed. I've listened very carefully to people describing the glories of their vacations and I don't see that it's a patch to what I feel when I am clicking away, smoothly and harmoniously, at my typewriter. So I said to her, 'Listen, if you're at my bedside when I'm about to read that Big Galley Proof in the Sky, you just bend close and get my last words because they're going to be, "Only a hundred?" '

I don't suppose I was entirely serious, but if I can hang on just a little while longer, till I complete what needs to be done to prepare this manuscript, the whole question will become academic.

For this, you see, is My Hundredth Book.

The idea for this precise book arose at a luncheon at Locke-Ober's here in Boston on September 28, 1968. With me were Austin Olney, Walter Lorraine, and Mary K. Harmon of Houghton Mifflin. I was about to have my ninety-second book published and the question arose as to how many other books I had in press. As I began to tick them off, we all realized that My Hundredth Book was upon me.

Various suggestions were made and finally someone (I think Austin) suggested that I make it a completely personal book in which I rattled on and on about myself and my writings, with selections from books, articles, and stories where those were appropriate.

I thought about it briefly, and said, 'Any writer who is a monster of vanity and egocentricity – like myself, for instance – would love to write a book like that. But who would buy it?'

'You let us worry about that, Isaac,' said Austin.

All right, then. I intend to have a lot of fun and as for you, Houghton Mifflin – worry!

PART 1

Astronomy

As you may know (and as any writer must know) there is a disease called 'writer's block' which is pitiful to see. A blocked writer can go days, months, years, without ever being able to satisfy an unbearable craving to write. He may stare for hours at a time at a blank sheet of paper in the typewriter; or he may type and tear, type and tear endlessly; or he may visit a psychiatrist to ask for the return of his compulsion neurosis.

So far, thank goodness, I have managed to escape this plague.

I do not attribute my escape to any superior intelligence or virtue on my part at all. I attribute it entirely to the lucky circumstance that I can write with equal readiness in a number of different branches of science, and in some fields that are far removed from science – to say nothing of fiction.

The result is that when, far off on the distant horizon, the faintest twinge of weariness with what I am doing makes itself felt, I merely pull the sheet out of the type-writer, adjust it neatly on Pile A, pull the top sheet off Pile B, and carry on with something else which may be so different in nature that I am once again overcome with total eagerness.

Consequently, if I have the liberty of selecting from my own material at will, I warn you that it will be a potpourri indeed. And I'll start with astronomy.

I have never really taken a single formal course in as-tronomy in college, but astronomy is the science for a science-fiction writer. I picked up quite a bit in my omni-vorous reading, and have kept on picking up quite a bit to this very day. This reflects itself in what I write and I suppose some future candidate for his master's degree can

*set a new record for research-topic inconsequentiality by
studying my output in chronological progression and de-
ducing the state of my educational advancement therefrom.*

*I shall save him part of his trouble right here by con-
sidering my treatment of the satellites of Jupiter at various
stages in my career.*

*The satellites of Jupiter appear in the earliest piece of
writing I ever published professionally, which makes it a
good subject to start with anyway.*

*No, it didn't appear in 'Marooned Off Vesta', which I
mentioned earlier as my first published story. That was
first published, but third written. The first written was
never published (its title was 'Cosmic Corkscrew', if you're
curious) and no longer exists. The second written was 'The
Callistan Menace'.*

*I wrote 'The Callistan Menace' in July, 1938, and it ap-
peared, eventually, in the April, 1940, issue of* Astonishing
Stories, *two years after 'Marooned off Vesta', though it had
been written a month earlier.*

*I wouldn't dream of presenting the entire story (it's
rather poor) but I will include the beginning – partly because they're the very first professional words of mine, and
partly because it represents my initial treatment of the
satellites of Jupiter:*

from 'The Callistan Menace' *(1940)*

'Damn Jupiter!' growled Ambrose Whitefield viciously,
and I nodded agreement.

'I've been on the Jovian satellite run,' I said, 'for fifteen
years and I've heard those two words spoken maybe a
million times. It's probably the most sincere curse in the
Solar System.'

Our watch at the controls of the scoutship *Ceres* had
just been relieved and we descended the two levels to our
room with dragging steps.

'Damn Jupiter – and damn it again,' insisted Whitefield

morosely. 'It's too big for the System. It stays out there
behind us and pulls and pulls and *pulls!* We've got to keep
the Atomos firing all the way. We've got to check our
course – completely – every hour. No relaxation, no coast-
ing, no taking it easy! Nothing but the rottenest kind of
work.'

There were tiny beads of perspiration on his forehead
and he swabbed at them with the back of his hand. He was
a young fellow, scarcely thirty, and you could see in his
eyes that he was nervous, and even a little frightened.

And it wasn't Jupiter that was bothering him, in spite of
his profanity. Jupiter was the least of our worries. It was
Callisto! It was that little moon which gleamed a pale blue
upon our visiplates that made Whitefield sweat and that
had spoiled four nights' sleep for me already. Callisto! Our
destination!

Even old Mac Steeden, grey moustachioed veteran who,
in his youth, had sailed with the great Peewee Wilson himself, went about his duties with an absent stare. Four days
out – and ten days more ahead of us – and panic was reaching out with clammy fingers.

We were all brave enough in the ordinary course of
events. The eight of us on the *Ceres* had faced the purple
Lectronics and stabbing Disintos of pirates and rebels and
the alien environments of half a dozen worlds. But it takes
more than run-of-the-mill bravery to face the unknown! to
face Callisto, the 'mystery world' of the Solar System.

One fact was known about Callisto – one grim, bare fact.
Over a period of twenty-five years, seven ships, progressively better equipped, had landed – and never been heard
from again. The Sunday supplements peopled the satellite
with anything from super-dinosaurs to invisible ghosts of
the fourth dimension, but that did not solve the mystery.

We were the eighth. We had a better ship than any of
those preceding. We were the first to sport the newly developed beryl-tungsten hull, twice as strong as the old steel
shells. We possessed super-heavy armaments and the very
latest Atomic Drive engines.

Still – we were only the eighth and every man jack of us knew it.

Don't worry; the mystery was solved. As I recall there was a wormlike creature on Callisto that could project a magnetic field that was intensified by the ordinary steel of ships and space suits. In this case, the spaceship had a nonferrous hull, but the space suits were still steel. The only nonferrous space suit was Peewee Wilson's undersized museum piece. Fortunately, a boy had stowed away on the ship –

And you can carry on from there.

But did you see what I did with the Jovian system? That's right; I did nothing. I merely mentioned Jupiter's gravitational pull, and I talked about Callisto's 'pale blue' appearance. (Why pale blue, I wonder?)

But, then, that was 1938. By the time a dozen years had passed, I had learned a good deal more about astronomy and about writing. I could handle that same system in greater detail and with more authority.

My chance came in one of the six novels which, between 1953 and 1958, I wrote for youngsters. They all dealt with David 'Lucky' Starr and his pint-sized pal, John Bigman Jones, who toured the Solar System, fighting criminals, pirates, spies, and the forces of evil in general.

It was Walter I. Bradbury of Doubleday who first suggested the idea that I write them. The intention was that of supplying a serial hero for television, so that both the publishers and I, myself, might make an honest dollar.

But I hesitated. I don't object to money, in principle, but I have a set of hang-ups about what I'm willing to do in exchange. I said, 'But the television people may ruin the stories and then I will be ashamed to have my name identified with them.'

So Brad said, 'Use a pseudonym.'

And I did. I chose Paul French and wrote all my Lucky Starr books under that name.

As it turned out, television turned out to be utterly unin-

terested in the Lucky Starr stories and the precaution was unnecessary. So if you want to know who Paul French is – he is I, Isaac Asimov. There's no reason to keep it secret anymore; nor has there been these dozen years and more.

I have been asked a thousand times, by the way, why I picked that particular pseudonym. Apparently, people expect something subtly disreputable to be at the bottom of it. No such thing. At the time I was selecting a pseudonym, I heard that the suspense writer, Cornell Woolrich, deliberately chose a nationality as his – William Irish. So I chose Paul French. Whether Woolrich was or was not of Irish descent and whether that weighed with him, either way, I don't know. But to keep the record sparkling clean, I'm not of French descent.

The fifth of my Paul French novels was Lucky Starr and the Moons of Jupiter (Doubleday, 1957). Its plot centred about an important scientific project which was aiming at the development of an anti-gravity device and the work was based on Jupiter's outermost satellite.

The project was in trouble, however. Information was leaking out to the Solar System's most inveterate enemies, the human colonies (long since independent and grown despotic and dangerous) in the Sirian system. Actually, the Sirian system is a poor place for human colonies because the star, Sirius, is too large, hot, and bright, and has a white-dwarf companion besides. However, I didn't intend to worry about it till I wrote a Lucky Starr novel set in the Sirian system – and I never got to it.

Lucky Starr and John Bigman Jones are, therefore, coming to the Jovian system to try to locate the source of the leak. Jupiter's outermost satellite is described in the first selection. Later in the book, they travel in towards Jupiter on the first anti-gravity (Agrav) ship, and that flight is described in the second selection:

from LUCKY STARR AND THE MOONS
OF JUPITER *(1957)*

Dropping down towards Jupiter Nine reminded Bigman
very strongly of similar manoeuvres in the asteroid belt.
As Lucky had explained on the voyage outward, most
astronomers considered Jupiter Nine to have been a true
asteroid to begin with; a rather large one that had been
captured by Jupiter's tremendous gravity field many
millions of years previously.

In fact, Jupiter had captured so many asteroids that here,
15,000,000 miles from the giant planet, there was a kind of
miniature asteroid belt belonging to Jupiter alone. The four
largest of these asteroid satellites, each from forty to a hundred miles in diameter, were Jupiter Twelve, Eleven, Eight,
and Nine. In addition there were at least a hundred additional satellites of less than a mile in diameter, unnumbered
and unregarded. Their orbits had been plotted only in the
last ten years when Jupiter Nine was first put to use as an
anti-gravity research centre, and the necessity of travelling
to and from it had made the population of surrounding
space important.

The approaching satellite swallowed the sky and became
a rough world of peaks and rocky channels, unsoftened by
any touch of air in the billions of years of its history.
Bigman, still thoughtful, said, 'Lucky, why in Space do they
call this Jupiter Nine, anyway? It isn't the ninth one out
from Jupiter according to the Atlas. Jupiter Twelve is a lot
closer.'

Lucky smiled. 'The trouble with you, Bigman, is that
you're spoiled. Just because you were born on Mars, you
think mankind has been cutting through space ever since
creation. Look boy, it's only a matter of a thousand years
since mankind invented the first spaceship . . . Before space
travel was invented, men were restricted to Earth and all
they knew about Jupiter was what they could see in a telescope. The satellites are numbered in the order they were
discovered, see?'

'Oh,' said Bigman. 'Poor ancestors!' He laughed, as he always did, at the thought of human beings cooped up on one world, peering out longingly.

Lucky went on. 'The four big satellites of Jupiter are numbered One, Two, Three, and Four, of course, but the numbers are hardly ever used. The names Io, Europa, Ganymede, and Callisto are familiar names. The nearest satellite of all, a small one, is Jupiter Five, while the farther ones have numbers up to Twelve. The ones past Twelve weren't discovered till after space travel was invented and men had reached Mars and the asteroid belt . . . Watch out now. We've got to adjust for landing.'

It was amazing, thought Lucky, how you could consider tiny a world eighty-nine miles in diameter as long as you were nowhere near it. Of course, such a world is tiny compared to Jupiter or even to Earth. Place it gently on Earth and its diameter is small enough to allow it to fit within the state of Connecticut without lapping over; and its surface area is less than that of Pennsylvania.

And yet, just the same, when you came to enter the small world, when you found your ship enclosed in a large lock and moved by gigantic grapples (working against a gravitational force of almost zero but against full inertia) into a large cavern capable of holding a hundred ships the size of the *Shooting Starr*, it no longer seemed so small.

And then when you came across a map of Jupiter Nine on the wall of an office and studied the network of underground caverns and corridors within which a complicated programme was being carried out, it began to seem actually large. Both horizontal and vertical projections of the work volume of Jupiter Nine were shown on the map, and though only a small portion of the satellite was being used, Lucky could see that some of the corridors penetrated as much as two miles beneath the surface and that others spread out just under the surface for nearly a hundred miles.

'A tremendous job,' he said softly to the lieutenant at his side.

Lieutenant Augustus Nevsky nodded briefly. His uniform was spotless and gleaming. He had a stiff little blond moustache, and his wide-set blue eyes had a habit of staring straight ahead as though he were at perpetual attention.

He said with pride, 'We're still growing.'

The days passed. Halfway to Jupiter, they passed the inner and more sparsely populated belt of small moons, of which only Six, Seven, and Ten were numbered. Jupiter Seven was visible as a bright star, but the others were far enough away to melt into the background of the constellations.

Jupiter itself had grown to the size of the Moon as seen from Earth. And because the ship was approaching the planet with the Sun squarely to its rear, Jupiter remained in the 'full' phase. Its entire visible surface was ablaze with sunlight. There was no shadow of night advancing across it.

Yet, though the size of the Moon, it was not so bright as the Moon by any means. Its cloud-decked surface reflected eight times as much of the light that reached it, as did the bare powdered rock of the Moon. The trouble was that Jupiter only received one twenty-seventh of the light per square mile that the Moon did. The result was that it was only one third as bright at that moment as the Moon appeared to be to human beings on Earth.

Yet it was more spectacular than the Moon. Its belts had become quite distinct, brownish streaks with soft fuzzy edges against a creamy-white background. It was even easy to make out the flattened straw-coloured oval that was the Great Red Spot as it appeared at one edge, crossed the face of the planet, then disappeared at the other.

Bigman said, 'Hey, Lucky, Jupiter looks as though it isn't really round. Is that just an optical illusion?'

'Not at all,' said Lucky. 'Jupiter really isn't round. It's flattened at the poles. You've heard that Earth is flattened at the poles, haven't you?'

'Sure. But not enough to notice.'

'Of course not. Consider! Earth is twenty-five thousand miles about its equator and rotates in twenty-four hours, so that a spot on its equator moves just over a thousand miles an hour. The resulting centrifugal force bulges the equator outwards so that the diameter of the Earth across its middle is about twenty-seven miles more than the diameter from North Pole to South Pole. The difference in the two diameters is only about a third of one percent, so that from space Earth looks like a perfect sphere.'

'Oh.'

'Now take Jupiter. It is two hunded and seventy-six thousand miles about its equator, eleven times the circumference of Earth, yet it rotates about its axis in only ten hours; five minutes less than that, to be exact. A point on its equator is moving at a speed of almost twenty-eight thousand miles an hour; or twenty-eight times as fast as any point on Earth. There's a great deal more centrifugal force and a much larger equatorial bulge, especially since the material in Jupiter's outer layers is much lighter than that in the Earth's crust. Jupiter's diameter across its equator is nearly six thousand miles more than its diameter from North Pole to South Pole. The difference in the diameters is a full fifteen percent, and that's an easy thing to see.'

Bigman stared at the flattened circle of light that was Jupiter and muttered, 'Sands of Mars!'

The Sun remained behind them and unseen as they sank towards Jupiter. They crossed the orbit of Callisto, Jupiter Four, outermost of Jupiter's major satellites, but did not see it to advantage. It was a world 1,500,000 miles from Jupiter and as large as Mercury, but it was on the other side of its orbit, a small pea close to Jupiter and heading into eclipse in its shadow.

Ganymede, which was Jupiter Three, was close enough to show a disc one-third as wide as the Moon seen from

Earth. It lay off to one side so that part of its night surface
could be seen. It was three-quarters full even so, pale white,
and featureless . . .

Everyone aboard the *Jovian Moon* was watching the day
Ganymede eclipsed Jupiter. It wasn't a true eclipse. Ganymede covered only a tiny part of Jupiter. Ganymede was
600,000 miles away, not quite half the size of the Moon as
seen from Earth. Jupiter was twice the distance, but it was
a swollen globe now, fourteen times as wide as Ganymede,
menacing and frightening.

Ganymede met Jupiter a little below the latter's equator,
and slowly the two globes seemed to melt together. Where
Ganymede cut in, it made a circle of dimmer light, for
Ganymede had far less of an atmosphere than Jupiter had
and reflected a considerably smaller portion of the light it
received. Even if that had not been so, it would have been
visible as it cut across Jupiter's belts.

The remarkable part was the crescent of blackness that
hugged Ganymede's rear as the satellite moved completely
onto Jupiter's disc. As the men explained to one another in
breathless whispers, it was Ganymede's shadow falling on
Jupiter.

The shadow, only its edge seen, moved with Ganymede,
but slowly gained on it. The sliver of black cut finer and
finer until in the mid-eclipse region, when Jupiter, Ganymede, and the *Jovian Moon* all made a straight line with
the Sun, the shadow was completely gone, covered by the
world that cast it.

Thereafter, as Ganymede continued to move on, the
shadow began to advance, appearing before it, first a sliver,
then a thicker crescent, until both left Jupiter's globe.

The entire eclipse lasted three hours.

The *Jovian Moon* reached and passed the orbit of Ganymede when that satellite was at the other end of its seven-
day orbit about Jupiter.

There was a special celebration when that happened.
Men with ordinary ships (not often, to be sure) had

reached Ganymede and landed on it, but no one, not one human being, had ever penetrated closer than that to Jupiter. And now the *Jovian Moon* did.

The ship passed within 100,000 miles of Europa, Jupiter Two. It was the smallest of Jupiter's major satellites, only 1,900 miles in diameter. It was slightly smaller than the Moon, but its closeness made it appear twice the size of the Moon as seen from Earth. Dark markings could be made out that might have been mountain ranges. Ships' telescopes proved they were exactly that. The mountains resembled those on Mercury, and there was no sign of Moonlike craters. There were brilliant patches, too, resembling ice fields.

And still they sank downwards, and left Europa's orbit behind.

Io was the innermost of Jupiter's major satellites, in size almost exactly equal to Earth's Moon. Its distance from Jupiter, moreover, was only 285,000 miles, or little more than that of the Moon from Earth.

But there the kinship ended. Whereas Earth's gentle gravitational field moved the Moon about itself in the space of four weeks, Io, caught in Jupiter's gravity, whipped about in its slightly larger orbit in the space of forty-two hours. Where the Moon moved about Earth at a speed of a trifle over 1,000 miles an hour, Io moved about Jupiter at a speed of 22,000 miles an hour, and a landing upon it was that much more difficult.

The ship, however, manoeuvred perfectly. It cut in ahead of Io and wiped out Agrav at just the proper moment.

With a bound, the hum of the hyperatomics was back, filling the ship with what seemed a cascade of sound after the silence of the past weeks.

The *Jovian Moon* curved out of its path, finally, subject once again to the accelerating effect of a gravitational field, that of Io. It was established in an orbit about the satellite at a distance of less than 10,000 miles, so that Io's globe filled the sky.

They circled about it from dayside to nightside, coming lower and lower. The ship's batlike Agrav fins were retracted in order that they might not be torn off by Io's thin atmosphere.

Then, eventually, there was the keen whistling that came with the friction of ship against the outermost wisps of that atmosphere.

Velocity dropped and dropped; so did altitude. The ship's sidejets curved it to face stern-downward towards Io, and the hyperatomic jets sprang into life, cushioning the fall. Finally, with one last bit of drop and the softest jar, the *Jovian Moon* came to rest on the surface of Io.

There was wild hysteria on board the *Jovian Moon*. Even Lucky and Bigman had their backs pounded by men who had been avoiding them constantly all voyage long.

One hour later, in the darkness of Io's night, with Commander Donahue in the lead, the men of the *Jovian Moon*, each in his space suit, emerged one by one onto the surface of Jupiter One.

Sixteen men. The first human beings ever to land on Io!

Notice that there is considerable detail about the satellite system in Lucky Starr and the Moons of Jupiter *and, while it isn't completely fair to judge only from a selection out of context, take my word for it that the astronomy didn't unduly slow the story.*

As a matter of fact, one of the special delights of writing science fiction is mastering the art of interweaving science and fiction; in keeping the science accurate and comprehensible without unduly stalling the plot. This is by no means easy to do, and it is as easy to ruin everything by loving science too much as by understanding it too little.

In my case, I loved science too much. I kept getting the urge to explain science without having to worry about plots and characterization.

As I shall explain later, I actually began to write non-fiction in the form of a textbook, which is a very constricted way of doing it. I wanted more freedom, and again I found the answer in the science-fiction magazines.

More and more, as time went on, science-fiction magazines were publishing 'science articles' – straightforward pieces on science, usually those branches of science that were felt to be of particular interest to science-fiction readers.

In 1955, I published my first science article of this sort. It was named 'Hemoglobin and the Universe' and appeared in the February, 1955, issue of Astounding Science Fiction. *I wrote fifteen more, most of them appearing in* Astounding, *and then came a turning point.*

Robert P. Mills, editor of Venture Science Fiction, *a new magazine, suggested I write a regular science column. It was to be a 1,500-word piece and I would write one every two months, for the magazine was a bimonthly. I could have my own choice of topics.*

I was delighted. 'Yes, indeed,' I said, 'yes, yes.'

The first of my regular columns appeared in the seventh issue of the magazine (January, 1958) but, alas, the magazine survived only through its tenth issue (July, 1958). I got to write only four articles altogether and worse yet, the dismal thought occurred to me that my articles might have helped kill the magazine.

Fortunately, I had the rudimentary good sense not to mention this gloomy hypothesis of mine to Robert P. Mills. He was editing another magazine, a more firmly established one named The Magazine of Fantasy and Science Fiction, *more commonly known as* F & SF, *and in 1959 he asked me to write a column for that. Apparently, he had not independently thought of the lethal characteristics of my writing and even went so far as to suggest 4,000 words instead of 1,500. Since* F & SF *was a monthly, this meant I would be writing five times as many words for* F & SF *as for* Venture. *Naturally, I was five times as happy.*

My first science article in F & SF *appeared in the November, 1958, issue. The articles are still appearing now, more than ten years later. I have never missed an issue and I am slowly beginning to relax a little bit, since I am almost convinced now that my monthly column may not be harming the magazine.*

In increasing my wordage five times, Mr Mills shrewdly increased my total payment four times; and in ten years, that payment hasn't been increased, either. But that's all right. I have no complaints. After all –

I am allowed to write on any subject I choose, and I have chosen them anywhere from pure mathematics to a belligerently controversial view on the social status of women. I am allowed to write in any manner I choose (consistent with good taste and human decency – and I'm glad to say I have never given the editors occasion to call me on either) and I get the proofs for correction before the articles appear. What fairer approach to writer's heaven can be desired, and what is money compared with that?

So here is a selection from one of those articles that deals with the satellites of Jupiter, without the bother of a fictional frame:

from 'View from Amalthea' *(1968)*

To begin with, Jupiter has twelve known satellites, of which four are giants with diameters in the thousands of miles, and the other eight are dwarfs with diameters of 150 miles or less.

Naturally, if we want to see a spectacular display, we would want to choose an observation post reasonably close to the four giants. If we do, then seven of the eight dwarfs are bound to be millions of miles away and would be seen as starlike points of lights at best.

Let's ignore the dwarfs then. There may be some interest in following a starlike object that shifts its position among the other stars, but that is not at all comparable to a satellite that shows a visible disc.

Concentrating on the four giant satellites, we will surely agree that we don't want to take up an observation post from which one or more of the satellites will spend much of its time in the direction of Jupiter. If that happens, we would be forced to watch it with Jupiter in the sky, and I defy anyone to pay much attention to any satellite when there is a close-up view of Jupiter in the field of vision.

For that reason, we would want our observation post in a position closer to Jupiter than are the orbits of any of the four giant satellites. Then we can watch all four of them with our back to Jupiter.

We could build a space station designed to circle Jupiter at close range and always watch from the side away from Jupiter, but why bother? There is a perfect natural station with just the properties we need. It is Jupiter's innermost satellite, a dwarf that is closer to the planet than any of the giants.

The four giant satellites of Jupiter were the first satellites to be discovered anywhere in the Solar System (except for our own Moon, of course). Three of them were discovered on January 7, 1610, by Galileo, and he spotted the fourth on January 13.

Those remained the only four known satellites of Jupiter for nearly 300 years. And then, on September 9, 1892, the American astronomer, Edward Emerson Barnard, detected a fifth one, much dimmer and therefore smaller, than the giant four, and also considerably closer to Jupiter.

The discovery came as somewhat of a shock, for the astronomical world had grown very accustomed to thinking of Jupiter as having four satellites and no more. The shock was so great, apparently, that astronomers could not bear to give the newcomer a proper name of its own. They called it 'Barnard's Satellite' after the discoverer, and also 'Jupiter V' because it was the fifth of Jupiter's satellites to be discovered. In recent years, however, it has come to be called Amalthea, after the nymph (or goat) who served as wet nurse for the infant Zeus (Jupiter).

Amalthea's exact diameter is uncertain (as is the diameter of every satellite in the Solar System but the Moon itself).

The usual figure given is 100 miles with a question mark after it. I have seen estimates as large as 150 miles. For our purposes, fortunately, the exact size doesn't matter.

There is no direct evidence, but it seems reasonable to suppose that Amalthea revolves about Jupiter with one face turned eternally towards the planet. On half the surface of the satellite, Jupiter's midpoint is always visible. When standing on the very edge of that 'sub-Jovian' side, the centre of Jupiter is right on the horizon. The planet (as seen from Amalthea) is so huge, however, that one must go a considerable distance into the other hemisphere before *all* of Jupiter sinks below the horizon.

From roughly one-quarter of the surface of Amalthea, all of Jupiter is externally below the horizon, and the night sky can be contemplated in peace and quiet. For our purposes, since we want to study the satellites of Jupiter, we will take a position (in imagination) at the very centre of this 'contra-Jovian' side of Amalthea.

One object that will be visible, every so often, in the contra-Jovian sky of Amalthea will be the Sun. Amalthea revolves about Jupiter in 11 hours and 50 minutes. That is its period of rotation, too, with respect to the stars and (with a correction too small to worry about) to the Sun as well. To an observer on Amalthea, the Sun will appear to make a complete circle of the sky in 11 hours and 50 minutes.

Since Amalthea revolves about Jupiter directly (or counterclockwise), the Sun will appear to rise in the east and set in the west, and there will be 5 hours and 55 minutes from sunrise to sunset.

With this statement, which I introduce only to assure you I am not unaware of the existence of the Sun, I will pass on to the matter of satellites exclusively for the remainder of the article.

The four giant satellites, reading outwards from Jupiter, are: Io, Europa, Ganymede, and Callisto. Sometimes they are called Jupiter I, Jupiter II, Jupiter III, and Jupiter IV respectively or, in abbreviated form, J-I, J-II, J-III, and J-IV.

Actually, for what we want, the abbreviations are very convenient. The names are irrelevant after all, and it is difficult to keep in mind which is nearer and which is farther if those names are all we go by. With the abbreviations, on the other hand, we can concentrate on the order of distances of the satellites in a very obvious way, and that's what we need to make the data meaningful.

Using the same system, I can and, on occasion, will, call Amalthea J-V. Generally, though, since it is to be our observation point and therefore a very special place, I will use its name.

So let's start with the basic statistics concerning the four giant satellites (see Table 1) with those for Amalthea also included for good measure. Of the data in Table 1, the least satisfactory are the values for the diameters. For instance, I have seen figures for Callisto as high as 3,220 and as low as 2,900. What I have given you is the rough consensus, as far as I can tell from the various sources in my library.

TABLE 1 – THE FIVE INNER JOVIAN SATELLITES

Satellite	Name	Diameter (miles)	Distance from Jupiter's centre (miles)
J-V	Amalthea	100	113,000
J-I	Io	2,300	262,000
J-II	Europa	1,950	417,000
J-III	Ganymede	3,200	666,000
J-IV	Callisto	3,200	1,170,000

For comparison, the diameter of our own Moon is 2,160 miles, so that we can say J-I is a little wider than our Moon, J-II a little thinner, and J-III and J-IV are considerably wider.

In terms of volume, the disparity in size between J-III and J-IV, on the one hand, and our Moon, on the other, is larger. Each of the two largest Jovian satellites is 3.3 times as voluminous as the Moon. However, they are apparently less dense than the Moon (perhaps there is more ice mixed with the rocks and less metal) so that they are not proportionately more massive.

Nevertheless, J-III is massive enough. It is not only twice as massive as the Moon; it is the most massive satellite in the Solar System. For the record, here are the figures on mass for the seven giant satellites of the Solar System (see Table 2). The table includes not only the four Jovian giants and our Moon (which we can call E-I), but Triton, which is Neptune's inner satellite and therefore N-I, and Titan, which I will call S-VI for reasons that will be made clear later.

TABLE 2 – MASSES OF SATELLITES

Satellite	Name	Mass (Moon = 1.0)
J-III	Ganymede	2.1
S-VI	Titan	1.9
N-I	Triton	1.9
J-IV	Callisto	1.3
E-I	Moon	1.0
J-I	Io	1.0
J-II	Europa	0.65

If we are going to view the satellites, not from Jupiter's centre (the point of reference for the figures on distance given in Table 1) but from the observation post on the contra-Jovian surface of Amalthea, then we have to take some complications into account.

When any of the satellites, say J-I, is directly above Amalthea's contra-Jovian point, it and Amalthea form a straight line with Jupiter. J-I's distance from Amalthea is then equal to its distance from Jupiter's centre minus the distance of Amalthea from Jupiter's centre. This represents the minimum distance of J-I from Amalthea.

As J-I draws away from this overhead position, its distance from the observation point increases and is considerably higher when it is on the horizon. The distance continues to increase as it sinks below the horizon until it reaches a point exactly on the opposite side of Jupiter from Amalthea. The entire width of Amalthea's orbit would have to be added to the distance between Amalthea and J-I.

Of course, from our vantage point on Amalthea's surface, we would only be able to follow the other satellites to the horizon. We will be faced with a minimum distance at zenith and a maximum distance at either horizon. Without troubling you with the details, I will present those distances in Table 3.

TABLE 3 – DISTANCES OF THE JOVIAN SATELLITES
FROM AMALTHEA

| Satellite | Distance from Amalthea (miles) | |
	at zenith	at horizon
J-I	149,000	236,000
J-II	304,000	403,000
J-III	553,000	659,000
J-IV	1,057,000	1,168,000

This change in distance from zenith to horizon is not something peculiar to Jupiter's satellites. It is true whenever the point of observation is not at the centre of the orbit. The distance of the Moon from a given point on the *surface* of the Earth is greater when the Moon is at the horizon than when it is at the zenith. The average distance of the centre of the Moon from a point on Earth's surface is 234,400 miles when the Moon is at zenith and 238,400 when it is at the horizon. This difference is very small because it is only the 4,000 mile radius of the Earth that is involved. When the Moon is at the horizon, we must look at it across half the thickness of the Earth, which we need not do when it is at the zenith.

From a point on Amalthea's surface, however, we must look across a considerable part of the 113,000 mile radius of its orbit, which makes more of a difference.

In the case of our Moon, we are dealing with an orbit that is markedly elliptical so that it can be as close as 221,500 miles at one point in its orbit and as far as 252,700 at another point. Fortunately for myself and this article, the orbits of the five Jovian satellites we are discussing, are all almost perfectly circular and ellipticity is a complication we don't have to face here.

Given the distance of each satellite from Amalthea, and the diameter of each satellite, it is possible to calculate the apparent size of each, as seen from our Amalthean viewpoint (see Table 4).

TABLE 4 – APPARENT SIZE OF JOVIAN SATELLITES
AS SEEN FROM AMALTHEA

Satellite	Diameter (minutes of arc)	
	at zenith	at horizon
J-I	53	34
J-II	23	17
J-III	20	17
J-IV	10	9

If you want to compare this with something familiar, consider that the average apparent diameter of the Moon is 31 minutes of arc. This means that J-I, for instance, is just slightly larger than the Moon when it rises, bloats out to a circle half again as wide as the Moon when it reaches zenith and shrinks back to its original size when it sets.

The other three satellites, being farther from Amalthea, do not show such large percentage differences in distance from horizon to zenith and therefore do not show such differences in apparent size either.

Notice that although J-III is considerably farther than J-II, it is also considerably larger. The two effects counterbalance as seen from Amalthea so that J-II and J-III appear indistinguishable in size, at least at the horizon. Of course, J-II, being closer, bloats just a little more at zenith. As for J-IV, it is smallest in appearance, and shows only $\frac{1}{3}$ the apparent diameter of our Moon.

The sky of Amalthea puts on quite a display, then. There are four satellites with visible discs, of which one is considerably larger than our Moon.

* * *

But never mind size; what about brightness? Here several factors are involved. First there is the apparent surface area of each satellite, then the amount of light received by it from the Sun, and finally the fraction of received Sunlight reflected by it (its albedo). In Table 5, I list each of these bits of data for each of the satellites, using the value for our own Moon as basis for comparison.

If we consider the figures in Table 5, we see that J-I as seen from Amalthea is remarkable. At zenith it will possess an area up to three times that of our Moon. The intensity of Sunlight it receives, however (as do the other Jovian satellites), is only $^3/_{80}$ that received by the Moon. This is not surprising. The Moon, after all, is at an average distance of 93,000,000 miles from the Sun as compared to 483,000,000 for the Jovian satellites.

TABLE 5 – THE JOVIAN SATELLITES AND OUR MOON

Satellite	Apparent area (Moon=1.0)		Sunlight received (Moon=1.0)	Albedo (Moon=1.0)
	Maximum	Minimum		
J-I	2.92	1.20	0.037	5
J-II	0.55	0.30	0.037	5.5
J-III	0.42	0.30	0.037	3
J-IV	0.10	0.084	0.037	0.4

The Moon has no atmosphere and therefore no clouds – and it is atmospheric clouds that contribute most to light reflection. The Moon, therefore, showing bare rock, reflects only about $^1/_{14}$ of the light it receives from the Sun, absorbing the rest.

The Moon's mark is bettered by J-I, J-II, and J-III. In fact J-II reflects about $^2/_5$ of the light it receives, which is every bit as good as the Earth can manage. This doesn't necessarily mean that these three satellites have an atmosphere and clouds like the Earth. It seems more likely that there are drifts of water-ice and ammonia-ice (or both) on the surfaces of the satellites, and that these drifts do the reflecting.

J-IV, for some reason, reflects only $^1/_{30}$ of the light it re-

ceives and is therefore less than half as reflective as the
Moon. Perhaps J-IV is composed of particularly dark rock.
Or is it conceivable that astronomers have badly overesti-
mated J-IV's diameter? (If it were smaller than astronomers think it is, it would have to reflect more light to
account for its brightness.)

Anyway, we can now calculate the apparent brightness
of each satellite (as compared with our Moon) by multiplying the area by the amount of Sunlight received by the
albedo. The results are given in Table 6.

TABLE 6 – APPARENT BRIGHTNESS OF THE JOVIAN SATELLITES

Satellite	Apparent brightness (Moon=1.0)	
	Maximum	Minimum
J-I	0.54	0.22
J-II	0.11	0.06
J-III	0.045	0.033
J-IV	0.0015	0.0012

As you see, not one of the Jovian satellites, as seen from
Amalthea, can compare in apparent brightness with our
Moon as seen from the Earth's surface. Even J-I, the
closest to Amalthea and therefore the brightest, is never
better than $1/2$ as bright as the Moon; J-II is less than $1/7$
as bright; J-II less than $1/20$; and J-IV less than $1/600$.

And yet who says brightness is everything? Our own
Moon is only $1/465,000$ as bright as the Sun, and if we consider beauty alone, it is all the better for that.

Perhaps the Jovian satellites as seen from Amalthea will
be still more beautiful than our Moon, for being so softly
illuminated. It will result, perhaps, in better contrast, so
that craters and maria will be more clearly visible. If the
satellites are partly ice-covered, patches of comparative
brilliance will stand out against the darkness of bare rock.
It will be all the more startling because on Amalthea there
will be no air to soften or blur the sharpness of the view.

Callisto may be most beautiful of all, though it may require a fieldglass to see it at its best. It would be a darkling

satellite, with its mysterious low albedo. Perhaps it might look rather like a lump of coal, with its very occasional patches of highly reflecting ice so interspersed by very dark rock that it would seem a cluster of diamonds in the sky, rather than a solid circle of light.

Scientists may go to Amalthea someday for a variety of reasons, but the average tourist may well go for the view alone.

One of the occupational hazards of writing science fiction (or, for that matter, science) is the certainty that you will be quite wrong quite often; that your readers, especially bright thirteen-year-olds, will point that out with great glee; and that you will feel very embarrassed.

Usually, this is because of one's own imperfect understanding of science, but for my own part, I can bear up under that. After all, a science-fiction writer must, on one occasion or another, speak knowingly, or at least with an affectation of knowledge, about every field of science that exists. He is bound to pull a boner every now and then. I am no exception to that general rule.

It is somehow much more irritating, however, to find that though you have gone to a great deal of trouble to be correct and accurate, and are *correct and accurate, as far as anyone can tell, at the time of writing – the scientists themselves change their minds. 'By the way, old chap', they tell us, 'all that stuff we had in all those books – We're going to change all that.'*

For instance, in the first of my Paul French novels, David Starr: Space Ranger (Doubleday, 1952), the action was placed on Mars, a Mars that I designed to match meticulously the best opinions of 1952 astronomy. It was a Mars without craters, and in 1965, astronomers discovered that Mars was loaded with craters.

Then, in Lucky Starr and the Oceans of Venus *(Doubleday, 1954) I pictured a Venus with a planet-wide ocean, and in* Lucky Starr and the Big Sun of Mercury *(Double-*

day, 1956) I pictured a Mercury where one side faced the Sun perpetually.

Both views were in careful accord with the best astronomical knowledge of the middle 1950s.

Unfortunately, by 1956, astronomers began to suspect that Venus was hot, and by 1962 they were certain. The surface temperature of Venus is something like 450° C. and water can exist on the planet only in gaseous form. Venus can have clouds of water but it cannot have an ocean of water.

And in 1965, astronomers bounced radar waves off Mercury and could tell from the nature of the bouncing that Mercury rotated more quickly than had been thought and did not *keep only one side towards the Sun.*

This is terribly embarrassing. All the Lucky Starr books are now out of print and they may have to stay out of print. Doubleday has thought of reprinting and, undoubtedly, a new generation of youngsters would be ready to buy them, but what about their scientific outdatedness?

The Mars setting of David Starr: Space Ranger *isn't too bad, since the matter of craters or no craters plays no part in the plot. I could go over the book and, with very little trouble, insert references to craters here and there.*

Not so in the case of the books set on Venus and on Mercury. Almost all the action in Lucky Starr and the Oceans of Venus *takes place under the ocean, including a fight with a two-mile-wide monster something like a giant jellyfish. And everything in* Lucky Starr and the Big Sun of Mercury *turns upon the relative motions of the planet and the Sun, with consequences which I described with meticulous (and, as it turned out, utterly wrong) detail. Those two books simply cannot be patched; they can only be scrapped.*

To reprint the series, then, would mean that I would have to add a special note to the books about Venus and Mercury, explaining that the astronomy was all wrong, and why. And that's rather clumsy and would cast a pall on the series – so maybe it's gone forever.

Just in case it is, I would like to include a passage from my favourite part of the entire series – the aforesaid fight with the giant jellyfish. It had risen out of the deeper portion of the Venusian ocean and had planted its vast cup over a section of the shallower ocean floor which included the ship carrying Lucky and Bigman. Lucky left the ship to find, if he could, a vulnerable spot in the mighty two-hundred-million-ton object:

from LUCKY STARR AND THE OCEANS OF VENUS *(1954)*

Fifty feet or less above, the light ended on a rough, greyish surface, streaked with deep corrugations. Lucky scarcely attempted to brake his rush. The monster's skin was rubbery and his own suit hard. Even as he thought that, he collided, pressing upwards and feeling the alien flesh give.

For a long moment, Lucky drew deep gasps of relief. For the first time since leaving the ship, he felt moderately safe. The relaxation did not last, however. At any time the creature could turn its attack on the ship. That must not be allowed to happen.

Lucky played his finger flash about his surroundings with a mixture of wonder and nausea.

Here and there in the undersurface of the monster were holes some six feet across into which, as Lucky could see by the flow of bubbles and solid particles, water was rushing. At greater intervals were slits, which opened occasionally into ten-foot-long fissures that emitted frothing gushes of water.

Apparently this was the way the monster fed. It poured digestive juices into the portion of the ocean trapped beneath its bulk, then sucked in water by the cubic yard to extract the nutriment it contained, and still later expelled water, debris, and its own wastes . . .

Lucky moved jerkily through no action of his own and,

in surprise, turned the beam of light on a spot closer to himself. In a moment of stricken horror, he realized the purposes of those deep corrugations he had noticed in the monster's undersurface. One such was forming directly to one side of him and was sucking inward, into the creature's substance. The two sides of the corrugation rubbed against one another, and the whole was obviously a grinding mechanism whereby the monster broke up and shredded particles of food too large to be handled directly by its intake pores.

Lucky did not wait. He could not risk his battered suit against the fantastic strength of the monster's muscles. The walls of his suit might hold, but portions of the delicate working mechanisms might not.

He swung his shoulder so as to turn the suit's jets directly against the flesh of the monster and gave them full energy. He came loose with a sharp smacking sound, then veered around and back.

He did not touch the skin again, but hovered near it and travelled along it, following the direction against gravity, mounting upwards, away from the outer edges of the thing, towards its centre.

He came suddenly to a point where the creature's undersurface turned down again in a wall of flesh that extended as far as his light would reach on either side. That wall quivered and was obviously composed of thinner tissue.

It was the blowpipe.

Lucky was sure that was what it was – a gigantic cavern a hundred yards across, out of which the fury of rushing water emerged. Cautiously Lucky circled it. Undoubtedly this was the safest place one could be, here at the very base of the blowpipe, and yet he picked his way gingerly.

He knew what he was looking for, however, and he left the blowpipe. He moved away in the direction in which the monster's flesh mounted still higher, until he was at the peak of the inverted bowl, and there it was!

At first, Lucky was aware only of a long-drawn-out rumble, almost too deep to hear. In fact, it was vibration that attracted his attention, rather than any sound. Then he spied the swelling in the monster's flesh. It writhed and beat; a huge mass, hanging thirty feet downwards and perhaps as big around as the blowpipe.

That *must* be the centre of the organism; its heart, or whatever passed for its heart, must be there. That heart must beat in powerful strokes, and Lucky felt dizzy as he tried to picture it. Those heartbeats must last five minutes at a time, during which thousand of cubic yards of blood (or whatever the creature used) must be forced through blood vessels large enough to hold the *Hilda*. That heartbeat must suffice to drive the blood a mile and back.

What a mechanism it must be, thought Lucky. If one could only capture such a thing alive and study its physiology!

Somewhere in that swelling must also be what brain the monster might have. Brain? Perhaps what passed for its brain was only a small clot of nerve cells without which the monster could live quite well.

Perhaps! But it couldn't live without its heart. The heart had completed one beat. The central swelling had contracted to almost nothing. Now the heart was relaxing for another beat five minutes or more from now, and the swelling was expanding and dilating as blood rushed into it.

Lucky raised his weapon and with his light beam full on that giant heart, he let himself sink down. It might be best not to be too close. On the other hand, he dared not miss.

For a moment a twinge of regret swept him. From a scientific standpoint it was almost a crime to kill this mightiest of nature's creatures.

He dared wait no longer. He squeezed the handgrip of his weapon. The wire shot out. It made contact, and Lucky's eyes were blinded by the flash of light in which the near wall of the monster's heart was burned through.

There is a borderline case of astronomical inaccuracy which bothers me far more than does the matter of the

*Paul French novels, because it involves an astronomic
description of which I am particularly proud.*

*It is to be found in a story called 'The Martian Way'
that deals with a colony of Earthmen on Mars. They must
import water from Earth and Earth, in a fit of isolationism,
refuses to grant further supplies. The Colonists, rather than
abandon their Martian homes, decide to trek out to Saturn
for their supplies.*

*But, before going on to the passage, I want to say that
the story was written at the height of the McCarthyist
period and I included in the story a McCarthy-type poli-
tician. My disapproval of Senator McCarthy was quite
manifest in the story and I expected repercussions. I didn't
particularly enjoy the thought of repercussions but I felt I
had to put myself on record, somehow. Apparently, what I
did was done so subtly, however (or so clumsily), that no one
either noticed or, possibly, cared. There wasn't a single re-
percussion and so much for Isaac Asimov, political satirist.*

*And now to the passage, which begins as the Martian
expedition is approaching Saturn:*

from 'The Martian Way' *(1952)*

Half a million miles above Saturn, Mario Rioz was cradled
on nothing and sleep was delicious. He came out of it
slowly and for a while, alone in his suit, he counted the
stars and traced lines from one to another . . .

They had aimed high to pass out of the ecliptic while
moving through the Asteroid Belt. That had used up water
and that had probably been unnecessary. Although tens
of thousands of worldlets look as thick as vermin in two-
dimensional projection upon a photographic plate, they are
nevertheless scattered so thinly through the quadrillions of
cubic miles that make up their conglomerate orbit that
only the most ridiculous of coincidences would have
brought about a collision.

Still, they passed over the Belt and someone calculated

the chances of collision with a fragment of matter large enough to do damage. The value was so low, so impossibly low, that it was perhaps inevitable that the notion of the 'space float' should occur to someone.

The days were long and many, space was empty, only one man was needed at the controls at any one time. The thought was a natural.

First, it was a particularly daring one who ventured out for fifteen minutes or so. Then another, who tried half an hour. Eventually, before the asteroids were entirely behind, each ship regularly had its off-watch member suspended in space at the end of a cable.

It was easy enough. The cable, one of those intended for operations at the conclusion of their journey, was magnetically attached at both ends, one to the space suit to start with. Then you clambered out the lock onto the ship's hull and attached the other end there. You paused awhile, clinging to the metal skin by the electromagnets in your boots. Then you neutralized those and made the slightest muscular effort.

Slowly, ever so slowly, you lifted from the ship and even more slowly the ship's larger mass moved an equivalently shorter distance downwards. You floated incredibly, weightlessly, in solid, speckled black. When the ship had moved far enough away from you, your gauntleted hand, which kept touch upon the cable, tightened its grip slightly. Too tightly, and you would begin moving back towards the ship and it towards you. Just tightly enough, and friction would halt you. Because your motion was equivalent to that of the ship, it seemed as motionless below you as though it had been painted against an impossible background while the cable between you hung in coils that had no reason to straighten out.

It was a half ship to your eye. One half was lit by the light of the feeble Sun, which was still too bright to look at directly without the heavy protection of the polarized space-suit visor. The other half was black on black, invisible.

Space closed in and it was like sleep. Your suit was warm, it renewed its air automatically, it had food and drink in special containers from which it could be sucked with a minimal motion of the head, it took care of wastes appropriately. Most of all, more than anything else, there was the delightful euphoria of weightlessness.

You never felt so well in your life. The days stopped being too long, they weren't long enough, and there weren't enough of them.

They has passed Jupiter's orbit at a spot some thirty degrees from its then position. For months, it was the brightest object in the sky, always excepting the glowing white pea that was the Sun. At its brightest, some of the Scavengers insisted they could make out Jupiter as a tiny sphere, one side squashed out of true by the night shadow.

Then over a period of additional months it faded, while another dot of light grew until it was brighter than Jupiter. It was Saturn, first as a dot of brilliance, then as an oval, glowing splotch.

('Why oval?' someone asked, and after a while, someone else said, 'The rings, of course,' and it was obvious.)

Everyone spacefloated at all possible times towards the end, watching Saturn incessantly.

('Hey, you jerk, come on back in, damn it. You're on duty.' 'Who's on duty? I've got fifteen minutes more by my watch.' 'You set your watch back. Besides, I gave you twenty minutes yesterday.' 'You wouldn't give two minutes to your grandmother.' 'Come on in, damn it, or I'm coming out anyway.' 'All right, I'm coming. Holy howlers, what a racket over a lousy minute.' But no quarrel could possibly be serious, not in space. It felt too good.)

Saturn grew until at last it rivalled and then surpassed the Sun. The rings, set at a broad angle to their trajectory of approach, swept grandly about the planet, only a small portion being eclipsed. Then, as they approached, the span of the rings grew still wider, yet narrower as the angle of approach constantly decreased.

The larger moons showed up in the surrounding

sky like serene fireflies.

Mario Rioz was glad he was awake so that he could watch again.

Saturn filled half the sky, streaked with orange, the night shadow cutting it fuzzily nearly one-quarter of the way in from the right. Two round little dots in the brightness were shadows of two of the moons. To the left and behind him (he could look over his left shoulder to see, and as he did so, the rest of his body inched slightly to the right to conserve angular momentum) was the white diamond of the Sun.

Most of all he liked to watch the rings. At the left, they emerged from behind Saturn, a tight, bright, triple band of orange light. At the right, their beginnings were hidden in the night shadow, but showed up closer and broader. They widened as they came, like the flare of a horn, growing hazier as they approached, until, while the eye followed them, they seemed to fill the sky and lose themselves.

From the position of the Scavenger fleet just inside the outer rim of the outermost ring, the rings broke up and assumed their true identity as a phenomenal cluster of solid fragments rather than the tight, solid band of light they seemed.

Below him, or rather in the direction his feet pointed, some twenty miles away, was one of the ring fragments. It looked like a large, irregular splotch, marring the symmetry of space, three-quarters in brightness and the night shadow cutting it like a knife. Other fragments were farther off, sparkling like stardust, dimmer and thicker, until, as you followed them down, they became rings once more.

The fragments were motionless, but that was only because the ships had taken up an orbit about Saturn equivalent to that of the outer edge of the rings.

The day before, Rioz reflected, he had been on that nearest fragment, working along with more than a score of others to mould it into the desired shape. Tomorrow he would be at it again.

Today – today he was spacefloating.

* * *

Ted Long wandered over the ridged surface of the ring fragment with his spirits as icy as the ground he walked on. It had all seemed perfectly logical back on Mars, but that was Mars. He had worked it out carefully in his mind in perfectly reasonable steps. He could still remember exactly how it went.

It didn't take a ton of water to move a ton of ship. It was not mass equals mass, but mass times velocity equals mass times velocity. It didn't matter, in other words, whether you shot out a ton of water at a mile a second or a hundred pounds of water at twenty miles a second. You got the same final velocity out of the ship.

That meant the jet nozzles had to be made narrower and the steam hotter. But then drawbacks appeared. The narrower the nozzle, the more energy was lost in friction and turbulence. The hotter the steam, the more refractory the nozzle had to be and the shorter its life. The limit in that direction was quickly reached.

Then, since a given weight of water could move considerably more than its own weight under the narrow-nozzle conditions, it paid to be big. The bigger the water-storage space, the larger the size of the actual travel-head, even in proportion. So they started to make liners heavier and bigger. But then the larger the shell, the heavier the bracings, the more difficult the weldings, the more exacting the engineering requirements. At the moment, the limit in that direction had been reached also.

And then he had put his finger on what had seemed to him to be the basic flaw – the original unswervable conception that the fuel had to be placed inside the ship; the metal had to be built to encircle a million tons of water.

Why? Water did not have to be water. It could be ice, and ice could be shaped. Holes could be melted into it. Travel-heads and jets could be fitted into it. Cables could hold travel-heads and jets stiffly together under the influence of magnetic field-force grips.

Long felt the trembling of the ground he walked on. He was at the head of the fragment. A dozen ships were blast-

ing in and out of sheaths carved in its substance, and the
fragment shuddered under the continuing impact.

The ice didn't have to be quarried. It existed in proper
chunks in the rings of Saturn. That's all the rings were –
pieces of nearly pure ice, circling Saturn. So spectroscopy
stated and so it had turned out to be. He was standing on
one such piece now, over two miles long, nearly one mile
thick. It was almost half a billion tons of water, all in one
piece, and he was standing on it.

*The colonists manage to overcome their difficulties, bring
back the huge fragment of ice from the rings of Saturn and
solve the water problems of Mars.*

*Why am I proud? – In the first place, I consider this the
best description of what it's like out there near Saturn that
anyone has ever written.*

*I admit that sounds conceited but how can anyone be a
writer and not be conceited? A modest person couldn't
possibly suppose that anyone would be willing to pay
money for his writings, and he would never get started. A
modest writer is a contradiction in terms.*

*Besides, I have made up my mind that in this book, at
least, I lay it right on the line. No stupid façades. If I can't
say what I please in My Hundredth Book, there was no
use writing the other ninety-nine.*

*My second reason for pride concerns my description of
the 'space-float', which is these days known under the misleading title of 'space walk'. When 'The Martian Way' was
published in 1952, no one had ever stepped out into space
at the end of a lifeline. When it finally happened, in the
mid-60s, the sensation (judging from the descriptions I
read) appears to have been euphoria, exactly as I described
it.*

*I described it accurately, perhaps, because I felt the sen-
sations so thoroughly in writing it. I have a bounding
imagination (that, too, like conceit, comes with the terri-*

tory) *and when I picture something, I picture it
thoroughly.*

*I think of that, sometimes, when I am teased about my
refusal to get into an aeroplane. Over and over again, I am
told, 'You don't know what you're missing.'*

*Hah! I've floated in Saturn's rings. They don't know
what* they're *missing.*

And now the only trouble rests in the question as to how
thick the rings of Saturn are, and how large the particles
within them are. Recent estimates of the thickness of the
rings have dropped enormously. At the time I wrote 'The
Martian Way', I accepted an estimate that made the rings
ten miles thick. In that case, they could easily be composed
of particles a mile or two long.

Now, however, estimates tend to be in the yards rather
than in the miles, and one suggestion is that the rings are
but one foot think. If so, the particles may be hunks of
gravel rather than hunks of mountain, and the story would
be ruined.

Everything has its other side, of course. If the changing
findings of science ruin a science-fiction story now and
then, they certainly make for exciting subject matter in
histories of science. At least, this is what I found when I
was writing my most ambitious book on astronomy, The
Universe (*Walker & Company, 1966*).

That book was not entirely ambitious to begin with, by
the way. Edward L. Burlingame, of *Walker & Company*,
had an idea that I might write a small book about the
recently discovered and fascinatingly mysterious quasars,
and I jumped at the chance.

The trouble is, though, that I have an unconquerable
aversion against explaining something without first presenting a reasonable background, so I decided to explain
a few things before talking about quasars, and then I
decided to explain a few other things before that, and then
a few other things before that, and so on.

The final result was that, after a short introduction, I

began with the statement, 'In 600 B.C., the Assyrian Empire had just fallen . . .' So what Ed got was a fairly large history of astronomy in which my discussion of quasars took up the fourth and final section of the nineteenth and final chapter. In a display of excellent good sportsmanship, Ed published the book anyway.

One of the most dramatic episodes in astronomical history occurred in the early 1920s when it first became clear that there was a vast Universe beyond the Milky Way. Step by step, certain cloudy masses in the heavens turned out to be enormously large and enormously distant systems of stars –

from THE UNIVERSE *(1966)*

Man's vision of the size of the Universe had increased enormously in 2,000 years. Let us recapitulate.

By 150 B.C., the Earth-Moon system had been accurately defined. The Moon's orbit was seen to be half a million miles across, and the diameter of the planetary orbits was suspected to be in the millions of miles.

By 1800 A.D., the scale of the Solar System had been defined. Its diameter was not merely in the millions of miles, but in the billions. The distance of the stars was still unknown but was suspected to be in the trillions of miles (that is, a couple of light-years) at least.

By 1850 A.D., the distance of the nearer stars had been defined as not merely trillions of miles, but tens and hundreds of trillions of miles. The diameter of the Galaxy was still unknown but was suspected to be in the thousands of light-years.

By 1920 A.D., the diameter of the Galaxy had been defined at not merely thousands of light-years but many tens of thousands of light-years.

At each new stage, the size of the regions of the Universe under investigation turned out to exceed the most optimistic estimates of the past. Furthermore, at each stage, there was the conservative opinion that the object whose size had been defined represented all, or almost all the Universe, and until 1920, that view had always turned out to be wrong.

The Earth-Moon system had shrunk to insignificance in the light of the size of the Solar System. The Solar System had in turn shrunk to insignificance when the distance of the nearby stars was determined. And the system of the nearby stars was insignificant in comparison with the Galaxy as a whole.

Would this process continue or did the Galaxy and its Magellanic satellites represent an end at last? Had astronomers finally probed to the end of the Universe?

Even as late as 1920, it seemed quite possible that the conservative view would finally triumph. The Galaxy and the Magellanic Clouds seemed very likely to contain all the matter in the Universe and beyond them, one could maintain, lay nothing . . .

And yet astronomers could not relax completely with their finite Universe 200,000 light-years across. There were grounds for some suspicion that numerous large objects might exist far outside the Galaxy, and it proved extraordinarily difficult to argue that suspicion out of existence.

A particularly troublesome item was a cloudy patch of light in the constellation Andromeda, an object that was called the 'Andromeda Nebula' because of its location and appearance.

The Andromeda Nebula is visible to the naked eye as a small object of the fourth magnitude that looks like a faint, fuzzy star to the unaided eye. Some Arab astronomers had noted it in their star maps, but the first to describe it in modern times was the German astronomer Simon Marius (1570–1624) in 1612. In the next century, Messier included it in his list of fuzzy objects that were not comets. It was thirty-first on his list, so that the Andromeda Nebula is often known as 'M31'.

There was no reason, at first, for thinking that the Andromeda Nebula was significantly different from other nebulae such as the Orion Nebula. The Andromeda Nebula seemed a luminous cloud and no more than that.

Some eighteenth-century astronomers even envisaged a place for such clouds in the scheme of things. What if stars developed out of distended rotating masses of gas? Under the effect of their own gravity, such clouds would begin to contract and condense, speeding their rotation as they did so. As they rotated more and more quickly, they would flatten into a lens shape and, eventually, eject a ring of gas from the bulging equator. Later, as rotation continued to speed up, a second ring would separate, then a third ring, and so on. Each ring would coalesce into a small planetary body, and finally what was left of the cloud would have condensed into a large glowing star that would find itself at the centre of a whole family of planets.

Such a theory would account for the fact that all the planets of the Solar System were situated nearly in a single plane, that all of them revolved about the Sun in the same direction. Each planet, moreover, tended to have a system of satellites that revolved about it in a single plane and in the same direction, as though the planets, in the process of contracting from gaseous rings, gave off smaller rings of their own.

The first to suggest such an origin of the Solar System was the German philosopher Immanuel Kant (1724–1804) in 1755. A half-century later, the French astronomer Pierre Simon de Laplace (1749–1827) published a similar theory (which he arrived at independently) as an appendix to a popular book on astronomy.

It is interesting that Kant and Laplace had opposing views on the Andromeda Nebula, views that kept astronomers at loggerheads for a century and a half.

Laplace pointed to the Andromeda Nebula as possibly representing a planetary system in the process of formation; indeed its structure is such that it seems to be in the obvious process of rapid rotation. You can almost make out (or convince yourself you are making out) a ring of gas about to be given off. For this reason, Laplace's suggestion as to the method of formation of planetary systems is known as the 'nebular hypothesis'.

If Laplace were correct and if the Andromeda Nebula were a volume of gas serving as precursor for a single planetary system, it cannot be a very large object and, in view of its apparent size in the telescope, it cannot be a very distant object.

Laplace's nebular hypothesis was popular among astronomers throughout the nineteenth century, and his view of the Andromeda Nebula represented a majority opinion through all that time. In 1907 a parallax determination was reported for the Andromeda Nebula, one that seemed to show it to be at a distance of nineteen light-years. Certainly, that seemed to settle matters.

Yet there was Kant's opposing view. Despite the fact that he, too, had originated a nebular hypothesis, he did not fall prey to the temptation of accepting the Andromeda Nebula as visible support of his theory. He suggested instead that the Andromeda Nebula, and similar bodies, might represent immensely large conglomerations of stars, which appeared as small, fuzzy patches only because they were immensely far away. He felt they might represent 'island universes', each one a separate galaxy, so to speak.

However, this suggestion of Kant's was not based on any observational data available to the astronomers of the time. It made very few converts and, if Kant's speculation was thought of at all, it was dismissed as a kind of science fiction.

But Kant's suggestion did not die. Every once in a while some small piece of evidence would arise that would not quite fit the orthodox Laplacian view. Chief among these was the matter of spectroscopic data.

Stars, generally, produce light which, on passing through a prism, broadens into an essentially continuous spectrum, broken by the presence of dark spectral lines. If, however, gasses or vapours of relatively simple chemical composition are heated until they glow, the light they emit, when passed through a prism, produces an 'emission spectrum' consisting of individual bright lines. (The exact position of the bright lines depends on the chemical composition of the gas or vapour.)

Then, too, a continuous spectrum usually (but not always) implies white light, while an emission spectrum is often the product of coloured light, since some of the bright lines of one particular colour or another might dominate the entire glow.

Many bright nebulae do indeed show very delicate colour effects (that do not show up in ordinary black-and-white photographs) . . .

The light from the Andromeda Nebula was a drab white, however, and in 1899 its spectrum was obtained and shown to be continuous . . .

White light and a continuous spectrum meant that the Andromeda Nebula might consist of a mass of stars and be so far off that those stars could not be made out separately. On the other hand, that conclusion was not inevitable, for gaseous nebulae might, under some circumstances, possess white light and continuous spectra.

This was so because emission spectra were produced by hot gases glowing with their own light. Suppose, though, that a mass of gas was cold and was serving merely as a passive reflector of starlight. In that case, the spectrum of the reflected starlight would be essentially the same as the spectrum of the original starlight itself (just as the spectrum of moonlight is like that of sunlight).

If the Andromeda Nebula were merely reflecting starlight, that would explain everything. Its spectrum would be consistent with the theory that it was a not-very-large patch of gas quite close to the Solar System.

But one catch remained. If the Andromeda Nebula were merely reflecting starlight, where were the stars whose light it was reflecting? . . . None could be found.

At least, no permanent stars could be found. Occasionally, a starlike object was found to be associated temporarily with the Andromeda Nebula. As this turned out to be highly significant, let us pause in order to take up the matter of temporary starlike objects in some detail.

To any casual observer of the heavens, the starry configu-
rations seem permanent and fixed. Indeed, the Greek
philosophers had differentiated between the sky and the
earth by this fact. On Earth, Aristotle suggested, there was
perpetual and continuing change, but the heavens were
absolutely changeless.

To be sure, there were occasional 'shooting stars' which
made it appear, to the uninitiated, that a star had fallen
from heaven. However, no matter how many shooting stars
appeared, no star was ever observed to be missing from its
place as a result. Consequently, such shooting stars were
considered to be atmospheric phenomena by the Greeks
and therefore, like the shifting of clouds or the falling of
rain, to be part of the changing earth and not of the
changeless heavens. The very word 'meteor' applied to
shooting stars is from a Greek term meaning 'things in the
air'.

The Greeks were correct in deciding that the flash of
light accompanying a shooting star was an atmospheric
phenomenon. The object causing that flash, though, was a
speeding body (a 'meteoroid') varying in size from less
than a pinpoint to a multi-ton object. Before entering the
Earth's atmosphere, a meteoroid is an independent body
of the Solar System. After entering the atmosphere, it heats
through friction to the point where it flashes brilliantly. If
small, it is consumed in the process; if large, a remnant
may survive to strike the Earth's surface as a 'meteorite'.

Another class of temporary inhabitants of the sky were
the occasional comets, often sporting long, cloudy projections that might be considered as flowing tails or streaming
hair. The ancients viewed it as the latter, for 'comet' is
from the Latin word for 'hair'. Comets came and went
erratically, so the Greek philosophers considered them to
be atmospheric phenomena also. Here, they were clearly
wrong, for the comets exist far beyond Earth's atmosphere
and are actually members of the Solar System, as inde-

pendent a set of members as the planets themselves.

Nevertheless, suppose we modify the Greek view and say that change is a property of the Solar System, but that the stars far beyond the Solar System are changeless. If we do this, we eliminate not only meteors and comets, but also such changes as the phases of the Moon, the spots on the Sun, and the complicated motions of the planets. Is this restricted view of changelessness tenable?

To the naked eye, it would almost seem to be. To be sure, the intensity of the light produced by some stars varies, but such cases are few and unspectacular, not obvious to the casual eye. Some stars also have significant proper motions, but this is even less noticeable, and it would take many centuries to be sure of the existence of such motions without a telescope.

One type of spectacular change, however, *could* take place in the heavens, and so clearly that the most casual observer could see it. I am referring to the actual appearance of a completely new, and sometimes very bright, star in the sky. Such stars were clearly stars and lacked all trace of the fuzziness of comets. Furthermore, they were not momentary flashes like meteors, but persisted for weeks and months.

Not only were such new stars evidence of change among the stars by the mere fact that they appeared and eventually disappeared, but also they changed brightness radically during the course of their brief stay in the sky as visible objects. Only the fact that such objects were so rarely encountered made it possible for the ancient astronomers to ignore their existence and to continue to accept the assumption of the changelessness of the heavens.

There is evidence, in fact, of only one such new star having appeared during the period of Greek astronomy, and that evidence is none too strong. Hipparchus is supposed to have recorded such a new star in 134 B.C. We do not have his word for this, for virtually none of his works has survived. The Roman encyclopaedist Pliny (23–79 A.D.), writing two centuries later, reported it, saying that it was this new star that inspired Hipparchus to prepare the first star map, in order that future new stars might be more easily detected.

Perhaps the most spectacular new star in historic times was not observed in Europe at all, for it appeared in the constellation Taurus in June, 1054, at a time when European astronomy was virtually nonexistent. That we know of it at all is thanks to the observations of Chinese and Japanese astronomers who recorded the appearance of what they called a 'guest star' at this time. It persisted for two years and grew so fiercely brilliant at its peak as to outshine Venus and become easily visible by day. For almost a month it was the brightest object in the sky next to the Sun and the Moon.

Then, in November, 1572, another such object, almost as bright, appeared in the constellation Cassiopeia, outshining Venus, at its peak, by five or ten times. By then, however, European astronomy was flourishing again, and an astronomer of the first rank was in his impressionable youth. This was the Danish astronomer Tycho Brahe, who observed the new star carefully and then, in 1573, published a small book about it. A short version of the Latin title of the book is *De Nova Stella* ('Concerning the New Star'). Ever since, a star that suddenly appears where none was observed before has been called a 'nova' ('new').

One of the important points made in connection with the nova of 1572 by Brahe was that it lacked a measurable parallax. This meant it had to be many times as distant as the Moon and could not be an atmospheric phenomenon and therefore part of the changeable Earth. (Brahe made the same observation in 1577 for a comet and showed that comets, too, were not atmospheric phenomena.)

Then, in 1604, still another nova appeared, this time in the constellation Ophiuchus. It was observed by Kepler and Galileo. While distinctly less bright than Brahe's nova, that of 1604 was still a remarkable phenomenon and, at its peak, rivalled the planet Jupiter in brilliance.

Oddly enough, no superlatively bright novae have graced

the sky in the three and a half centuries since 1604. This is rather a pity, for the telescope was invented a few years after 1604, and astronomy entered a new era in which such spectacular novae could have been studied much more profitably than before.

Nevertheless the telescopic revolution in astronomy at once affected the views concerning these novae. In the first place, it was quickly seen that the stars visible to the naked eye were not all the stars there were by any means. A nova, therefore, need not be a truly new star, despite its name. It might merely be a dim star – too dim to be seen by the naked eye, ordinarily – which, for some reason, brightened sufficiently to become visible. As astronomers began to discover more and more variable stars, such changes in brightness came to seem neither phenomenal nor even unusual in themselves. What was unusual about novae was not the fact that their brightness changed, but the *extent* to which it changed. Novae could be classified as a type of variable star, but a particular type called 'cataclysmic variables'. Their changes in brightness seemed not merely the result of some more or less quiet periodic process, but rather the consequence of some vast cataclysm – somewhat like the difference between a periodic geyser spout and an erratic and unpredictable volcanic eruption.

Then, too, whereas in pretelescopic days, only those sudden brightenings which reached unusual peaks could readily be observed, the telescope made it possible to observe much less drastic events.

Since novae were associated with such brightness, dim ones were not searched for, and for two and a half centuries no novae were reported. Then, in 1848, the English astronomer John Russell Hind (1823–1895) happened to observe a star in Ophiuchus that suddenly brightened. At its brightest, it only reached the fifth magnitude so that it was never anything more than a dim star to the naked eye, and in pretelescope days it might easily have gone unnoticed. Nevertheless, it was a nova.

Thereafter, novae of all brightness were searched for and discovered in surprising numbers. One of them, ap-

pearing in the constellation of Aquila in 1918 ('Nova
Aquilae'), shone, briefly, as brightly as Sirius. None, however, approached the planetary brightness of the novae of
1054, 1572, and 1604.

It is now estimated that some two dozen novae appear
each year, here and there in the Galaxy, although relatively
few of them are so situated as to be visible from the Earth.

The matter of the novae entered the problem of the Andromeda Nebula when, in 1885, one appeared in the
central portions of the nebula. For the first time, a
prominent star was seen in connection with the Andromeda
Nebula.

There were two possibilities here. The star might exist
between the Andromeda Nebula and ourselves and be seen
in the nebula only because that object was in the line of
sight. In that case the star and the nebula would have no
true connection. The second possibility was that the
Andromeda Nebula was made up of stars too dim to be
seen and that one of them had flared up into a nova and
had become visible in a telescope.

If the latter were the case, it might be possible to determine the distance of the Andromeda Nebula if one assumed
that novae always reached about the same peak of
luminosity. In that case, variations in apparent brightness
would be caused entirely by a difference in distance. If the
distance of any nova could be determined, the distance of
all the rest could then be calculated. The opportunity came
with a nova that appeared in the constellation Perseus
('Nova Persei') in 1901. It was an unusually close nova and
its distance was estimated by parallax to be about 100
light-years.

The nova that had appeared in the Andromeda Nebula,
referred to now as 'S Andromedae', reached only the
seventh magnitude at its peak (so that it would never have
been visible without a telescope) as compared with a magnitude of 0.2 reached by Nova Persei. If the two novae had
indeed attained the same luminosity, S Andromedae would
have to be some sixteen times as distant as Nova Persei to

account for the difference in brightness. It was argued in 1911, then, that the distance of S Andromedae was 1,600 light-years.

If S Andromedae were indeed part of the Andromeda Nebula, that meant the nebula, too, was 1,600 light-years distant. If S Andromedae were merely in the line of sight of the nebula, the latter would have to be beyond the nova and even more than 1,600 light-years from us. In either case, the nebula was at least 800 times as far from us as had been calculated from the apparent parallactic data obtained in 1907. If the nebula were 1,600 light-years distant, it had to be quite large to seem as large in our telescopes as it does. It could scarcely represent a single planetary system in the process of formation as Laplace had supposed. Still, one could not yet accept the Kantian view either. Even at 1,600 light-years, the Andromeda Nebula had to be merely a feature of the Galaxy.

This line of argument assumed, however, that S Andromedae and Nova Persei actually reached the same luminosity. What if this assumption were not valid? What if S Andromedae were actually much more luminous than Nova Persei ever was? Or much less luminous? How could one tell?

The American astronomer Heber Doust Curtis (1872–1942) believed that the one way of deciding this matter was to search for more novae in the Andromeda Nebula. What could not be judged in the case of one specimen might become clear in the comparative study of many. He therefore tracked down and studied a number of novae in the Andromeda Nebula, and found himself able to make two points.

First, the number of novae located in the nebula was so high that there was no possibility that they were not associated with the nebula. To suppose that all those novae just happened to spring up among stars located in the line of sight between ourselves and the nebula was ridiculous. Such a fortuitous concentration of novae was completely unlikely. This further implied that the Andromeda Nebula was not merely a cloud of dust and gas passively reflecting sunlight. It had to consist of numerous stars – a very large number indeed to have so many novae (a very rare type of star) appear among them. That such stars could not be made out even by large telescopes argued that the nebula was at a great distance. Secondly, all the novae observed in the Andromeda Nebula after 1885 were far dimmer than S Andromedae had been. Curtis suggested in 1918 that these other novae should be compared with Nova Persei, and that S Andromedae was an exceptional, extra-ordinarily bright nova.

If the ordinary novae in the Andromeda Nebula were set equal in luminosity to Nova Persei, then the distance that would account for the unusual dimness of the former would have to be in hundreds of thousands of light-years, at the very least. Such a distance would also account for the fact that the nebula could not be resolved into stars. At such a distance, individual stars were simply too faint to be made out – unless they brightened enormously, nova-fashion.

But if the Andromeda Nebula were indeed at such a distance, it must be far outside the limits of the Galaxy and, to appear as large as it does, it must be a huge conglomeration of a vast number of stars. It was indeed an island universe of the type Kant had once described.

Curtis's conclusion was by no means accepted by other astronomers, and even Shapley was opposed to him.

Entering the lists, however, was the American astronomer Edwin Powell Hubble (1889–1953). It seemed clear to him that the argument involving novae would always seem inconclusive since not enough was known about them. If, however, the Andromeda Nebula were actually an island universe, then perhaps a new telescope – more powerful than any available to nineteenth-century astronomers – might settle the issue by revealing the individual stars in the nebula. From the ordinary stars, far less mysterious than the novae, it might be possible to draw firmer conclusions concerning the nebula.

In 1917, a new telescope had been installed on Mt Wilson, just northeast of Pasadena. It had a mirror that was an unprecedented 100 inches in diameter, making it by far the most powerful telescope in the world (and it was to remain the most powerful for a generation).

Hubble turned the Mt Wilson telescope on the Andromeda Nebula and succeeded in making out individual stars on the outskirts. That was the final settlement of one problem: the nebula consisted of stars and not of gas and dust . . .

By the mid-1920s, then, the matter was settled, and it has not been questioned since. The Andromeda Nebula is not a member of the Galaxy but is located far beyond its bounds. It is a vast and independent conglomeration of stars, an island universe indeed. Kant was right; Laplace was wrong.

There is more than one dimension to writing, of course. Not only can you write on different subjects, you can also aim at different audiences. And since I am the greediest writer alive and want to write on every subject for every audience, I fall easy prey to certain propositions.

Mrs Julian May Dikty, of the Follett Publishing Company, wrote to me in 1965, reminding me that we had met at a recent science-fiction convention in Chicago, and suggesting I write a series of books on astronomy for eight-year-olds.

I am easily reached by an appeal to sentiment, as it happens. I told myself that Mrs Dikty was a fellow conventioneer and that requests from fellow conventioneers deserved special considerations, so I agreed.

But I was cheating, you know, just to give myself a good argument for doing what I wanted to do. I knew very well that I had never been to that particular science-fiction convention (it's a long story but, through no fault of my own, I was manoeuvred into being in Chicago a week after the convention) and that Mrs Dikty only thought she had met me.

Oh, well, I have by now written four of those little books, and a fifth is in press.

One of the little books is Galaxies *(Follett, 1968) and I treat the Andromeda Galaxy, for eight-year-olds, as follows:*

from GALAXIES *(1968)*

Our Sun is part of a great gathering of many billions of stars. This is shaped like a pinwheel and it turns around and around in space. There is a thick cluster of stars at the centre of the pinwheel, and streams of stars called spiral arms come from the centre. Our Sun is out in one of the spiral arms, far from the centre.

When we look through the pinwheel of stars longways, we can see a band of many faint stars that make a dim, milky glow in the sky. This is called the Milky Way.

The great group of stars we belong to is called a Galaxy . . .

Elsewhere in space there are Galaxies just as huge as our own. In the constellation of Andromeda, we can see a small hazy spot of light. A large telescope shows that this spot is another great Galaxy, more than two million light-years away from our Milky Way Galaxy.

Our own Galaxy is shaped like the Andromeda Galaxy.

Beyond the Andromeda Galaxy in every direction are still other Galaxies. Many of them have pinwheel shapes and are called spiral Galaxies. Other Galaxies without spiral arms look like great balls of stars or have no special shape.

All the Galaxies put together and the space between them make up the Universe.

That may sound like pretty hard going for eight-year-olds, but I'm only quoting the words, of course. There are useful and accurate pictures on every page of these little books, which help the young readers over the hurdles, and for them I can claim no credit, of course. The illustrators of Galaxies *are Alex Ebel and Denny McMains.*

PART 2

Robots

My name in science fiction is most often associated with robots. I had occasion recently to explain why in an article written for a British popular-science magazine, Science Journal, *at the request of its editor, Robin Clarke.*

You may wonder why so specialized a subject as my relationship to robots appeared in so estimable a periodical, and I can only say that it happens now and then. I get a request to speak or write on a vastly complicated and specialized subject and I answer, as I must, that I am not really an authority on that particular subject. (I am not really an authority on any subject, but I hate to say so too openly.)

Invariably, the answer comes back: 'Oh, we know that, but we want you to speak or write on this vastly complicated and specialized subject in its relation to the future.'

Well, Science Journal *was preparing a special issue labelled 'Machines Like Men', for October, 1968, and after planning a progression of serious articles on progressively more complex robots, they decided on a final article on the ultimate robots of the future and so they asked me to do an article, entitled 'The Perfect Machine'.*

Part of its beginning went as follows:

from 'The Perfect Machine' (1968)

The science-fiction writers . . . could not rid themselves of the notion that the manufacture of robots involved forbidden knowledge, a wicked aspiration on the part of man to abilities reserved for God. The attempt to create artificial life was an example of hubris and demanded punishment. In story after story, with grim inevitability, the robot destroyed its creator before being itself destroyed. There were exceptions, to be sure, and occasional tales were written in which robots were sympathetic or even virtuous. But it was not until 1939 that, for the first time as far as I know, a science-fiction writer approached the robots from a systematic engineering standpoint.

Without further coyness, I will state that the science-fiction writer was myself. Since then I have written some two dozen short stories and two novels in which robots were treated as machines, created by human beings to fulfil human purposes. There was no hint of 'forbidden knowledge', only rational engineering. Those robot stories killed the Frankenstein motif in respectable science fiction as dead as ever 'Don Quixote' killed knight errantry.

To me, the applied science of manufacturing robots, of designing them, of studying them, was 'robotics'. I used this word because it seemed the obvious analogue of physics, mechanics, hydraulics, and a hundred other terms. In fact, I was sure it was an existing word. Recently, however, it was pointed out to me that 'robotics' does not appear in any edition of Webster's unabridged dictionary so I suppose I invented the word.

My engineering attitude towards robots did not spring to life, full blown. I can trace the development neatly through the stories themselves.

I wrote my first robot story in 1939 and had trouble selling it at first. (As a matter of fact, it was not until 1941 that rejection slips and I became almost total – never quite total, of course – strangers.)

It was about a robot nursemaid, named 'Robbie'. It was loved by the little girl it cared for and distrusted by the little girl's mother. The mother finally got rid of the robot, the little girl was inconsolable, and, eventually, events twisted themselves in such a fashion that the little girl found the robot, had her life saved by it, and all were re-united in a perfect happy ending.

I called the story 'Robbie' but the editor, Frederik Pohl, who finally accepted and published it, changed the title to 'Strange Playfellow'. Fred, an amiable fellow, exceedingly intelligent, and a friend of mine of thirty years' standing (since before I was a writer and he an editor), does have a tendency in that direction. Some editors are more inveterate title changers than others, and Fred is a title-change addict. On rare occasions, he improves a title by changing it; but this, in my opinion, was not one of those occasions.

Anyway, the important thing about the story was the existence of one paragraph. The girl's mother is expressing her doubts about Robbie, and the girl's father says:

from 'Strange Playfellow' *(1940)*

'Dear! A robot is infinitely more to be trusted than a human nursemaid. Robbie was constructed for only one purpose – to be the companion of a little child. His entire "mentality" has been created for the purpose. He just can't help being faithful and loving and kind. He's a machine – *made so.*'

It is the reverse of the Frankenstein attitude, you see, but I don't go any farther than to say 'made so'.

The question of being 'made so' grew sharper in my mind with time. My third robot story was 'Liar!' It was about a robot who could read minds, and who thus knew what people wanted to hear. It had to tell them what they wanted to hear even when that was a lie, for otherwise it would make them feel bad. The robot, reading minds, would sense their unhappiness so that truth-telling was, in those cases, inadmissible.

The robot caused considerable trouble before this was understood.

Susan Calvin, the robopsychologist (who appears in a number of my robot stories), is the first to understand. Here's a passage as she begins to explain:

from 'Liar!' *(1941)*

Lanning's voice was hostile. 'What is all this, Dr Calvin?'

She faced them and spoke wearily. 'You know the fundamental law impressed upon the positronic brain of all robots, of course.'

The other two nodded together. 'Certainly,' said Bogert. 'On no condition is a human being to be injured in any way, even when such injury is directly ordered by another human.'

What had been a simple 'made so' in 'Strange Playfellow' had now become a 'fundamental law' of robotics.

There was more than that, though. In the course of a discussion with John W. Campbell, Jr, editor of Astounding Science Fiction, *sometime in 1941, two more laws were added, and thus were evolved the 'Three Laws of Robotics'. These, in some form or another will, I honestly think, eventually form the basis of robotics when the science is truly developed and it is for them, if anything, that I may be remembered by posterity.*

They were first mentioned specifically in my fifth robot story, 'Runaround', which was set on Mercury (with only one side facing the Sun, of course). A robot had gone out of order and it was necessary that it be repaired quickly, or else disaster would follow. The two heroes of the story, Gregory Powell and Mike Donovan, their lives in balance, try to figure out what to do and decide to go back to fundamentals:

from 'Runaround' *(1942)*

Powell's radio voice was tense in Donovan's ear: 'Now, look, let's start with the three fundamental Rules of Robotics – the three rules that are built most deeply into a robot's positronic brain.' In the darkness, his gloved fingers ticked off each point.

'We have: One, a robot may not injure a human being under any conditions – and, as a corollary, must not permit a human being to be injured because of inaction on his part.'

'Right!'

'Two,' continued Powell, 'a robot must follow all orders given by qualified human beings as long as they do not conflict with Rule One.'

'Right!'

'Three: a robot must protect his own existence, as long as that does not conflict with Rules One and Two.'

'Right! Now where are we?'

By 1950, nine of my robot stories were collected into a book – I, Robot. This was my second book and after all these years it is still in print and is still selling briskly, to my infinite satisfaction. Its first few years were rocky, however.

You see, although Doubleday and Houghton Mifflin publish the lion's share of my books (sixty of the Hundred between the two of them) the rest have been distributed for a variety of reasons among thirteen other publishers. My relations with all of these but one have always been entirely satisfactory. The exception was Gnome Press which, in the early 1950s, published I, Robot and three other books. All four books have since been taken over, to my delight, by Doubleday.

In the collection, I adjusted the stories in minor ways to remove internal inconsistencies and to place the Three Laws firmly in those stories which preceded 'Runaround'. I also changed the title of the first story from 'Strange Playfellow' back to 'Robbie'. (A snap of the finger to you, Fred Pohl, old friend.)

Just before the contents page of I, Robot was a special listing of the Three Laws, and these give the 'official version' which differed only inconsequentially from the word-

ing in 'Runaround' but which I ought to present here:

from I, ROBOT *(1950)*

THE THREE LAWS OF ROBOTICS

1. A robot may not injure a human being or, through inaction, allow a human being to come to harm.

2. A robot must obey the orders given it by human beings except where such orders would conflict with the First Law.

3. A robot must protect its own existence as long as such protection does not conflict with the First or Second Law.

– HANDBOOK OF ROBOTICS
56th Edition, 2058 A.D.

The concept of robots continued to develop in my mind and I could see no limits to their perfection. Computers, it seems to me (and a robot's brain is, after all, merely a compact computer), can grow complex and versatile without foreseeable limit. Why not a computer (or robot), then, as intelligent as man. For that matter, why not a computer (or robot) more intelligent than man.

I took up this matter as the final and climactic paragraphs of a book entitled The Intelligent Man's Guide to Science *which had its ups and downs.*

Its history began in May, 1959, when an editor from Basic Books asked me to do a book on twentieth-century science. I agreed, but then, exactly as in the case of the later Universe, *I found it necessary to go back to ancient times in every branch of science which I discussed. The book turned out to be more than twice as long as the editor had anticipated – nearly 400,000 words long.*

The editor agreed to do it anyway, but when I received the galley proof, I hit the ceiling and bounced. It seems that the editor, wielding his blue pencil with an energy and intensity I had never encountered before (or since), had greatly condensed my book. When the book was published in 1960, I refused to read it or, indeed, even to open it.

I must interrupt here to say that I generally read my own books after they are published. In part, this is to catch any still-surviving errors so that they may be corrected in the next printing (if any). Mostly, though, I am forced to admit it is because I love to read my own books for their own sake.

This sounds ridiculous, perhaps, but why not? I like the way I write. How else could I write as much as I do, if I didn't enjoy my own writing? Think of it! I've got to read the stuff as it comes out of the typewriter, and then again when I correct the first draft, and then again when I retype it, and then again when I read the final copy, and then again in copyedited version, and then again in galley proof and in page proof. If I didn't like my writing, how could I stand it all?

Of course, I could hire a secretary to do most of this, but since I like reading my writing I don't have to. I can thus remain a one-man operation, running at my own speed without interference, and without the frictional delay of having to deal with typists, secretaries, agents, or any other middlemen at all.

But to get back to The Intelligent Man's Guide to Science –

It was a critical and financial success, so I cannot and do not say that the editorial modifications in any way damaged the book. What's more, my relationship with Basic Books did not suffer. However, what made me unhappy was that the book was not *mine. A book with my name on it doesn't have to be a critical or a financial success; but it does have to be* mine.

Anyway, in 1964, Basic Books asked me to bring the book up to date, and this time I was not to be caught again. I set my conditions. I was to see all changes before the galley-proof stage, and I implied that the fewer I saw the happier I would be. I was assured that this would be so (and this agreement was honoured rigorously by them).

I got to work with great vigour, therefore, made a thoroughgoing revision of the book and produced The New Intelligent Man's Guide to Science *which is my book, and which I love, and open and read frequently. And it is a critical and financial success also.*

Let me quote the last two paragraphs then, which deal with the ultimate end of the computer and which are the same, as it happens, in both editions:

from THE INTELLIGENT MAN'S GUIDE TO SCIENCE *(1960)*

All these attempts to mimic the mind of man are in their earliest infancy. Not in the foreseeable future can we envision any possibility of a machine matching the human brain. The road, however, is open, and it conjures up thoughts which are exciting but also, in some ways, frightening. What if man eventually were to produce a mechanical creature equal or superior to himself in all respects, including intelligence and creativity? Would it replace man, as the superior organisms of the earth have replaced or subordinated the less well adapted in the long history of evolution?

It is a queasy thought: that we represent, for the first time in the history of life on the Earth, a species capable of bringing about its own possible replacement. Of course, we have it in our power to prevent such a regrettable dénouement by refusing to build machines that are too intelligent. But it is tempting to build them nevertheless. What achievement could be grander than the creation of an object that surpasses the creator? How could we consummate the victory of intelligence over nature more gloriously than by passing on our heritage, in triumph, to a greater intelligence – of our own making.

And here we come to an advantage science fiction holds over straightforward science exposition. When it comes to really far-out ideas, much more can be done in a fictional frame. Several years before I wrote the above passage, I had written a story called 'The Last Question'.

This story has a rather curious aftermath. More people have written me to ask if I were the author of this particular story than of any other story I have ever written. They not only can't remember for sure that I am the author; they also can't remember where they read it; and, invariably, they can't remember the title.

Perhaps this is because it is a bad title, but I don't think so. I think that the content of the story attracts them, yet frightens them, too. Unconsciously, they try to forget and don't quite succeed.

It is also the only story of mine that (as far as I know) was the subject of a sermon. It was read from the pulpit in a Unitarian church at Bedford, Massachusetts, while I sat quietly in the back row (I didn't tell them I was coming) and listened.

Anyway, it is one of the three or four stories I am most pleased with having written. It represents my ultimate thinking on the matter of computers/robots and so I am presenting it here, in full:

'The Last Question' *(1956)*

The last question was asked for the first time, half in jest, on May 21, 2061, at a time when humanity first stepped into the light. The question came about as a result of a five-dollar bet over highballs, and it happened this way:

Alexander Adell and Bertram Lupov were two of the faithful attendants of Multivac. As well as any human beings could, they knew what lay behind the cold, clicking, flashing face – miles and miles of face – of that giant computer. They had at least a vague notion of the general plan of relays and circuits that had long since grown past the point where any single human could possibly have a firm grasp of the whole.

Multivac was self-adjusting and self-correcting. It had to be, for nothing human could adjust and correct it quickly enough or even adequately enough. So Adell and Lupov attended the monstrous giant only lightly and superficially, yet as well as any men could. They fed it data, adjusted questions to its needs, and translated the answers that were issued. Certainly they, and all others like them, were fully entitled to share in the glory that was Multivac's.

For decades, Multivac had helped design the ships and plot the trajectories that enabled man to reach the Moon, Mars, and Venus, but past that, Earth's poor resources could not support the ships. Too much energy was needed for the long trips. Earth exploited its coal and uranium with increasing efficiency, but there was only so much of both.

But slowly Multivac learned enough to answer deeper questions more fundamentally, and on May 14, 2061, what had been theory, became fact.

The energy of the Sun was stored, converted, and utilized directly on a planet-wide scale. All Earth turned off its burning coal, its fissioning uranium, and flipped the switch that connected all of it to a small station, one mile in diameter, circling the Earth at half the distance of the Moon. All Earth ran by invisible beams of sunpower.

Seven days had not sufficed to dim the glory of it, and Adell and Lupov finally managed to escape from the public function and to meet in quiet where no one would think of looking for them, in the deserted underground chambers, where portions of the mighty buried body of Multivac showed. Unattended, idling, sorting data with contented lazy clickings, Multivac, too, had earned its vacation and the boys appreciated that. They had no intention, originally, of disturbing it.

They had brought a bottle with them, and their only concern at the moment was to relax in the company of each other and the bottle.

'It's amazing when you think of it,' said Adell. His broad

face had lines of weariness in it, and he stirred his drink slowly with a glass rod, watching the cubes of ice slur clumsily about. 'All the energy we can possibly ever use for free. Enough energy, if we wanted to draw on it, to melt all Earth into a big drop of impure liquid iron, and still never miss the energy so used. All the energy we could ever use, forever and forever and forever.'

Lupov cocked his head sideways. He had a trick of doing that when he wanted to be contrary, and he wanted to be contrary now, partly because he had had to carry the ice and glassware. 'Not forever,' he said.

'Oh, hell, just about forever. Till the Sun runs down, Bert.'

'That's not forever.'

'All right, then. Billions and billions of years. Twenty billion, maybe. Are you satisfied?'

Lupov put his fingers through his thinning hair as though to reassure himself that some was still left and sipped gently at his own drink. 'Twenty billion years isn't forever.'

'Well, it will last our time, won't it?'

'So would the coal and uranium.'

'All right, but now we can hook up each individual spaceship to the Solar Station, and it can go to Pluto and back a million times without ever worrying about fuel. You can't do *that* on coal and uranium. Ask Multivac, if you don't believe me.'

'I don't have to ask Multivac. I know that.'

'Then stop running down what Multivac's done for us,' said Adell, blazing up. 'It did all right.'

'Who says it didn't? What I say is that the Sun won't last forever. That's all I'm saying. We're safe for twenty billion years, but then what?' Lupov pointed a slightly shaky finger at the other. 'And don't say we'll switch to another star.'

There was silence for a while. Adell put his glass to his lips only occasionally, and Lupov's eyes slowly closed. They rested.

Then Lupov's eyes snapped open. 'You're thinking we'll switch to another star when our Sun is done, aren't you?'

'I'm not thinking.'

'Sure you are. You're weak on logic, that's the trouble with you. You're like the guy in the story who was caught in a sudden shower and who ran to a grove of trees and got under one. He wasn't worried, you see, because he figured when one tree got wet through, he would just get under another one.'

'I get it,' said Adell. 'Don't shout. When the Sun is done, the other stars will be gone, too.'

'Darn right they will,' muttered Lupov. 'It all had a beginning in the original cosmic explosion, whatever that was, and it'll all have an end when all the stars run down. Some run down faster than others. Hell, the giants won't last a hundred million years. The Sun will last twenty billion years and maybe the dwarfs will last a hundred billion for all the good they are. But just give us a trillion years and everything will be dark. Entropy has to increase to maximum, that's all.'

'I know all about entropy,' said Adell, standing on his dignity.

'The hell you do.'

'I know as much as you do.'

'Then you know everything's got to run down someday.'

'All right. Who says they won't?'

'You did, you poor sap. You said we had all the energy we needed, forever. You said "forever".'

It was Adell's turn to be contrary. 'Maybe we can build things up again someday,' he said.

'Never.'

'Why not? Someday.'

'Never.'

'Ask Multivac.'

'You ask Multivac. I dare you. Five dollars says it can't be done.'

Adell was just drunk enough to try, just sober enough to be able to phrase the necessary symbols and operations

into a question which, in words, might have corresponded
to this: Will mankind one day without the net expenditure
of energy be able to restore the Sun to its full youthfulness
even after it had died of old age?

Or maybe it could be put more simply like this: How
can the net amount of entropy of the universe be massively
decreased?

Multivac fell dead and silent. The slow flashing of lights
ceased, the distant sounds of clicking relays ended.

Then, just as the frightened technicians felt they could
hold their breath no longer, there was a sudden springing to
life of the teletype attached to that portion of Multivac.
Five words were printed: INSUFFICIENT DATA FOR MEAN-
INGFUL ANSWER.

'No bet,' whispered Lupov. They left hurriedly.

By next morning, the two, plagued with throbbing head
and cottony mouth, had forgotten the incident.

Jerrodd, Jerrodine, and Jerrodette I and II watched the
starry picture in the visiplate change as the passage through
hyperspace was completed in its non-time lapse. At once,
the even powdering of stars gave way to the predominance
of a single bright marble-disc, centred.

'That's X-23,' said Jerrodd confidently. His thin hands
clamped tightly behind his back and the knuckles
whitened.

The little Jerrodettes, both girls, had experienced the
hyperspace passage for the first time in their lives and
were self-conscious over the momentary sensation of
inside-outness. They buried their giggles and chased one
another wildly about their mother, screaming, 'We've
reached X-23 – we've reached X-23 – we've –'

'Quiet, children,' said Jerrodine sharply. 'Are you sure,
Jerrodd?'

'What is there to be but sure?' asked Jerrodd, glancing
up at the bulge of featureless metal just under the ceiling.
It ran the length of the room, disappearing through the
wall at either end. It was as long as the ship.

Jerrodd scarcely knew a thing about the thick rod of metal except that it was called a Microvac, that one asked it questions if one wished; that if one did not it still had its task of guiding the ship to a preordered destination; of feeding on energies from the various Sub-galactic Power Stations; of computing the equations for the hyperspatial jumps.

Jerrodd and his family had only to wait and live in the comfortable residence quarters of the ship.

Someone had once told Jerrodd that the *ac* at the end of 'Microvac' stood for 'analogue computer' in ancient English, but he was on the edge of forgetting even that.

Jerrodine's eyes were moist as she watched the visiplate. 'I can't help it. I feel funny about leaving Earth.'

'Why, for Pete's sake?' demanded Jerrodd. 'We had nothing there. We'll have everything on X-23. You won't be alone. You won't be a pioneer. There are over a million people on the planet already. Good Lord, our great-grand-children will be looking for new worlds because X-23 will be overcrowded.' Then, after a reflective pause, 'I tell you, it's a lucky thing the computers worked out interstellar travel the way the race is growing.'

'I know, I know,' said Jerrodine miserably.

Jerrodette I said promptly, 'Our Microvac is the best Microvac in the world.'

'I think so, too,' said Jerrodd, tousling her hair.

It *was* a nice feeling to have a Microvac of your own and Jerrodd was glad he was part of his generation and no other. In his father's youth, the only computers had been tremendous machines taking up a hundred square miles of land. There was only one to a planet. Planetary AC's they were called. They had been growing in size steadily for a thousand years and then, all at once, came refinement. In place of transistors had come molecular valves so that even the largest Planetary AC could be put into a space only half the volume of a spaceship.

Jerrodd felt uplifted, as he always did when he thought that his own personal Microvac was many times more complicated than the ancient and primitive Multivac that had first tamed the Sun, and almost as complicated as Earth's Planetary AC (the largest) that had first solved the problem of hyperspatial travel and had made trips to the stars possible.

'So many stars, so many planets,' sighed Jerrodine, busy with her own thoughts. 'I suppose families will be going out to new planets forever, the way we are now.'

'Not forever,' said Jerrodd, with a smile. 'It will all stop someday, but not for billions of years. Many billions. Even the stars run down, you know. Entropy must increase.'

'What's entropy, Daddy?' shrilled Jerrodette II.

'Entropy, little sweet, is just a word which means the amount of running-down of the universe. Everything runs down, you know, like your little walkie-talkie robot, remember?'

'Can't you just put in a new power unit, like with my robot?'

'The stars *are* the power units, dear. Once they're gone, there are no more power units.'

Jerrodette I at once set up a howl. 'Don't let them, Daddy. Don't let the stars run down.'

'Now look what you've done,' whispered Jerrodine, exasperated.

'How was I to know it would frighten them?' Jerrodd whispered back.

'Ask the Microvac,' wailed Jerrodette I. 'Ask him how to turn the stars on again.'

'Go ahead,' said Jerrodine. 'It will quiet them down.' (Jerrodette II was beginning to cry, also.)

Jerrodd shrugged. 'Now, now, honeys. I'll ask Microvac. Don't worry, he'll tell us.'

He asked the Microvac, adding quickly, 'Print the answer.'

Jerrodd cupped the strip of thin cellufilm and said cheerfully, 'See now, the Microvac says it will take care of everything when the time comes so don't worry.'

Jerrodine said, 'And now, children, it's time for bed.

We'll be in our new home soon.'

Jerrodd read the words on the cellufilm again before destroying it : INSUFFICIENT DATA FOR MEANINGFUL ANSWER.

He shrugged and looked at the visiplate. X-23 was just ahead.

VJ-23X of Lameth stared into the black depths of the three-dimensional, small-scale map of the Galaxy and said, 'Are we ridiculous, I wonder, in being so concerned about the matter?'

MQ-17J of Nicron shook his head. 'I think not. You know the Galaxy will be filled in five years at the present rate of expansion.'

Both seemed in their early twenties, both were tall and perfectly formed.

'Still,' said VJ-23X, 'I hesitate to submit a pessimistic report to the Galactic Council.'

"I wouldn't consider any other kind of report. Stir them up a bit. We've got to stir them up.'

VJ-23X sighed. 'Space is infinite. A hundred billion Galaxies are there for the taking. More.'

'A hundred billion is *not* infinite and it's getting less infinite all the time. Consider! Twenty thousand years ago, mankind first solved the problem of utilizing stellar energy, and a few centuries later, interstellar travel became possible. It took mankind a million years to fill one small world and then only fifteen thousand years to fill the rest of the Galaxy. Now the population doubles every ten years –'

VJ-23X interrupted. 'We can thank immortality for that.'

'Very well. Immortality exists and we have to take it into account. I admit it has its seamy side, this immortality. The Galactic AC has solved many problems for us, but in solving the problem of preventing old age and death, it has undone all its other solutions.'

'Yet you wouldn't want to abandon life, I suppose.'

'Not at all,' snapped MQ-17J, softening it at once to, 'Not yet. I'm by no means old enough. How old are you?'

'Two hundred and twenty-three. And you?'

'I'm still under two hundred. – But to get back to my point. Population doubles every ten years. Once this Galaxy is filled, we'll have filled another in ten years. Another ten years and we'll have filled two more. Another decade, four more. In a hundred years, we'll have filled a thousand Galaxies. In a thousand years, a million Galaxies. In ten thousand years, the entire known Universe. Then what?'

VJ-23X said, 'As a side issue, there's a problem of transportation. I wonder how many sunpower units it will take to move Galaxies of individuals from one Galaxy to the next.'

'A very good point. Already, mankind consumes two sunpower units per year.'

'Most of it's wasted. After all, our own Galaxy alone pours out a thousand sunpower units a year and we only use two of those.'

'Granted, but even with a hundred percent efficiency, we only stave off the end. Our energy requirements are going up in a geometric progression even faster than our population. We'll run out of energy even sooner than we run out of Galaxies. A good point. A very good point.'

'We'll just have to build new stars out of interstellar gas.'

'Or out of dissipated heat?' asked MQ-17J, sarcastically.

'There may be some way to reverse entropy. We ought to ask the Galactic AC.'

VJ-23X was not really serious, but MQ-17J pulled out his AC-contact from his pocket and placed it on the table before him.

'I've half a mind to,' he said. 'It's something the human race will have to face someday.'

He stared sombrely at his small AC-contact. It was only two inches cubed and nothing in itself, but it was connected through hyperspace with the great Galactic AC that served all mankind. Hyperspace considered, it was an integral part of the Galactic AC.

MQ-17J paused to wonder if someday in his immortal

life he would get to see the Galactic AC. It was on a little world of its own, a spider webbing of force-beams holding the matter within which surges of sub-mesons took the place of the old clumsy molecular valves. Yet despite its sub-ethnic workings, the Galactic AC was known to be a full thousand feet across.

MQ-17J asked suddenly of his AC-contact, 'Can entropy ever be reversed?'

VJ-23X looked startled and said at once, 'Oh, say, I didn't really mean to have you ask that.'

'Why not?'

'We both know entropy can't be reversed. You can't turn smoke and ash back into a tree.'

'Do you have trees on your world?' asked MQ-17J.

The sound of the Galactic AC startled them into silence. Its voice came thin and beautiful out of the small AC-contact on the desk. It said: THERE IS INSUFFICIENT DATA FOR A MEANINGFUL ANSWER.

VJ-23X said, 'See!'

The two men thereupon returned to the question of the report they were to make to the Galactic Council.

Zee Prime's mind spanned the new Galaxy with a faint interest in the countless twists of stars that powered it. He had never seen this one before. Would he ever see them all? So many of them, each with its load of humanity – but a load that was almost a dead weight. More and more, the real essence of men was to be found out here, in space.

Minds, not bodies! The immortal bodies remained back on the planets, in suspension over the eons. Sometimes they roused for material activity but that was growing rarer. Few new individuals were coming into existence to join the incredibly mighty throng, but what matter? There was little room in the Universe for new individuals.

Zee Prime was roused out of his reverie upon coming across the wispy tendrils of another mind.

'I am Zee Prime,' said Zee Prime. 'And you?'

'I am Dee Sub Wun. Your Galaxy?'

'We call it only the Galaxy. And you?'

'We call ours the same. All men call their Galaxy their Galaxy and nothing more. Why not?'

'True. Since all Galaxies are the same.'

'Not all Galaxies. On one particular Galaxy the race of man must have originated. That makes it different.'

Zee Prime said, 'On which one?'

'I cannot say. The Universal AC would know.'

'Shall we ask him? I am suddenly curious.'

Zee Prime's perceptions broadened until the Galaxies themselves shrank and became a new, more diffuse powdering on a much larger background. So many hundreds of billions of them, all with their immortal beings, all carrying their load of intelligences with minds that drifted freely through space. And yet one of them was unique among them all in being the original Galaxy. One of them had, in its vague and distant past, a period when it was the only Galaxy populated by man.

Zee Prime was consumed with curiosity to see this Galaxy and he called out: 'Universal AC! On which Galaxy did mankind originate?'

The Universal AC heard, for on every world and throughout space, it had its receptors ready, and each receptor led through hyperspace to some unknown point where the Universal AC kept itself aloof.

Zee Prime knew of only one man whose thoughts had penetrated within sensing distance of Universal AC, and he reported only a shining globe, two feet across, difficult to see.

'But how can that be all of Universal AC?' Zee Prime had asked.

'Most of it,' had been the answer, 'is in hyperspace. In what form it is there I cannot imagine.'

Nor could anyone, for the day had long since passed, Zee Prime knew, when any man had any part of the making of a Universal AC. Each Universal AC designed and constructed its successor. Each, during its existence of a million years or more, accumulated the necessary data to

build a better and more intricate, more capable successor
in which its own store of data and individuality would be
submerged.

The Universal AC interrupted Zee Prime's wandering
thoughts, not with words, but with guidance. Zee Prime's
mentality was guided into the dim sea of Galaxies and one
in particular enlarged into stars.

A thought came, infinitely distant, but infinitely clear.
THIS IS THE ORIGINAL GALAXY OF MAN.

But it was the same after all, the same as any other, and
Zee Prime stifled his disappointment.

Dee Sub Wun, whose mind had accompanied the other,
said suddenly, 'And is one of these stars the original star
of Man?'

The Universal AC said, MAN'S ORIGINAL STAR HAS GONE
NOVA. IT IS A WHITE DWARF.

'Did the men of its system die?' asked Zee Prime,
startled and without thinking.

The Universal AC said, A NEW WORLD, AS IN SUCH CASES
WAS CONSTRUCTED FOR THEIR PHYSICAL BODIES IN TIME.

'Yes, of course,' said Zee Prime, but a sense of loss
overwhelmed him even so. His mind released its hold on
the original Galaxy of Man, let it spring back and lose itself
among the blurred pinpoints. He never wanted to see it
again.

Dee Sub Wun said, 'What is wrong?'

'The stars are dying. The original star is dead.'

'They must all die. Why not?'

'But when all energy is gone, our bodies will finally die,
and you and I with them.'

'It will take billions of years.'

'I do not wish it to happen even after billions of years.
Universal AC! How may stars be kept from dying?'

Dee Sub Wun said in amusement, 'You're asking how
entropy might be reversed in direction.'

And the Universal AC answered: THERE IS AS YET IN-
SUFFICIENT DATA FOR A MEANINGFUL ANSWER.

Zee Prime's thoughts fled back to his own Galaxy. He

gave no further thought to Dee Sub Wun, whose body might be waiting on a Galaxy a trillion light-years away, or on the star next to Zee Prime's own. It didn't matter.

Unhappily, Zee Prime began collecting interstellar hydrogen out of which to build a small star of his own. If the stars must someday die, at least some could yet be built.

Man considered with himself, for in a way, Man, mentally, was one. He consisted of a trillion, trillion, trillion ageless bodies, each in its place, each resting quiet and incorruptible, each cared for by perfect automatons, equally incorruptible, while the minds of all the bodies freely melted one into the other, indistinguishable.

Man said, 'The Universe is dying.'

Man looked about at the dimming Galaxies. The giant stars, spendthrifts, were gone long ago, back in the dimmest of the dim far past. Almost all stars were white dwarfs, fading to the end.

New stars had been built of the dust between the stars, some by natural processes, some by Man himself, and those were going, too. White dwarfs might yet be crashed together and of the mighty forces so released, new stars built, but only one star for every thousand white dwarfs destroyed, and those would come to an end, too.

Man said, 'Carefully husbanded, as directed by the Cosmic AC, the energy that is even yet left in all the Universe will last for billions of years.'

'But even so,' said Man, 'eventually it will all come to an end. However it may be husbanded, however stretched out, the energy once expended is gone and cannot be restored. Entropy must increase forever to the maximum.'

Man said, 'Can entropy not be reversed? Let us ask the Cosmic AC.'

The Cosmic AC surrounded them but not in space. Not a fragment of it was in space. It was in hyperspace and made of something that was neither matter nor energy. The question of its size and nature no longer had meaning in any terms that Man could comprehend.

'Cosmic AC,' said Man, 'how may entropy be reversed?'

The Cosmic AC said, THERE IS AS YET INSUFFICIENT DATA FOR A MEANINGFUL ANSWER.

Man said, 'Collect additional data.'

The Cosmic AC said, I WILL DO SO. I HAVE BEEN DOING SO FOR A HUNDRED BILLION YEARS. MY PREDECESSORS AND I HAVE BEEN ASKED THIS QUESTION MANY TIMES. ALL THE DATA I HAVE REMAINS INSUFFICIENT.

'Will there come a time,' said Man, 'when data will be sufficient or is the problem insoluble in all conceivable circumstances?'

The Cosmic AC said, NO PROBLEM IS INSOLUBLE IN ALL CONCEIVABLE CIRCUMSTANCES.

Man said, 'When will you have enough data to answer the question?'

The Cosmic AC said, THERE IS AS YET INSUFFICIENT DATA FOR A MEANINGFUL ANSWER.

'Will you keep working on it?' asked Man.

The Cosmic AC said, I WILL.

Man said, 'We shall wait.'

The stars and Galaxies died and snuffed out, and space grew black after ten trillion years of running down.

One by one, Man fused with AC, each physical body losing its mental identity in a manner that was somehow not a loss but a gain.

Man's last mind paused before fusion, looking over a space that included nothing but the dregs of one last dark star and nothing besides but incredibly thin matter, agitated randomly by the tag ends of heat wearing out, asymptotically, to an equilibrium level near absolute zero.

Man said, 'AC, is this the end? Can this chaos not be reversed into the Universe once more? Can that not be done?'

AC said, THERE IS AS YET INSUFFICIENT DATA FOR A MEANINGFUL ANSWER.

Man's last mind fused and only AC existed – and that in hyperspace.

* * *

Matter and energy had ended and with it space and time. Even AC existed only for the sake of the one last question that it had never answered from the time a half-drunken computer attendant ten trillion years before had asked the question of a computer that was to AC far less than was a man to Man.

All other questions had been answered, and until this last question was answered also, AC might not release his consciousness.

All collected data had come to a final end. Nothing was left to be collected.

But all collected data had yet to be completely correlated and put together in all possible relationships.

A timeless interval was spent in doing that.

And it came to pass that AC learned how to reverse the direction of entropy.

But there was now no man to whom AC might give the answer of the last question. No matter. The answer – by demonstration – would take care of that, too.

For another timeless interval, AC thought how best to do this. Carefully, AC organized the programme.

The consciousness of AC encompassed all of what had once been a Universe and brooded over what was now Chaos. Step by step, it must be done.

And AC said, LET THERE BE LIGHT!

And there was light –

PART 3

Mathematics

When I was in grade school, I had an occasional feeling that I might be a mathematician when I grew up. I loved the maths classes because they seemed so easy. As soon as I got my maths book at the beginning of a new school term, I raced through it from beginning to end, found it all beautifully clear and simple, and then breezed through the course without trouble.

It is, in fact, the beauty of mathematics, as opposed to almost any other branch of knowledge, that it contains so little unrelated and miscellaneous factual material one must memorize. Oh, there are a few definitions and axioms, some terminology – but everything else is deduction. And, if you have a feel for it, the deduction is all obvious, or becomes obvious as soon as it is once pointed out.

As long as this holds true, mathematics is not only a breeze, it is an exciting intellectual adventure that has few peers. But then, sooner or later (except for a few transcendent geniuses), there comes a point when the breeze turns into a cold and needle-spray storm blast. For some it comes quite early in the game: long division, fractions, proportions, something shows up which turns out to be no longer obvious no matter how carefully it is explained. You may get to understand it but only by constant concentration; it never becomes obvious.

And at that point mathematics ceases to be fun.

When there is a prolonged delay in meeting that barrier, you feel lucky, but are you? The longer the delay, the greater the trauma when you do meet the barrier and smash into it.

I went right through high school, for instance, without finding the barrier. Maths was always easy, always fun, always an 'A-subject' that required no studying.

To be sure, I might have had a hint there was something wrong. My high school was Boys High School of Brooklyn and in the days when I attended (1932 to 1935) it was renowned throughout the city for the skill and valour of its maths team. Yet I was not a member of the maths team.

I had a dim idea that the boys on the maths team could do mathematics I had never heard of, and that the problems they faced and solved were far beyond me. I took care of that little bit of unpleasantness, however, by studiously refraining from giving it any thought, on the theory (very widespread among people generally) that a difficulty ignored is a difficulty resolved.

At Columbia I took up analytical geometry and differential calculus and, while I recognized a certain unaccustomed intellectual friction heating up my mind somewhat, I still managed to get my A's.

It was when I went on to integral calculus that the dam broke. To my horror, I found that I had to study; that I had to go over a point several times and that even then it remained unclear; that I had to sweat away over the homework problems and sometimes either had to leave them unsolved or, worse still, worked them out incorrectly. And in the end, in the second semester of the year course, I got (oh shame!) a B.

I had, in short, reached my own particular impassable barrier, and I met that situation with a most vigorous and effective course of procedure– I never took another maths course.

Oh, I've picked up some additional facets of mathematics on my own since then, but the old glow was gone. It was never the shining gold of 'Of course' anymore, only the dubiously polished pewter of 'I think I see it.'

Fortunately, a barrier at integral calculus is quite a high one. There is plenty of room beneath it within which to run and jump, and I have therefore been able to write books on mathematics. I merely had to remember to keep this side of integral calculus.

In June, 1958, Austin Olney of Houghton Mifflin (whose

*acquaintance I had first made the year before and whose suggestion is responsible for this book you are holding)
asked me to write a book on mathematics for youngsters.
I presume he thought I was an accomplished mathematician and I, for my part, did not see my way clear to
disabusing him. (I suppose he is disabused now, though.)*

*I agreed readily (with one reservation which I shall come
to in due course) and proceeded to write a book called*
Realm of Numbers *which was as far to the safe side of
integral calculus as possible.*

*In fact, it was about elementary arithmetic, to begin with,
and it was not until the second chapter that I as much as
got to Arabic numerals, and not until the fourth chapter
that I got to fractions.*

*However, by the end of the book I was talking about
imaginary numbers, hyperimaginary numbers, and transfinite numbers – and that was the real purpose of the book.
In going from counting to transfinites, I followed such a
careful and gradual plan that it never stopped seeming
easy.*

*Anyway, here's part of a chapter from the book, rather
early on, while I am still revelling in the simplest matters,
but trying to get across the rather subtle point of the importance of zero.*

from REALM OF NUMBERS *(1959)*

The Hindus began with nine different symbols, one for
each of the numbers from one through nine. These have
changed through history but reached their present form in
Europe in the sixteenth century and are now written: 1,
2, 3, 4, 5, 6, 7, 8, and 9.

This in itself was not unique. The Greeks and Hebrews,
for instance, used nine different symbols for these numbers.
In each case, the symbols were the first nine letters of their
alphabets. The Greeks and Hebrews went on, though, to
use the next nine letters of their alphabets for ten, twenty,

thirty, and so on; and the nine letters after that for one hundred, two hundred, three hundred, and so on. If the alphabet wasn't long enough for the purpose (twenty-eight letters are required to reach a thousand by this system) archaic letters or special forms of letters were added.

The use of letters for numbers gave rise to confusion with words. For instance, the Hebrew number 'fifteen' made use of the two letters that began the name of God (in the Hebrew language) and so some other letter combination had to be used.

On the other hand, ordinary words could be converted into numbers by adding up the numerical value of the letters composing it. This was done especially for words and names in the Bible (a process called 'gematria') and all sorts of mystical and occult meanings were read into it. The most familiar example is the passage in the Revelation of St John where the number of the 'beast' is given as six hundred and sixty-six. This undoubtedly meant that some contemporary figure, whom it was unsafe to name openly (probably the Roman Emperor Nero) had a name which, in Hebrew or Greek letters, added up to that figure. Ever since then, however, people have been trying to fit the names of their enemies into that sum.

Where the Hindus improved on the Greek and Hebrew system, however, was in using the same nine figures for tens, hundreds, and indeed for any rung of the abacus. Out of those nine figures, they built up all numbers. All that was necessary was to give the figures positional values.

For instance, the number twenty-three, on the abacus, consisted of three counters moved to the right on the 'ones' rung and two on the 'tens' rung. The number can therefore be written 23, the numeral on the right representing the bottom rung on the abacus and the one on the left the next higher one.

Obviously, thirty-two would then be written 32 and the positional values become plain since 23 and 32 are not the same number. One is two tens plus three ones and the other three tens plus two ones.

It is very unlikely that the clever Greeks did not think of this; they thought of many much more subtle points. What must have stopped them (and everyone else until the day of the unknown Hindu genius) was the dilemma of the untouched rung on the abacus.

Suppose you wanted, instead of twenty-three, to write two hundred and three. On the abacus, you would move two counters on the 'hundreds' rung and three on the 'ones' rung. The 'tens' rung would remain untouched. Using the Hindu system, it might seem you would still have to write 23, only this time the 2 means 'two hundreds', not 'two tens'.

For that matter, how would you write two thousand and three, or two thousand and thirty, or two thousand three hundred? In each case, you would have to move two counters on one rung and three on another. They would all seem to be 23.

One solution might be to use different symbols for each rung, but that was what the Greeks did and that was unsatisfactory. Or you might use some sort of symbol above each figure to indicate the rung. You might write twenty-three as

23 and two hundred and three as 23, indicating that in the second case, the 2 was in the third or 'hundreds' rung, rather than in the second or 'tens' rung. This would make the numbers rather difficult to read in a hurry, though the system would work in theory.

No, the great Hindu innovation was the *invention of a special symbol for an untouched abacus row*. This symbol the Arabs called 'sifr', meaning 'empty', since the space at the right end of an untouched abacus rung was empty. This word has come down to us as 'cipher' or, in more corrupt form, as 'zero'.

Our symbol for zero is 0, and so we write twenty-three as 23, two hundred and three as 203, two thousand and three as 2,003, two hundred and thirty as 230, two thousand and thirty as 2,030, two thousand three hundred as

2,300, and so on. In each case, we show the untouched rungs on the abacus by using zeros.

(Twenty-three could be written as 0023 or 0000000023, depending on the size of the abacus, but this is never done. It is always assumed that all rungs of the abacus above the first one mentioned and all numerals to the left of the first one mentioned are zero.)

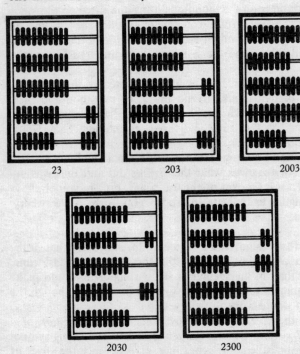

NUMBERS WITH ZERO ON ABACUS

It was the zero that made our so-called Arabic numerals practical and revolutionized the use of numbers. (Strange that the discovery of 'nothing' could be so world-shakingly important; and stranger still that so many great mathematicians never saw that 'nothing'.)

Such is the importance of zero that, to this day, one word for the manipulation of numbers is 'ciphering' and when we work out a problem (even one not involving numbers), we 'decipher' it. The awe in which the numerals were held by people who didn't understand their working is recalled to us by the fact that any secret writing, usually called a 'cryptogram', may also be called a 'cipher'.

The best part of Realm of Numbers *was that it restored my long-lost feeling about maths that I had before the integral-calculus disaster. More than any other book I've ever written it poured out the typewriter in a series of 'Of courses'. The whole thing was written – first draft, correction, final copy, everything – in thirteen days.*

My wife, who is shrewd and practical-minded, urged me to put the manuscript aside for, say, six months, and then walk into the Houghton Mifflin offices with a work-worn and haggard look on my face. She said that if I brought in a manuscript two weeks after starting it, they would be convinced it was no good.

I saw the reasoning behind her argument but found myself incapable of putting it into practice. A completed manuscript simply burns a hole in my desk. It must *be brought to the publishers. What's more, I can't possibly manage to make myself work-worn and haggard, for there is something about a completed manuscript that gives me an expression of eager delight.*

So I brought it in promptly and capered about in my usual fashion and thank goodness no one seemed to think any the less of the manuscript as a result.

In fact, it was followed up by similar books on measuring units and on algebra. It was my intention (and still is) to sneak up on calculus by very small steps and, eventually, live dangerously indeed by manoeuvring myself immediately under my impassable barrier.

The trouble is I get easily sidetracked. A new book appeared which gave a method for quickly manipulating numbers in one's head through the use of shortcut rules.

The only trouble was that memorizing the rules and keeping them straight seemed to me to be infinitely harder than going about it by pencil and paper.

I felt that what was needed was only the very simplest rules for handling only the very simplest problems. It was my theory, you see, that most people are faced with those very simplest problems ninety percent of the time. The difficult problems that involve complicated rules and feats of memory come up only infrequently and they can be handled by pen and paper.

So I wrote Quick and Easy Math, *of which part of a chapter is included here:*

from QUICK AND EASY MATH (1964)

I think it would be generally agreed that addition and subtraction are the simplest of the arithmetical operations. Even without timesaving devices, most people would accept them without much trouble. Multiplication, however, is considerably harder and more tedious; mistakes are easier to make; and most people hesitate more over working out particular problems.

Yet multiplication is only a form of addition, and is itself a kind of shortcut.

Thus, let's consider the multiplication problem 9 times 8, or to use the 'multiplication sign' ($\times$), 9×8. The number 9 is the 'multiplicand' in this case (from a Latin word meaning 'that which is to be multiplied') while the number 8 is the 'multiplier'. As you all surely know, $9 \times 8 = 72$, and 72 is the 'product'.

But what is there in $9 \times 8 = 72$ that makes the problem a kind of addition? Remember that you can read 9×8 as 'nine times eight'. You are asked to take 8 'nine times'. Well, if you take nine 8s and add them together: $8 + 8 + 8 + 8 + 8 + 8 + 8 + 8 + 8$, you do indeed get 72.

Because multiplication is a form of addition, it shares

some of the properties of addition. Just as $a + b = b + a$, so $a \times b = b \times a$. (In algebra, the multiplication sign is generally omitted, so we can express the last statement as $ab = ba$.) Consequently if $9 \times 8 = 72$, then $8 \times 9 = 72$. Sure enough, if you add eight 9s together: $9 + 9 + 9 + 9 + 9 + 9 + 9 + 9$, the sum there too comes to 72.

The fact that multiplication is a shortcut for at least some problems in addition is at once plain. It is easier to memorize that $8 \times 9 = 72$ than to have to add all those 9s and 8s.

In the third grade or so we are usually set to memorizing the 'multiplication table', a table which gives the products of all possible combinations of single digits. As a result, it soon becomes second nature for us to say $3 \times 2 = 6$, $7 \times 7 = 49$, $5 \times 9 = 45$, and so forth. We ought to be able to rattle off any combination from $0 \times 0 = 0$ to $9 \times 9 = 81$.

The multiplication table I learned as a child ran all the way up through 12, so that I also learned that $8 \times 11 = 88$, $11 \times 12 = 132$, and $12 \times 12 = 144$. It might not be a bad idea for people who want to make multiplication easier for themselves to memorize all the combinations up to 20 so that they can say, at the drop of a hat, $6 \times 15 = 90$, $17 \times 12 = 204$, $18 \times 19 = 342$, and $20 \times 20 = 400$. However, these extra memorizations, involving two-digit numbers, though handy, are not absolutely necessary. You can make out perfectly well if you memorize a multiplication table that takes you only to 9×9.

The simplest part of multiplication involves zero. Any number at all, no matter how large, when multiplied by zero gives zero as the product. We can say that $2 \times 0 = 0$; $75 \times 0 = 0$; $6,354,876 \times 0 = 0$. And, of course, $0 \times 0 = 0$.

This behaviour of zero simplifies certain types of multiplication problems. Suppose, for instance, you want to multiply 10 by 10 and that you decide to do it by the step-by-step method you were taught in school. First, you multiply 10 by 0, writing down the answer; then you multiply 10 by 1, indenting the second answer; finally you add the two answers. I am sure that you all know how to do this and, in fact, that you do this sort of thing every time you multiply. The problem 10×10 would then be worked out as follows:

$$
\begin{array}{r}
10 \\
\times \quad 10 \\
\hline
00 \\
10 \\
\hline
100
\end{array}
$$

The numbers that lie between the two horizontal lines are called 'partial products'. Notice that the first partial product comes out 00, because that partial product is the result of multiplying 10 by 0, and all multiplications by 0 yield 0. We might write 00 or 000 or even 000000000000, but all numbers made up only of zeros are equal to 0.

We get these zeros as partial products whenever there is a zero as one of the digits in the multiplier. Let's take some more cases of multiplications involving numbers made up of a 1 followed by several zeros.

$$
\begin{array}{r}
100 \\
\times \quad 100 \\
\hline
000 \\
0\,00 \\
10\,0 \\
\hline
10,000
\end{array}
\qquad
\begin{array}{r}
1,000 \\
\times \quad 10 \\
\hline
0\,000 \\
10\,00 \\
\hline
10,000
\end{array}
$$

In short, $100 \times 100 = 10,000$ and $1000 \times 10 = 10,000$. If we stick to numbers of this type and study the answers, we find that the product contains as many zeros as do the multiplicand and multiplier put together.

In multiplying 10×10, multiplicand and multiplier end in one zero apiece and the product 100 ends in two zeros. In multiplying 100×100, multiplicand and multiplier end in two zeros apiece and the product, 10,000, ends in four zeros. Again, in multiplying $1,000 \times 10$, the total number of zeros in multiplicand and multiplier is four and the product is also 10,000.

Without bothering to multiply out in full, you can tell that 10,000 × 1,000 with a total of seven zeros, must have a product of 10,000,000.

If the numbers being multiplied contain but a single digit before the various zeros and one or both of these digits is not 1, things are hardly any more complicated. Suppose that we wish to multiply 300 by 500. We can write 300 as 3 × 100 and 500 as 5 × 100. This means that 300 × 500 = 3 × 100 × 5 × 100. But we know from the multiplication table that 3 × 5 = 15 and we know from adding zeros that 100 × 100 = 10,000. Therefore 3 × 100 × 5 × 100 = 15 × 10,000, or 150,000.

If you consider this preceding paragraph carefully, you see that what we are doing is to add the zeros of multiplicand and multiplier and put the product of the non-zero digits in front of the sum of those zeros.

In multiplying 300 × 500 we could, without ado, count zeros and see that the answer must end in four zeros, 0000. We then multiply 3 × 5 and place the product, 15, in front of the four zeros. That gives us our complete answer, 150,000.

Using this system, you can see quickly that 700 × 4,000 has an answer in which 28 (that is, 7 × 4) is followed by five zeros. Therefore 700 × 4,000 = 2,800,000. In the same way 5 × 50 has as its product 25 followed by a single zero, or 250; 100×80 = 8,000; 20×60 = 1,200, and so on.

Sometimes it is possible to have more zeros in the product than you might expect from merely counting the zeros in multiplicand and multiplier. Suppose you were multiplying 40 × 50. You know the answer will end in two zeros, 00, and that these will be preceded by the product of 4 × 5, which is 20. Therefore, 40 × 50 = 2000, which, as it turns out, ends in three zeros, not in two. The third zero, however, was added by way of the product of 4 × 5, and not by adding the zeros in multiplicand and multiplier.

This is not a matter of concern, of course. The method

of counting zeros and putting the product of the single digits before those zeros will give the correct answer in any case. If an additional zero is needed, it will be added automatically.

What we see, then, is that we have learned more from the multiplication table than we perhaps supposed. In memorizing the product of 8 × 9 as 72, we also made it possible for ourselves to tell, at a glance, the product of 80 × 9, of 8 × 90, of 80 × 90, of 8,000 × 900, and so on.

But if we think that's all there is to multiplication, we are living in a fool's paradise. What if one of the numbers contains more than one digit that is not zero? What if it is not the product of 8 × 9 that we want but the product of 83 × 9?

This is something we haven't memorized in any multiplication table. Instead, we usually work it out digit by digit in the manner taught us in school. First, we multiply the 3 by the 9, which gives us 27. We put down 7 and carry 2. Then we multiply 8 × 9, which gives us 72. Adding the 2 we have carried, gives us the sum of 74. Writing this down before the 7 we had previously written down, the answer is 747. This system of multiplying without actually writing down the partial products is 'short multiplication'. If we multiply 83 × 9 by short multiplication, it would look like this:

$$
\begin{array}{r}
83 \\
\times \quad 9 \\
\hline
2 \\
\hline
747
\end{array}
$$

If we wrote out the partial products in full, we would have 'long multiplication', thus:

$$
\begin{array}{r}
83 \\
\times \quad 9 \\
\hline
27 \\
72 \\
\hline
747
\end{array}
$$

Is there any way of simplifying this? Yes, there is, if we follow our basic principle of changing a difficult problem into an easy one. We have already decided that once the multiplication table is memorized it is easy to multiply numbers that consist of only single digits, plus zeros. How, then, can we convert 83 into such numbers? The logical way is to write 83 as 80 + 3. The number 3 is a single digit, and the number 80 is a single digit plus a zero.

But how can one multiply 80 + 3 by 9?

Using algebraic symbolism we are multiplying a sum $a + b$ by a number c and this is written $(a + b)c$. If we clear parentheses, we find that $(a + b)c = ac + bc$. In other words, to multiply 80 + 3 by 9, we first multiply 80×9, then 3×9, then add the two products.

This may strike you as a step backwards. How can we make a multiplication simpler by changing it into two multiplications? Are we not just making it harder? Not at all. We are converting one difficult multiplication into two easy ones, and this is a step forwards, not backwards. We know at a glance that $80 \times 9 = 720$, and that $3 \times 9 = 27$. Since $720 + 27 = 747$, there is our answer.

You can do this in your head without trouble, in all likelihood, but if you want to do it on paper it would look like this:

$$\begin{array}{r} 80 + 3 \\ \times 9 \\ \hline 720 + 27 = 747 \end{array}$$

Naturally you can use this method on numbers involving final zeros. If you are faced with the multiplication 83×90, work out 83×9 and add the zero. Since you know that $83 \times 9 = 747$, then $83 \times 90 = 7,470$. Furthermore, $830 \times 9 = 7,470$ also, $8,300 \times 900 = 7,470,000$, and so on.

Now let's look back a bit to the point where I multiplied 83×9 by the usual method of long multiplication. The partial products were:

$$\begin{array}{r} 27 \\ 72 \\ \hline \end{array}$$

The indented 72 might just as well have a zero after it, for that would not change things. In that case we would have:

$$
\begin{array}{r}
83 \\
\times\ \ 9 \\
\hline
27 \\
720 \\
\hline
747
\end{array}
$$

This means that in ordinary long multiplication we are adding 27 and 720 to get 747, while in the method I recommend, we are adding 720 and 27. Since we are doing the same thing either way, why should one method be preferable to the other?

The answer is this: the school method works from right to left. This is to simplify the written work. Any number you write down will not have to be changed as a result of any number that you will later carry (just as in addition). The trouble is that we think the numbers from left to right, no matter how much we may work with them from right to left, and that makes for confusion.

If we try to multiply 83×9 mentally, in the usual manner, we begin by saying $3 \times 9 = 27$, put down 7 and carry 2, but since we think of 27 as 'two-seven' we might carelessly put down 2 and carry 7. We then end with a completely wrong answer.

In the left-to-right method, however, we are thinking of numbers in the customary left-to-right way. We say $(80 + 3) \times 9 = 720 + 27 = 747$. It may not be any easier arithmetically, but it is certainly easier psychologically.

In the same way you can say $44 \times 6 = (40 + 4) \times 6 = 240 + 24 = 264$; and $46 \times 7 = (40 + 6) \times 7 = 280 + 42 = 322$; and so on.

Furthermore, the left-to-right method is more versatile in that it allows subtractions as well as additions. The school method of right-to-left does not allow this.

Suppose that we must multiply 89×7. We can write this $(80 + 9) \times 7 = 560 + 63 = 623$. However, adding 560 and 63 mentally might produce a bit of hesitation. Why not, then, consider 89 to be 90 −1, rather than 80 + 9? Now we can say that $89 \times 7 = (90 - 1) \times 7 = 630 - 7 = 623$.

Most people would find it easier to deal with $630 - 7$ than with $560 + 63$, and the left-to-right method allows such people to make the necessary shift from addition to subtraction.

In the same way, $49 \times 8 = (50 - 1) \times 8 = 400 - 8 = 392$. And $38 \times 3 = (40 - 2) \times 3 = 120 - 6 = 114$.

Of course, you can pass this system on to numbers with more than two digits. The problem 546×6 can be expressed as $(500 + 40 + 6) \times 6 = 3,000 + 240 + 36 = 3,276$. Or, $329 \times 5 = (300 + 30 - 1) \times 5 = 1,500 + 150 - 5 = 1,645$.

If you try this technique on larger numbers, you may well find it difficult to keep all the partial products in your head while trying to sum them. Enough practice will make it easier to do so but if you would rather not devote the necessary time to such practice, all is not yet lost. You can use pencil and paper after all.

In multiplying $7,625 \times 7$, you can mentally break up 7,625 into $7,000 + 600 + 20 + 5$, and multiply each of these portions by 7. You then write down the partial products only:

$$
\begin{array}{r}
49,000 \\
4,200 \\
140 \\
35 \\
\hline
53,375
\end{array}
$$

You may still find this faster than the usual method taught in school.

When the British edition of this book came out, it seemed to me I found an egregious error on the book jacket. This sometimes happens but, fortunately, very rarely. Still, it remains the nightmare of all right-thinking authors and editors.

In the case of Realm of Numbers, *for instance, the worst of all book-jacket mistakes took place – my name was misspelled. Houghton Mifflin had to paint in a black strip on every book jacket and place my name, correctly spelled, on that strip. If you have a copy of that book, you will see the black strip. – And now you will know why, unless Houghton Mifflin censors out this paragraph in order to hide their shame.*

For that matter, in the first printing of my story collection The Martian Way and Other Stories *published in 1955 by Doubleday, my name was misspelled on the spine of the book itself. Usually I never think to remove the book jacket and look at the book itself, but some obscure inner feeling drove me to do it that time and waves of horror broke wildly over me.*

My second name received an unwanted Z. *Actually the name is pronounced as though that letter were a* Z, *and it should be a* Z. *It was my father that misspelled it, through ignorance of the Latin alphabet (though he had the Hebrew and Cyrillic alphabets down cold). Still, it is an* S *now and it must stay an* S. *It is* A-S-I-M-O-V. *I've reached the ridiculous point now where I snap at strangers who write me letters in which the* Z *is present in my name and insist they write again before I answer properly.*

I tell myself that I do this because name recognition is my greatest asset and that I owe it to my writing career to keep my name purely and wholesomely spelled – but that's just rationalization. Actually, I'm a nut.

The mistake I found on the British edition of Quick and Easy Math *(to get back from the digression – and I suspect this book will turn out to be little more than a collection of digressions) was in the title, so I could afford to smile tolerantly. The innocent Englishmen had written it* Quick and Easy Maths. *I pointed out this mistake to Houghton Mifflin, laughing heartily, and they told me that 'maths' was the standard British abbreviation for 'mathematics'.*

Well, it's their language, I suppose.

Of course, having indicated how to do simple problems

in one's head, I had to write another book on how to do complicated problems on a slide rule.

Here I had a momentary hesitation. After all, there are a number of books telling people how to use a slide rule. In fact, any decent slide rule comes equipped with a little booklet explaining how to use it. Did I have to add another?

But that kind of argument must be squelched. There are also books written on every other subject I discuss in my own volumes and if I begin worrying about one item, I will have to worry about every other item I add to the set of infinitely-retold tales.

So I reasoned it out once and for all. I write on a subject, however often it has previously been treated, because it is my pleasure to do so and because it is an honest living. Then, too, I have managed to convince myself I do it better than anyone else, and I'll thank you not to disillusion me in this respect.

Mathematics has an oddly uncomfortable relationship to science fiction. It is easy to write a science-fiction story centred about an astronomic idea, or a chemical one, or a physical, or biological one. Every time some startling new discovery is made in the natural sciences, there are bound to be a rash of science-fiction stories exploiting it. Heavens, when the atom bomb dropped, atomic-doom science-fiction stories grew to be so numerous that editors began refusing them on sight.

But what do you do with mathematics? Generally, it doesn't lend itself to exciting science fiction, and new and startling mathematical discoveries are generally so rarefied that expounding them in fictional guise is almost impossible.

To be sure, something can be done. I've tried my own hand at mathematical science fiction, remaining as carefully below the integral calculus ceiling in fiction as in fact. Indeed, I got down to the simplest of arithmetic in a tale that was a fictional precursor of Realm of Numbers. *And just*

*to show you what can be done with the most elementary
of arithmetic, here's the story (not a very long one) in full:*

'The Feeling of Power' *(1958)*

Jehan Shuman was used to dealing with the men in
authority on long-embattled Earth. He was only a civilian
but he originated programming patterns that resulted in
self-directing war computers of the highest sort. Generals
consequently listened to him. Heads of congressional com-
mittees, too.

There was one of each in the special lounge of New
Pentagon. General Weider was space-burned and had a
small mouth puckered almost into a cipher. Congressman
Brant was smooth-cheeked and clear-eyed. He smoked
Denebian tobacco with the air of one whose patriotism was
so notorious, he could be allowed such liberties.

Shuman, tall, distinguished, and Programmer-first-class,
faced them fearlessly.

He said, 'This, gentlemen, is Myron Aub.'

'The one with the unusual gift that you discovered quite
by accident,' said Congressman Brant placidly. 'Ah.' He
inspected the little man with the egg-bald head with
amiable curiosity.

The little man, in return, twisted the fingers of his hands
anxiously. He had never been near such great men before.
He was only an ageing low-grade Technician who had long
ago failed all tests designed to smoke out the gifted ones
among mankind and had settled into the rut of unskilled
labour. There was just this hobby of his that the great
Programmer had found out about and was now making
such a frightening fuss over.

General Weider said, 'I find this atmosphere of mystery
childish.'

'You won't in a moment,' said Shuman. 'This is not
something we can leak to the firstcomer. – Aub!' There
was something imperative about his manner of biting off

that one-syllable name, but then he was a great Programmer speaking to a mere Technician. 'Aub! How much is nine times seven?'

Aub hesitated a moment. His pale eyes glimmered with a feeble anxiety. 'Sixty-three,' he said.

Congressman Brant lifted his eyebrows. 'Is that right?'

'Check it for yourself, Congressman.'

The congressman took out his pocket computer, nudged the milled edges twice, looked at its face as it lay there in the palm of his hand, and put it back. He said, 'Is this the gift you brought us here to demonstrate. An illusionist?'

'More than that, sir. Aub has memorized a few operations and with them he computes on paper.'

'A paper computer?' said the general. He looked pained.

'No, sir,' said Shuman patiently. 'Not a paper computer. Simply a sheet of paper. General, would you be so kind as to suggest a number?'

'Seventeen,' said the general.

'And you, Congressman?'

'Twenty-three.'

'Good! Aub, multiply those numbers and please show the gentlemen your manner of doing it.'

'Yes, Programmer,' said Aub, ducking his head. He fished a small pad out of one shirt pocket and an artist's hairline stylus out of the other. His forehead corrugated as he made painstaking marks on the paper.

General Weider interrupted him sharply. 'Let's see that.'

Aub passed him the paper, and Weider said, 'Well, it looks like the figure seventeen.'

Congressman Brant nodded and said, 'So it does, but I suppose anyone can copy figures off a computer. I think I could make a passable seventeen myself, even without practice.'

'If you will let Aub continue, gentlemen,' said Shuman without heat.

Aub continued, his hand trembling a little. Finally he

said in a low voice, 'The answer is three hundred and ninety-one.'

Congressman Brant took out his computer a second time and flicked it, 'By Godfrey, so it is. How did he guess?'

'No guess, Congressman,' said Shuman. 'He computed that result. He did it on this sheet of paper.'

'Humbug,' said the general impatiently. 'A computer is one thing and marks on paper are another.'

'Explain, Aub,' said Shuman.

'Yes, Programmer. – Well, gentlemen, I write down seventeeen and just underneath it, I write twenty-three. Next, I say to myself: seven times three –'

The congressman interrupted smoothly, 'Now, Aub, the problem is seventeen times twenty-three.'

'Yes, I know,' said the little Technician earnestly, 'but I *start* by saying seven times three because that's the way it works. Now seven times three is twenty-one.'

'And how do you know that?' asked the congressman.

'I just remember it. It's always twenty-one on the computer. I've checked it any number of times.'

'That doesn't mean it always will be, though, does it?' said the congressman.

'Maybe not,' stammered Aub. 'I'm not a mathematician. But I always get the right answers, you see.'

'Go on.'

'Seven times three is twenty-one, so I write down twenty-one. Then one times three is three, so I write down a three under the two of twenty-one.'

'Why under the two?' asked Congressman Brant at once.

'Because –' Aub looked helplessly at his superior for support. 'It's difficult to explain.'

Shuman said, 'If you will accept his work for the moment, we can leave the details for the mathematicians.'

Brant subsided.

Aub said, 'Three plus two makes five, you see, so the twenty-one becomes a fifty-one. Now you let that go for a while and start fresh. You multiply seven and two, that's fourteen, and one and two, that's two. Put them down like this and it adds up to thirty-four. Now if you put the thirty-four under the fifty-one this way and add them, you get three hundred and ninety-one and that's the answer.'

There was an instant's silence and then General Weider said, 'I don't believe it. He goes through this rigmarole and makes up numbers and multiplies and adds them this way and that, but I don't believe it. It's too complicated to be anything but horn-swoggling.'

'Oh no, sir,' said Aub in a sweat. 'It only *seems* complicated because you're not used to it. Actually, the rules are quite simple and will work for any numbers.'

'Any numbers, eh?' said the general. 'Come then.' He took out his own computer (a severely styled GI model) and struck it at random. 'Make a five seven three eight on the paper. That's five thousand seven hundred and thirty-eight.'

'Yes, sir,' said Aub, taking a new sheet of paper.

'Now' (more punching of his computer), 'seven two three nine. Seven thousand two hundred and thirty-nine.'

'Yes, sir.'

'And now multiply those two.'

'It will take some time,' quavered Aub.

'Take the time,' said the general.

'Go ahead, Aub,' said Shuman crisply.

Aub set to work, bending low. He took another sheet of paper and another. The general took out his watch finally and stared at it. 'Are you through with your magic-making, Technician?'

'I'm almost done, sir. – Here it is, sir. Forty-one million, five hundred and thirty-seven thousand, three hundred and eighty-two.' He showed the scrawled figures of the result.

General Weider smiled bitterly. He pushed the multiplication contact on his computer and let the numbers whirl to a halt. And then he stared and said in a surprised squeak, 'Great Galaxy, the fella's right.'

The President of the Terrestrial Federation had grown haggard in office and, in private, he allowed a look of settled melancholy to appear on his sensitive features. The Denebian war, after its early start of vast movement and great popularity, had trickled down into a sordid matter of manoeuvre and countermanoeuvre, the discontent rising steadily on Earth. Possibly, it was rising on Deneb, too.

And now Congressman Brant, head of the important Committee on Military Appropriations, was cheerfully and smoothly spending his half-hour appointment spouting nonsense.

'Computing without a computer,' said the President impatiently, 'is a contradiction in terms.'

'Computing,' said the congressman, 'is only a system for handling data. A machine might do it, or a human brain might. Let me give you an example.' And, using the new skills he had learned, he worked out sums and products until the president, despite himself, grew interested.

'Does this always work?'

'Every time, Mr President. It is foolproof.'

'Is it hard to learn?'

'It took me a week to get the real hang of it. I think you would do better.'

'Well,' said the President, considering, 'it's an interesting parlour game, but what is the use of it?'

'What is the use of a newborn baby, Mr President? At the moment there is no use, but don't you see that this points the way towards liberation from the machine. Consider, Mr President,' the congressman rose and his deep voice automatically took on some of the cadences he used in public debate, 'that the Denebian war is a war of computer against computer. Their computers forge an impenetrable shield of counter-missiles against our missiles, and ours forge one against theirs. If we advance the efficiency of our computers, so do they theirs, and for five years a precarious and profitless balance has existed.

'Now, we have in our hands a method of going beyond the computer, leapfrogging it, passing through it. We will combine the mechanics of computation with human thought; we will have the equivalent of intelligent computers; billions of them. I can't predict what the consequences will be in detail but they will be incalculable. And if Deneb beats us to the punch, they may be unimaginably catastrophic.'

The President said, troubled, 'What would you have me do?'

'Put the power of the administration behind the establishment of a secret project on human computation. Call it Project Number, if you like. I can vouch for my committee, but I will need the administration behind me.'

'But how far can human computation go?'

'There is no limit. According to Programmer Shuman, who first introduced me to this discovery –'

'I've heard of Shuman, of course.'

'Yes. Well, Dr Shuman tells me that in theory there is nothing the computer can do that the human mind can not do. The computer merely takes a finite amount of data and performs a finite number of operations upon them. The human mind can duplicate the process.'

The President considered that. He said, 'If Shuman says this. I am inclined to believe him – in theory. But, in practice, how can anyone know how a computer works?'

Brant laughed genially. 'Well, Mr President, I asked the same question. It seems that at one time computers were designed directly by human beings. Those were simple computers, of course, this being before the time of the rational use of computers to design more advanced computers had been established.'

'Yes, yes. Go on.'

'Technician Aub apparently had, as his hobby, the reconstruction of some of these ancient devices and in so doing he studied the details of their workings and found he could imitate them. The multiplication I just performed for you is an imitation of the workings of a computer.'

'Amazing!'

The congressman coughed gently. 'If I may make another point, Mr President – the further we can develop this thing, the more we can divert our Federal effort from computer production and computer maintenance. As the human brain takes over, more of our energy can be directed into peacetime pursuits and the impingement of war on the ordinary man will be less. This will be most advantageous for the party in power, of course.'

'Ah,' said the President, 'I see your point. Well, sit down, Congressman, sit down. I want some time to think about this. — But meanwhile, show me that multiplication trick again. Let's see if I can't catch the point of it.'

Programmer Shuman did not try to hurry matters. Loesser was conservative, very conservative, and liked to deal with computers as his father and grandfather had. Still, he controlled the West European computer combine, and if he could be persuaded to join Project Number in full enthusiasm, a great deal would be accomplished.

But Loesser was holding back. He said, 'I'm not sure I like the idea of relaxing our hold on computers. The human mind is a capricious thing. The computer will give the same answer to the same problem each time. What guarantee have we that the human mind will do the same?'

'The human mind, Computer Loesser, only manipulates facts. It doesn't matter whether the human mind or a machine does it. They are just tools.'

'Yes, yes. I've gone over your ingenious demonstration that the mind can duplicate the computer but it seems to me a little in the air. I'll grant the theory but what reason have we for thinking that theory can be converted to practice?'

'I think we have reason, sir. After all, computers have not always existed. The cave men with their triremes, stone axes, and railroads had no computers.'

'And possibly they did not compute.'

'You know better than that. Even the building of a railroad or a ziggurat called for some computing, and that must have been without computers as we know them.'

'Do you suggest they computed in the fashion you demonstrate?'

'Probably not. After all, this method – we call it "graphitics", by the way, from the old European word "grapho" meaning "to write" – is developed from the computers themselves so it cannot have antedated them. Still, the cave men must have had *some* method, eh?'

'Lost arts! If you're going to talk about lost arts –'

'No, no. I'm not a lost-art enthusiast, though I don't say there may not be some. After all, man was eating grain before hydroponics, and if the primitives ate grain, they must have grown it in soil. What else could they have done?'

'I don't know, but I'll believe in soil-growing when I see someone grow grain in soil. And I'll believe in making fire by rubbing two pieces of flint together when I see that, too.'

Shuman grew placative. 'Well, let's stick to graphitics. It's just part of the process of etherealization. Transportation by means of bulky contrivances is giving way to direct mass-transference. Communications devices become less massive and more efficient constantly. For that matter, compare your pocket computer with the massive jobs of a thousand years ago. Why not, then, the last step of doing away with computers altogether? Come, sir, Project Number is a going concern; progress is already headlong. But we want your help. If patriotism doesn't move you, consider the intellectual adventure involved.'

Loesser said sceptically, 'What progress? What can you do beyond multiplication? Can you integrate a transcendental function?'

'In time, sir. In time. In the last month I have learned to handle division. I can determine, and correctly, integral quotients and decimal quotients.'

'Decimal quotients? To how many places?'

Programmer Shuman tried to keep his tone casual. 'Any number!'

Loesser's lower jaw dropped. 'Without a computer?'

'Set me a problem.'

'Divide twenty-seven by thirteen. Take it to six places.'

Five minutes later, Shuman said, 'Two point zero seven

nine six two three.'

Loesser checked it. 'Well, now, that's amazing. Multiplication didn't impress me too much because it involved integers after all, and I thought trick manipulation might do it. But decimals –'

'And that is not all. There is a new development that is, so far, top secret and which, strictly speaking, I ought not to mention. Still – We may have made a breakthrough on the square-root fronts.'

'Square roots?'

'It involves some tricky points and we haven't licked the bugs yet, but Technician Aub, the man who invented the science and who has an amazing intuition in connection with it, maintains he has the problem almost solved. And he is only a Technician. A man like yourself, a trained and talented mathematician, ought to have no difficulty.'

'Square roots,' muttered Loesser, attracted.

'Cube roots, too. Are you with us?'

Loesser's hand thrust out suddenly, 'Count me in.'

General Weider stumped his way back and forth at the head of the room and addressed his listeners after the fashion of a savage teacher facing a group of recalcitrant students. It made no difference to the general that they were the civilian scientists heading Project Number. The general was the overall head, and he so considered himself at every waking moment.

He said, 'Now square roots are all fine. I can't do them myself and I don't understand the methods, but they're fine. Still, the Project will not be sidetracked into what some of you call the fundamentals. You can play with graphitics any way you want to after the war is over, but right now we have specific and very practical problems to solve.'

In a far corner, Technician Aub listened with painful attention. He was no longer a Technician, of course, having been relieved of his duties and assigned to the Project, with a fine-sounding title and good pay. But, of course, the social distinction remained and the highly placed scientific leaders could never bring themselves to admit him to their ranks on a footing of equality. Nor, to do Aub justice, did he, himself, wish it. He was as uncomfortable with them as they were with him.

The general was saying, 'Our goal is a simple one, gentlemen; the replacement of the computer. A ship that can navigate space without a computer on board can be constructed in one-fifth the time and at one-tenth the expense of a computer-laden ship. We could build fleets five times, ten times as great as Deneb could if we could but eliminate the computer.

'And I see something even beyond this. It may be fantastic now; a mere dream; but in the future I see the manned missile!'

There was an instant murmur from the audience.

The general drove on. 'At the present time, our chief bottleneck is the fact that missiles are limited in intelligence. The computer controlling them can only be so large, and for that reason they can meet the changing nature of anti-missile defences in an unsatisfactory way. Few missiles, if any, accomplish their goal, and missile warfare is coming to a dead end; for the enemy, fortunately, as well as for ourselves.

'On the other hand, a missile with a man or two within, controlling flight by graphitics, would be lighter, more mobile, more intelligent. It would give us a lead that might well mean the margin of victory. Besides which, gentlemen, the exigencies of war compel us to remember one thing. A man is much more dispensable than a computer. Manned missiles could be launched in numbers and under circumstances that no good general would care to undertake as far as computer-directed missiles are concerned –'

He said much more but Technician Aub did not wait.

Technician Aub, in the privacy of his quarters, laboured long over the note he was leaving behind. It read finally as follows:

'When I began the study of what is now called graphitics, it was no more than a hobby. I saw no more in it than an interesting amusement, an exercise of mind.

'When Project Number began, I thought that others were wiser than I; that graphitics might be put to practical use as a benefit to mankind, to aid in the production of really practical mass-transference devices perhaps. But now I see it is to be used only for death and destruction.

'I cannot face the responsibility involved in having invented graphitics.'

He then deliberately turned the focus of a protein-depolarizer on himself and fell instantly and painlessly dead.

They stood over the grave of the little Technician while tribute was paid to the greatness of his discovery.

Programmer Shuman bowed his head along with the rest of them but remained unmoved. The Technician had done his share and was no longer needed, after all. He might have started graphitics, but now that it had started, it would carry on by itself overwhelmingly, triumphantly, until manned missiles were possible with who knew what else.

Nine times seven, thought Shuman with deep satisfaction, is sixty-three, and I don't need a computer to tell me so. The computer is in my own head.

And it was amazing the feeling of power that gave him.

Two things come to mind in connection with 'The Feeling of Power'. One involves the matter of anthologization. Almost every one of my science-fiction short stories and novelettes has been anthologized in one place or another (one of them in fifteen different collections so far, with three more in press at the moment of writing). Usually, though, these collections are devoted to science fiction exclusively.

Some of my stories, however, are anthologized in collections that are intended for general reading in the classroom,

*and here 'The Feeling of Power' is particularly prominent.
Perhaps that is because the story deals with arithmetic as a
method of making a rather subtle (I think) point. And the
'satire' in the story usually receives particular attention in
the questions placed at the end of the story in such collections.*

*I always read those questions with profound interest.
When I was in school myself I was forever being asked
questions about literary works and I used to wonder
whether the writers themselves could have answered the
questions satisfactorily. Since I try not to let even the most
fugitive of thoughts go to waste, I wrote a short-short based
on that notion in 1953, long after I was out of school. In
the tale, Shakespeare is brought into the present and is
enrolled in a college course on his own plays. You guessed
it! He flunked!*

*Anyway, I now had a chance to see for myself. For in-
stance, here are some of the questions asked about the
story in these collections:*

*'Any good science-fiction story is based upon certain
assumptions as to what is going to happen during the next
few centuries. What are the assumptions in this story?'*

*'What general failings of the human race are satirized
in this story?'*

*'What is the main interest for the reader in this story? Is
it in the action, the character, or the theme? Support your
answer.'*

*'What details which are casually introduced into the
story establish that it takes place in the far-distant future?'*

*I think I can answer all those questions, but what would
happen if I did and sneaked them into a class which had
been reading my story. Would they be the best set of
answers in the class? Would the teacher write 'Very Good'
on them, or would she write, 'I think you missed the
point'? Would I pass?*

Well, I'm not going to try.

*As a matter of fact, I don't even feel guilty about it. I just
write my stories, clickety-click, as they come pouring out*

of me. I don't sit around and analyse them, either before I write them or after I write them. That's for the reader to do, if he wishes. If he happens to see something there that was more or less vaguely in my mind as I wrote, I'm happy for both of us – but if he sees something that wasn't anywhere in my mind (as far as I know) who's to say he's wrong?

I once listened to a German philosopher (he was really German and he was a professor of philosophy) discuss one of my stories in detail, when he didn't know I was in the audience. After his lecture, I came up to dispute the points he had made in his interpretation and presented him with what I felt was a blockbuster when I said, 'After all, I happen to be the author of the story.'

'Oh,' said he, 'are you Isaac Asimov? I'm pleased to meet you and I admire your work but tell me – What makes you think, just because you wrote the story that you know anything at all about it?'

I've tried never to forget that little lesson.

The second item that comes to mind in connection with 'The Feeling of Power' concerns the disconcerting effect a literal mind can have.

I know a very fine man, the soul of kindness and generosity, who publishes a magazine devoted to computers. He asked if he might reprint one of my stories dealing with computers so I sent him a copy of 'The Feeling of Power'.

He sent it right back with the simple comment, 'I don't believe it is possible for human beings to forget how to do arithmetic.'

It isn't easy to strike me speechless (as you may guess from this book alone) but he managed it with that comment.

PART 4

Physics

I once took a course in high school physics which, for some reason forever buried in the murky mind of the teacher, began with a long and detailed study of the incandescent lamp. I never recovered.

I did poorly in the course, naturally, and I did not do remarkably well in my college course in the science, either. Press the button marked 'physics' in my brain and the first free-association response is 'Electric lights. Fooey.'

My chance for recovery came in 1962, when Mr Truman M. Talley (Mac, for short) of New American Library set about talking me into doing a whole series of small introductory paperback books on science. For the purpose, I remember, he came up to Boston, had me out to dinner, and spun such a web of charm about me that, at the crucial moment, when he whipped out the contract all set for my signing – I signed it.

Mac calmly placed his copy of the contract in his inner jacket pocket and said, 'Which science do you want to handle first?'

At once I said, 'If you don't mind, I'd like to tackle physics.'

You see, here was my chance. At last I would sit down and undo the electric-light damage that had been done me in high school. I would introduce physics the way it ought to be introduced; or, at the very least, the way I thought it ought to be introduced.

Mac and the New American Library were only going to handle the paperback version of the books, of course, and the hard-cover editions were signed over to Walker & Company. (Part of the reason for this was that Ed Burlingame, whom I mentioned before in connection with The Universe, *was Mac's associate at the time I was work-*

ing on the book. When he resigned to become editor in chief of Walker & Company, he had inside knowledge of the book's existence and grabbed it. Editors sometimes carry me around like a virus when they change jobs, and that's one of the reasons I have so many publishers.)

The book came out under the title Understanding Physics *but it was in three volumes. That was by no means intentional to begin with.*

The agreement was that I was to do books, not more than 90,000 words long, on each of the sciences. But who counts? When I'm writing and having fun, the last thing in the world I want to do is to cut myself short. I hadn't gone very far in my lovingly slow explanation of physics before I realized that there wasn't the slightest possibility of covering the necessary ground in 90,000 words. A quick estimate showed me that I would, by then, have dealt with only one-third of the subject matter.

So I devoted the first book to 'Motion, Sound, and Heat', the second book to 'Light, Magnetism, and Electricity', and the third book to 'The Electron, Proton, and Neutron'. In other words I had three introductions: one to Mechanics, one to Electromagnetics, and one to Subatomics.

I handed them in to New American Library as three separate books, but Mac decided to run them as three volumes of a single book. This publishing decision was accepted by Walker & Company, and out it came as a single book in three volumes.

This presented me with a serious problem. Do I count the book as one book or as three books in my list?

And don't ask what difference it makes.

It makes a lot of difference. When the book came out in 1966, I was three-quarters of the way towards My Hundredth Book and three books would give me three times the push ahead that one book would. I wanted it to be three books – yet I also wanted to be honest.

I told myself that I had written it as three separate books; I had submitted it as three separate books; that it had been entirely a publisher's decision to count it as a single book – and yet I couldn't quite convince myself that I wasn't just stretching matters for the sake of that Hundredth.

So I asked Ed Burlingame. I said, 'Ed, when you publish Understanding Physics, *do you think of it as one book or as three books?'*

And Ed said with a phenomenally straight face, 'Why three books of course, Isaac.'

I went off in a state of high satisfaction to enter them on my list in that fashion, refusing to let myself consider for one moment that Ed, as a good editor, knew what was bugging me and felt it his first duty to give me the answer I wanted.

The three volumes of Understanding Physics *approached the science from a historical viewpoint. I believe in the historical approach for a number of reasons and make use of it whenever I can.*

The most elaborate historical account of science I have yet attempted arose out of a suggestion made to me in 1961 by T. O'Conor Sloane of Doubleday. His letter aroused the liveliest interest in me because when I was a nine-year-old and picked up the August, 1929, issue of Amazing Stories, *the very first science-fiction magazine I ever read, its editor had been T. O'Conor Sloane. That editor had been an aged man at the time and had since died, but surely there must be some connection.*

There was! T. O'Conor Sloane III was the grandson of the onetime editor.

Could I refuse under those circumstances?

Tom Sloane asked me to do 250 short biographies of the most important scientists in history, arranged chronologically. In principle, that was easy, but it was clearly going to be a difficult task to pick out the 250 most important scientists, so I avoided the necessity of too many decisions by writing 1,000 short biographies.

By the time I was finished I was extremely nervous about the length of the book, and it seemed to me there was a dis-

tinct possibility that Tom might kill me when I brought it in. So I used strategy.

I plunked six boxes full of manuscript in front of him and said, 'I have finished the original plus carbon of the book.'

He looked at it in astonishment and said, 'It looks a little on the long side.'

I let that sink in, hoping he would estimate three boxes original and three boxes carbon. When I thought he had adjusted himself sufficiently, I brought in the other six boxes which I had hidden outside his door and said, 'And this is the carbon I spoke of.'

Fortunately, he had a sense of humour and started laughing.

Then came the problem of naming the book. I had called it on my manuscript: A Biographical History of Science and Technology, *which was a perfect description. However, publishers are concerned about the selling aspects of titles even more than about their descriptive aspects. Tom said 'history' was a bad title word and 'encyclopedia' was a good one from the sales point of view, so it became* A Biographical Encyclopedia of Science and Technology.

And then Tom said he thought my name had become sufficiently well known to add lustre to the title and, to my horror, suggested it become Asimov's Biographical Encyclopedia of Science and Technology. *That, indeed, proved to be the final title.*

I'm not kidding about my horror. I really did object. Partly it was because, although I am terribly fond of myself, I am not as conceited as all that. *Besides, if the book did badly I might not be able to persuade myself it wasn't my name in the title that had turned the trick and then I would feel rotten. But neither Tom nor anyone else at Doubleday would listen, and it came out with my name in the title, bold as brass.*

And it did well, at that. Doubleday has since put my name at the head of the title of two more books, and may even continue doing so, too.

Among the scientific biographies contained in the book were some that were as short as 100 words and others that were as long as 10,000 words, and I must admit that the choice of whom to include and how thoroughly to deal with him was entirely a matter of my own prejudices. If he were someone I liked, he got in at considerable length and that's all there was to it.

One of the scientists I particularly like is Galileo, so he got a pretty full treatment and here he is:

from ASIMOV'S BIOGRAPHICAL ENCYCLOPEDIA OF SCIENCE AND TECHNOLOGY *(1964)*

GALILEO (gahl-ih-lay'oh)
Italian astronomer and physicist
Born: Pisa, February 15, 1564
Died: Arcetri (near Florence), January 8, 1642

Universally known by his first name only, Galileo's full name is Galileo Galilei. He was born three days before Michelangelo died; a kind of symbolic passing of the palm of learning from the fine arts to science.

Galileo was destined by his father, a mathematician, to the study of medicine and was deliberately kept away from mathematics. In those days (and perhaps in these) a physician earned thirty times a mathematician's salary. Galileo would undoubtedly have made a good physician, as he might also have made a good artist or musician, for he was a true Renaissance man, with many talents.

However, fate took its own turning and the elder Galilei might as well have saved himself the trouble. The young student, through accident, happened to hear a lecture on geometry. He promptly talked his reluctant father into letting him study mathematics and science.

This was fortunate for the world, for Galileo's career was a major turning point in science. He was not content merely to observe; he began to measure, to reduce things to quantity, to see if he could not derive some mathematical relationship that would describe a phenomenon with simplicity and generality. He was not the first to do this, for it had been done even by Archimedes eighteen centuries before, but Galileo did it more extensively than his predecessors and, what is more, he had the literary ability (another talent) to describe his work so clearly and beautifully that he made his quantitative method famous and fashionable.

The first of his startling discoveries took place in 1581, when he was a teenager studying medicine at the University of Pisa. Attending services at the Cathedral of Pisa, he found himself watching a swinging chandelier, which air currents shifted now in wide arcs, now in small ones. To Galileo's quantitative mind, it seemed that the time of swing was the same regardless of the amplitude. He tested this by his pulsebeat. Then, upon returning home, he set up two pendulums of equal length and swung one in larger, one in smaller sweeps. They kept together and he found he was correct.

(In later experiments, Galileo was to find that the difficulty of accurately measuring small intervals of time was his greatest problem. He had to continue using his pulse, or to use the rate at which water trickled through a small orifice and accumulated in a receiver. It is ironic then, that after Galileo's death Huygens was to use the principle of the pendulum, discovered by Galileo, as the means by which to regulate a clock, thus solving the problem Galileo himself could not. Galileo also attempted to measure temperature, devising a thermoscope for the purpose in 1593. This was a gas thermometer which measured temperature by the expansion and contraction of gas. It was grossly inaccurate, and not until the time of Amontons, a century later, was a reasonable beginning made in thermometry. It should never be forgotten that the rate of advance of science depends a great deal on advances in techniques of measurement.)

In 1586 Galileo published a small booklet on the design

of a hydrostatic balance he had invented and this first brought him to the attention of the scholarly world.

Galileo began to study the behaviour of falling bodies. Virtually all scholars still followed the belief of Aristotle that the rate of fall was proportional to the weight of the body. This, Galileo showed, was a conclusion erroneously drawn from the fact that air resistance slowed the fall of light objects that offered comparatively large areas to the air. (Leaves, feathers, and snowflakes are examples.) Objects that were heavy enough and compact enough to reduce the effect of air resistance to a quantity small enough to be neglected, fell at the same rate. Galileo conjectured that in a vacuum *all* objects would fall at the same rate. (A good vacuum could not be produced in his day, but when it finally was, Galileo was proved to be right.)

Legend has it that Galileo demonstrated his views by simultaneously dropping two cannonballs, one ten times heavier than the other, from the Leaning Tower of Pisa. Both were seen and heard to strike the ground simultaneously. This seems to be nothing more than a legend, but a similar experiment was actually performed, or at least described, some years earlier by Stevinus.

Nevertheless, the experiments that Galileo did indeed perform were quite sufficient to upset Aristotelian physics.

Since his methods for measuring time weren't accurate enough to follow the rate of motion of a body in free fall, he 'diluted' gravity by allowing a body to roll down an inclined plane. By making the slope of the inclined plane a gentle one, he could slow the motion as much as he wished. It was then quite easy to show the rate of fall of a body was quite independent of its weight.

He was also able to show that a body moved along an inclined plane at a constantly accelerated velocity; that is, it moved more and more quickly. Da Vinci had noted this a century earlier but had kept it to himself.

This settled an important philosophic point. Aristotle had held that in order to keep a body moving, a force had to be continually applied. From this it followed, according to some medieval philosophers, that the heavenly bodies, which were continually moving, had to be pushed along by the eternal labours of angels. A few even used such arguments to deduce the existence of God. On the other hand, some philosophers of the late Middle Ages, such as Buridan, held that constant motion required no force after the initial impulse. By that view, God in creating the world could have given it a start and then let it run by itself forever after. If a continuous force *were* applied, said these philosophers, the resulting motion would become ever more rapid.

Galileo's experiments decided in favour of this second view and against Aristotle. Not only did the velocity of a falling ball increase steadily with time under the continuous pull of the earth, but the total distance it covered increased as the square of the time.

He also showed that a body could move under the influence of two forces at one time. One force, applying an initial force horizontally (as the explosion of a gun), could keep a body moving horizontally at a constant velocity. Another force, applied constantly in a vertical direction, could make the same body drop downwards at an accelerated velocity. The two motions superimposed would cause the body to follow a parabolic curve. In this way Galileo was able to make a science out of gunnery.

This concept of one body influenced by more than one force also explained how it was that everything on the surface of the earth, including the atmosphere, birds in flight, and falling stones, could share in the earth's rotation and yet maintain their superimposed motions. This disposed of one of the most effective arguments against the theories of Copernicus and showed that one need not fear that the turning and revolving earth would leave behind those objects not firmly attached to it.

(Galileo's proofs were all reached by the geometric methods of the Greeks. The application of algebra to geometry and the discovery of infinitely more powerful methods of mathematical analysis than those at Galileo's disposal had to await Descartes and Newton. Yet Galileo made do with what he had and his discoveries marked the beginning of the science of mechanics and served as the basis a century later for the three laws of motion propounded by Newton.)

In his book on mechanics Galileo also dealt with the strength of materials, founding that branch of science as well. He was the first to show that if a structure increased in all dimensions equally it would grow weaker – at least he was the first to explain the theoretical basis for this. This is what is now known as the square cube law. The volume increases as the cube of linear dimensions, but the strength only as the square. For that reason larger animals require proportionately sturdier supports than small ones. A deer expanded to the size of an elephant and kept in exact proportion would collapse. Its legs would have to be thickened out of proportion for proper support.

The success of Galileo and his successors, particularly Newton, in accounting for motion by pushes and pulls ('forces') gave rise to the thought that everything in the universe capable of measurement could be explained on the basis of pushes and pulls no more complicated in essence than the pushes and pulls of levers and gears within a machine. This mechanistic view of the universe was to gain favour until a new revolution in science three centuries after Galileo showed matters to be rather more complicated than the mechanists had assumed.

Galileo's work made him unpopular at Pisa and he moved to a better position at Padua. Galileo was always making himself unpopular with influential people, for he had a brilliant and caustic wit and he could not resist using that wit to make jackasses – and therefore bitter enemies – of those who disagreed with him. Even as a college student, he had been nicknamed 'the wrangler' because of his argumentativeness. Besides, he was so brilliant a lecturer that students flocked to hear him while his colleagues mumbled away in empty halls, and nothing will infuriate a colleague more than that.

In Padua, Galileo was corresponding with the great astronomer Kepler and came to believe in the truth of the theories of Copernicus, though he prudently refrained for a while from saying so publicly. However, in 1609, he heard that a magnifying tube, making use of lenses, had been invented in Holland. Before six months had passed, Galileo had devised his own version of the instrument, one that had a magnifying power of thirty-two, and had turned it on the heavens. Thus began the age of telescopic astronomy.

Using his telescope, Galileo found that the Moon had mountains and the Sun had spots, which showed once again that Aristotle was wrong in his thesis that the heavens were perfect and that only on Earth was there irregularity and disorder. Tycho Brahe had already refuted Aristotle in his studies on his nova and his comet, and Fabricius had done it in his studies of a variable star, but Galileo's findings attacked the Sun itself. (Other astronomers discovered the sunspots at almost the same time as Galileo and there was wrangling over priority, which made Galileo additional enemies. Galileo, however, whether he had priority in the discovery or not, did more than merely see the spots. He used them to show that the Sun rotated about its axis in twenty-seven days, by following individual spots around the Sun. He even determined the orientation of the Sun's axis in that fashion.)

The stars, even the brighter ones, remained mere dots of light in the telescope, while the planets showed as little globes. Galileo deduced from this that the stars must be much farther away than the planets and that the universe might be indefinitely large.

Galileo also found that there were many stars in existence that could be seen by telescope but not by naked eye. The Milky Way itself owed its luminosity to the fact that it was composed of myriads of such stars.

More dramatically, he found that Jupiter was attended by four subsidiary bodies, visible only by telescope, that circled it regularly. Within a few weeks of observation he was able to work out the periods of each. Kepler gave these latter bodies the name of satellites and they are still known as the Galilean satellites. They are known singly by the mythological names of Io, Europa, Ganymede, and Callisto. Jupiter with its satellites was a model of a Copernican system – small bodies circling a large one. It was definite proof that not all astronomical bodies circled the Earth.

Galileo observed that Venus showed phases entirely like those of the Moon, from full to crescent, which it must do if the Copernican theory was correct. According to the Ptolemaic theory, Venus would have to be a perpetual crescent. The discovery of the phases of Venus definitely demonstrated, by the way, the fact that planets shine by reflected sunlight. Galileo discovered that the dark side of the Moon had a dim glow that could only arise from light shining upon it from the Earth ('Earthshine'). This showed that Earth, like the planets, gleamed in the Sun, and removed one more point of difference between the Earth and the heavenly bodies.

All these telescopic discoveries meant the final establishment of Copernicanism more than half a century after Copernicus had published his book.

Galileo announced his discoveries in special numbers of a periodical he called *Sidereus Nuncius* ('Starry Messenger'), and these aroused both great enthusiasm and profound anger. He built a number of telescopes and sent them all over Europe, including one to Kepler, so that others might confirm his findings. Galileo visited Rome in 1611, where he was greeted with honour and delight, though not everyone was happy. The thought of imperfect heavens, of invisible objects shining there, and worst of all of the Copernican system enthroned and the Earth demoted from its position as centre of the universe was most unsettling. Galileo's conservative opponents persuaded Pope Pius V to declare Copernicanism a heresy, and Galileo was forced into silence in 1616.

Intrigue continued. Now Galileo's friends, now his enemies, seemed to have gained predominance. In 1632 Galileo was somehow persuaded that the Pope then reigning (Urban VIII) was friendly and would let him speak out. He therefore published his masterpiece, *Dialogue on the Two Chief World Systems*, in which he had two people, one representing the view of Ptolemy and the other the view of Copernicus, present their arguments before an intelligent layman. (Amazingly enough, despite his long friendship with Kepler, Galileo did not mention Kepler's modification of Copernicus' theory, a modification that improved it beyond measure.)

Galileo of course gave the Copernican the brilliant best of the battle. The Pope was persuaded that Simplicio, the character who upheld the views of Ptolemy in the book, was a deliberate and insulting caricature of himself. Galileo was brought before the Inquisition on charges of heresy (his indiscreet public statements made it easy to substantiate the charge) and was forced to renounce any views that were at variance with the Ptolemaic system. Romance might have required a heroic refusal to capitulate, but Galileo was nearly seventy and he had the example of Bruno to urge him to caution.

Legend has it that when he rose from his knees, having completed his renunciation, he muttered, *'Eppur si muove!'* ('And yet it moves' – referring to the Earth). This was indeed the verdict given by the world of scholarship, and the silencing of Galileo for the remaining few years of his old age (during which – in 1637 – he made his last astronomical discovery, that of the slow swaying or 'liberation' of the Moon as it revolves) was an empty victory for the conservatives. When he died they won an even shallower victory by refusing him burial in consecrated ground.

The Scientific Revolution begun with Copernicus had been opposed for nearly a century at the time of Galileo's trial, but by then the fight was lost. The Revolution not only existed, but also had prevailed, although, to be sure, there remained pockets of resistance. Harvard, in the year of its founding (1636), remained firmly committed to the Ptolemaic theory.

My bad habit of exceeding all planned bounds, either because I have too much to say, or because I want to 'begin at the beginning' makes itself felt in one way or another in almost all my books. In one of my smaller books on physics, The Neutrino –

But let me begin at the beginning. (You see?)

My first book editor was, as I mentioned earlier, Walter I. Bradbury of Doubleday. After I had done a baker's dozen of science-fiction books with him, he left Doubleday and took a position with Henry Holt. This was profoundly disturbing to me, for all my editors quickly become father figures to me (even when, as is increasingly true lately, they are younger than I am).

After all, editors let me make long-distance collect calls to them whenever my attic becomes lonely; they treat me to lunches at the slightest excuse, or none at all; and, most of all, they are indefatigable in reassuring me that everyone at the publishing house, from the president to the elevator operator, loves me. (I can't help it. Writing is a lonely occupation.)

Naturally, losing a father figure rattles one, and the interval that passes before one gets an appropriate fixation on the next editor is cold and dismal. What's more, the longer and closer an editor has been with you, the greater the trauma of separation when it comes. At my two major publishing houses, particularly (Houghton Mifflin and Doubleday) the various editors with whom I am involved now have strict instructions never to resign, whatever purely material advantages may be held out to them elsewhere. (They all assure me in the most soothing way that they never will and, to give them credit, they say it with the most serious expressions you can imagine.)

But Brad did leave and I was lost for a while until it occurred to me that perhaps I might write a book for him

*at his new place. I eventually visited him at Holt and we
talked about a book, and then, a few days later, I got a
letter from him telling me that for reasons entirely uncon-
nected with my visit, he had resigned his position.*

*Eventually, he was at Harper's, and eventually, I tried
again. One effort came to naught under circumstances I
will describe later. A second time, though, we again discussed a book and this time we actually got as far as
signing a contract – and then Brad left Harper's and returned to Doubleday!*

*Quite aware that I would be terrified of being left with
strangers, he arranged to carry the contract with him and,
when the book was finally completed, it was Doubleday
that published it. It turned out to be* The Neutrino.

*This was the first time Brad was involved with a manu-
script of mine that was non-fiction, and he wasn't used to
my meandering. When I said that I was going to write a
book about the neutrino, I suppose he thought I would
start more or less: 'Once upon a time there was a neutrino.'*

*I didn't. I had to pave the way in my own fashion. I
began by laying a solid foundation and discussing the
development of the conservation laws in physics. At precisely the mid-point of the book, I began a section which
bore the subheading, 'Enter the Neutrino', and Brad pen-
cilled lightly in the margin, 'At last!'*

*I have my reasons for meandering, of course. One of my
problems, for instance, is that I have a fixation on counting.
No matter what the subject may be on which I am writing,
if I reach a place where it is possible to compare numbers
(especially large numbers), I detour. I made a point of this
in the introduction to* Only a Trillion, *which I'll come back
to later but which I'll now content myself with describing
as the very first collection of my science articles to be
published:*

from ONLY A TRILLION *(1957)*

One of the stories my mother likes to tell about me as a

child is that once, when I was nearly five, she found me standing rapt in thought at the kerbing in front of the house in which we lived. She said, 'What are you doing, Isaac?' and I answered, 'Counting the cars as they pass.'

I have no personal memory of this incident but it must have happened, for I have been counting things ever since. At the age of nearly five I couldn't have known many numbers and, even allowing for the relatively few cars roaming the streets thirty years ago, I must have quickly reached my limit. Perhaps it was the sense of frustration I then experienced that has made me seek ever since for countable things that would demand higher and higher numbers.

With time I grew old enough to calculate the number of snowflakes it would take to bury Greater New York under ten feet of snow and the number of raindrops it would take to fill the Pacific Ocean. There is even a chance that I was subconsciously driven to make chemistry my lifework out of a sense of gratitude to that science for having made it possible for me to penetrate beyond such things and take – at last – to counting atoms.

There is a fascination in large numbers which catches at most people, I think, even those who are easily made dizzy.

For instance, take the number one million; a 1 followed by six zeros; 1,000,000 or, as expressed by physical scientists, 10^6, which means $10 \times 10 \times 10 \times 10 \times 10 \times 10$.

Now consider what 'one million' means.

How much time must pass in order that a million seconds may elapse? – Answer: just over $11\frac{1}{2}$ days.

What about a million minutes? – Answer: just under 2 years.

How long a distance is a million inches? – Answer: just under 16 miles.

Assuming that every time you take a step your body moves forward about a foot and a half, how far have you gone when you take a million steps? – Answer: 284 miles.

In other words:

The secretary who goes off for a week to the mountains has less than a million seconds to enjoy herself.

The professor who takes a year's Sabbatical leave to write a book has just about half a million minutes to do it in.

Manhattan Island from end to end is less than a million inches long.

And, finally, you can walk from New York to Boston in less than a million steps.

Even so, you may not be impressed. After all, a jet plane can cover a million inches in less than a minute. At the height of World War II, the United States was spending a million dollars every six minutes.

So – let's consider a trillion. A trillion is a million million; a 1 followed by 12 zeros; 1,000,000,000,000; 10^{12}.

A trillion seconds is equal to 31,700 years.

A trillion inches is equal to 15,800,000 miles.

In other words, a trillion seconds ago, Stone Age man lived in caves, and mastodons roamed Europe and North America.

Or, a trillion-inch journey will carry you 600 times around the Earth, and leave more than enough distance to carry you to the Moon and back.

And yet . . . even a trillion can become a laughably small figure in the proper circumstances.

After considerable computation one day recently I said to my long-suffering wife: 'Do you know how rare astatine-215 is? If you inspected all of North and South America to a depth of ten miles, atom by atom, do you know how many atoms of astatine-215 you would find?'

My wife said, 'No. How many?'

To which I replied, 'Practically none. Only a trillion.'

This fetish of mine was one thing that slowed up The Neutrino. *At the point where I got a chance to talk about solar energy, I went into it in far greater detail than I had to because I could not resist playing with numbers –*

from THE NEUTRINO *(1966)*

Consider the Sun. The most obvious characteristic of that body is the quantity of light and heat it delivers despite the fact that it is 93,000,000 miles from us. It lights and warms all the Earth and has done so constantly through all of history.

The energy in the form of light and heat pouring down from the noonday Sun upon a single square centimetre of the Earth's surface in a single minute is 1.97 calories. This quantity, 1.97 cal/cm²/min, is called the *solar constant.*

A cross section of the Earth in a plane perpendicular to the radiation reaching it from the Sun is about 1,280,000,-000,000,000,000 or 1.28×10^{18} square centimetres in area. Therefore the total radiation striking the Earth each minute is about 2,510,000,000,000,000,000 or 2.51×10^{18} calories.

Even this by no means expresses all the radiation of the Sun. The Sun radiates energy in all directions and only very little of it strikes the tiny Earth.

Imagine a huge, hollow sphere with the Sun enclosed at its centre, with every part of the sphere 93,000,000 miles from the Sun. The Sun would light and heat every part of that sphere just as it does the Earth, and the area of this huge sphere would be over two billion times the cross-sectional area of the Earth. That means that the Sun radiates more than two billion times as much energy as the Earth manages to intercept.

The total energy radiated by the Sun is 5,600,000,000,-000,000,000,000,000,000 or 5.6×10^{27} cal/min. What's more the Sun has been radiating 5.6×10^{27} cal/min through all of recorded history and for an indefinitely long period before that, with only slight variations.

Here, then, is the crucial question: Where is all that energy coming from? If the law of conservation of energy applies to the Sun as well as to the Earth, then the incredibly vast supply of energy being poured into space by the Sun cannot be created out of nothing. Energy can only be changed from one form to another, and therefore the

Sun's radiation must be at the expense of another form of energy. But what other form?

A person pondering the problem might think first of chemical energy, as the form of the disappearing energy. A coal fire, for example, delivers light and heat as the Sun does, when the carbon of the coal and the oxygen of the air combine to form carbon dioxide.

Can it be, then, that the Sun is nothing more than a vast coal fire and that its radiant energy is obtained at the expense of chemical energy?

This possibility can be eliminated without trouble. Chemists know quite well exactly how much energy is given off by the burning of a given quantity of coal. Suppose the Sun's enormous mass (which is 333,500 times that of the Earth) were nothing but coal and oxygen and that the two were combining at such a rate as to produce 5.6×10^{27} cal/min. The Sun would then, indeed, be a coal fire lighting and heating the solar system as it is observed to do. But how long could such a coal fire continue to burn at such a rate before nothing is left but carbon dioxide? The answer is easily determined and works out to be a trifle over 1,500 years.

This is a small stretch of time. It covers only a fraction of the civilized history of mankind (to say nothing of the long aeons before that). Since the Sun was shining in its present fashion at the time of the height of the Roman Empire then we know without further investigation that it cannot be a coal fire, for it would be extinguished by now. Indeed, there is no known chemical reaction which would supply the Sun with the necessary energy for even a fraction of mankind's civilized existence.

Some alternatives to chemical energy must be examined, and one of them involves kinetic energy. We on Earth have a good display of the meaning of such energy every time a meteor strikes the upper atmosphere. Its kinetic energy is converted into heat by the effect of air resistance. Even a tiny meteor, the size of a pinhead, is heated to a temperature that causes it to blaze out for miles. A meteorite weighing a gram and moving at an ordinary velocity for meteorites (say, twenty miles per second) would have a kinetic energy of more than 5,000,000,000,000 or 5×10^{12} ergs – or about 120,000 calories.

A similar meteorite striking the Sun rather than the Earth would be whipped by the Sun's far stronger gravitational force to a far greater velocity. It would therefore deliver considerably more energy to the Sun. It is estimated, in fact, that a gram of matter falling into the Sun from a great distance would supply the Sun with some 44,000,000 calories of radiation. To take care of all the Sun's radiation, therefore, about 120,000,000,000,000,000,000 or 1.2×10^{20} grams of meteoric matter would have to strike the Sun every minute. This is equivalent to over a hundred trillion tons of matter.

This works well on paper but astronomers would view such a situation with the deepest suspicion. In the first place, there is no evidence that the solar system is rich enough in meteoric material to supply the Sun with a hundred trillion tons of matter every minute over long aeons of history.

Besides, this would affect the mass of the Sun. If meteoric material were collecting on the Sun at this rate then its mass would be increasing at the rate of about one percent in 300,000 years. This may not seem much, but it would seriously affect the Sun's gravitational pull, which depends upon its mass. If the Sun were increasing its mass even at this apparently slow rate, the Earth would be moving steadily closer to the Sun and our year would be growing steadily shorter. Each year would, in fact, be two seconds shorter than the one before, and astronomers would detect that fact at once, if it were indeed a fact. Since no such variation in the length of the year is observed, the possibility of meteorites serving as the source of the Sun's radiation must be abandoned.

Helmholtz, one of the architects of the law of conservation of energy, came up with a more reasonable alternative in 1853. Why consider meteorites falling into the Sun,

when the Sun's own material might be falling? The Sun's
surface is fully 432,000 miles from the Sun's centre.
Suppose that surface were slowly falling. The kinetic
energy of that fall could be converted into radiation.
Naturally, if a small piece of the Sun's surface fell a short
way towards the Sun's centre, very little energy would be
made available. However, if all the Sun's vast surface fell,
that is, if the Sun were contracting, a great deal of energy
might be made available.

Helmholtz showed that if the Sun were contracting at a
rate of 0.014 centimetres per minute, that would account
for its radiation. This was a very exciting suggestion, for it
involved no change in the Sun's mass and therefore no
change in its gravitational effects. Furthermore, the change
in its diameter as a result of its contraction would be small.
In all the six thousand years of man's civilized history, the
Sun's diameter would have contracted by only 560 miles
which, in a total diameter of 864,000 miles, can certainly
be considered insignificant. The shrinkage in diameter over
the two hundred fifty years from the invention of the
telescope to Helmholtz's time would be only twenty-three
miles, a quantity that would pass unnoticed by astronomers.

The problem of the Sun's radiation seemed solved, and
yet a flaw – a most serious one – remained. It was not
only during man's civilized history that the Sun had been
radiating, but for extended stretches of time before mankind had appeared upon the Earth.

How long those extended stretches had been no one
really knew in Helmholtz's time. Helmholtz, however, felt
this could be reasoned out. If the material of the Sun had
fallen inward from a great distance, say from the distance
of the earth's orbit, enough energy could have been supplied to allow the Sun to radiate at its present rate for
18,000,000 years. This would mean that the Earth could
not be more than 18,000,000 years old, however, for it
could scarcely be in existence in anything like its present
form when the matter of the Sun extended out to the

regions through which the Earth is now passing.

It might have seemed that a lifetime of 18,000,000 years for the Earth was enough for even the most demanding theorist, but it was not. Geologists, who studied slow changes in the Earth's crust, estimated by what seemed irrefutable arguments that to achieve the present situation, the Earth must have been in existence not for merely tens of millions of years, but for hundreds of millions of years, possibly for billions of years; and that through all that time, the Sun must have been shining in much its present fashion.

Then, too, in 1859, the theory of evolution by natural selection had been advanced by the English naturalist Charles Robert Darwin. If evolution was to have proceeded as biologists were then beginning to think it must have, then, again, the Earth had to be in existence for hundreds of millions of years at least, with the Sun shining throughout that time much as it is today.

During the second half of the nineteenth century, therefore, the law of conservation of energy was shored up, with respect to the Sun, in a most controversial fashion. A plausible theory had been proposed which astronomers were willing to accept, but which geologists and biologists objected to vigorously.

Apparently there were three alternatives:

1) The law of conservation of energy did not hold everywhere in the universe and, in particular, did not hold on the Sun – in which case 'all bets were off'.

2) The law of conservation did hold on the Sun, and the geologists and biologists were somehow wrong in their interpretation of the evidence they had mustered, so that the Earth was only a brief few million years old.

3) The law of conservation did hold on the Sun, but there was some source of energy as yet unknown to science which, when discovered, would allow for the Sun's radiating in its present fashion for billions of years, thus reconciling physical theory with the views of geologists and biologists.

In the end, it was alternative 3 which won out.

The Neutrino *was by no means the first book I had devoted to subatomics. The very first book I had written on physics was, in fact,* Inside the Atom, *where for the first time, I wrote up a serious description, for youngsters, of the development of the atomic bomb.*

I have always been ambivalent about the atomic bomb. Of all the recent discoveries of science, the atomic bomb was the first that was clearly 'science fictional'.

For one thing, work on it had been held utterly secret, so that it burst upon the world as a horrid surprise. For another, science-fiction writers had been dealing with such bombs in their stories all through the early 1940s. It is my understanding that the FBI, at one time, tried to stop the stories, but they were, very properly, informed that to stop atomic-bomb stories would give away the whole deal to 50,000 science-fiction fans at once. For a wonder, the FBI saw the point, and the stories were allowed to continue.

So, with no one but science-fiction writers saying anything, it ended up seeming science-fictional indeed.

My own personal science-fiction output, however, never included any reference to atomic bombs. This was not because I was unaware of the possibility, but precisely because I was aware and detested the possibility. I preferred instead to foresee the peaceful uses of atomic power. Thus, I had a passage in a story called 'Superneutron' (a very poor story for which I have never permitted anthologization) in which atomic power plants were described, in essence, with reasonable accuracy. The passage was written in late 1940, nearly fourteen years before such plants were actually established.

I claim no great foresight for making the prediction; everyone in science fiction was doing the same. Anyway, in the story a group of men are talking and here are two paragraphs of that conversation:

from 'Superneutron' *(1941)*

'Good,' agreed Hayes, 'but we'll pass on to another point for a moment. Do any of you remember the first atomic power plants of a hundred and seventy years ago and how they operated?'

'I believe,' muttered Levin, 'that they used the classic uranium fission method for power. They bombarded uranium with slow neutrons and split it up into masurium, barium, gamma rays and more neutrons, thus establishing a cyclic process.'

Exactly right!

Except that three years before the story was written, the element I call 'masurium' was formed by atomic bombardment. The earlier 'discovery' of that element had proved erroneous and the new formation was the first real isolation of the element. The element was therefore given the new and permanent name of 'technetium'.

I had been able to foresee fourteen years into the future with crystal clarity, but, alas, I had not been able to look three years into the past.

Well, the atomic bomb came, and it finally made science fiction 'respectable'. For the first time, science-fiction writers appeared to the world in general to be something more than a bunch of nuts; we were suddenly Cassandras whom the world ought to have believed.

But I tell you, I would far rather have lived and died a nut in the eyes of all the world than to have been salvaged into respectability at the price of nuclear war hanging like a sword of Damocles over the world forever.

PART 5

Chemistry

Although I have written on every branch of science and at every level, chemistry is the field in which I have received formal training. At least I majored in chemistry in college and then took a whole mess of additional chemistry courses in graduate school. As a result the three degrees I obtained from Columbia (B.S. 1939; M.A. 1941; and Ph.D. 1948) were all in chemistry.

But then, when Boston University School of Medicine offered me a faculty position in 1949, it was in the department of biochemistry.

You may ask: So what?

So a lot. There's a difference. Biochemistry is the study of the chemical processes that go on within living tissue and it has strong physiological and medical components. (That's why it is taught in a medical school.) It is a highly specialized branch of chemistry and it is one that is growing with enormous celerity. No one who has received his education only in 'straight' chemistry is entirely fit to teach biochemistry.

As it happened, I had had no courses in biochemistry at all and was therefore not entirely fit to teach biochemistry. But I wasn't going to toss away what (at that time) seemed like a good position. I reasoned that in a medical school no one faculty member teaches the entire course; we were each assigned specific lectures. I felt that I might be lucky and be assigned lectures that were among the more heavily 'straight' and the less heavily 'bio'. – And if not, I could teach myself biochemistry when no one was looking and stay a lecture ahead of the students. Besides, I was still under the impression, in 1949, that I preferred research to teaching and it was in research (I thought) that I would make my mark.

So I kept a cheerful smile on my face, did my best to exude self-confidence and accepted the position.

I managed. Fortunately my science-fiction writing had inured me to self-education, and I got away with it. In fact, so sure of myself did I grow that I had not been at the job much more than a year when I let myself be talked into co-authoring a medical school text on biochemistry.

I told the story of the birth of the textbook and some of what it meant to write it (and in collaboration, yet) in an article of mine called 'The Sound of Panting' in which I discussed the difficulties of keeping up with the subject in general. Here is the way the article begins:

from 'The Sound of Panting' *(1955)*

Back in September of 1950, Dr William C. Boyd, Professor of Immunochemistry at Boston University School of Medicine – where I work – having just come back from several months in Egypt, and feeling full of spirit, lured me to one side and suggested that we write a textbook on biochemistry for medical students. This struck me as a terrific idea. Dr Boyd had already written textbooks on blood-grouping, on immunology, and on anthropology, so there was no doubt in my mind that he could supply the experience. As for myself, although a science-fiction writer, I am not too proud to write textbooks, so I felt I could supply enthusiasm. We then rung in Dr Burnham S. Walker, who is the head of our Department of Biochemistry and who has an encyclopaedic knowledge of the subject. He went along not only with the notion but also with alacrity.

There followed a hectic interval in which we laid our plans, corralled a publisher, and had a lot of fun. But there came a time when all the preliminaries were over and we came face to face with a typewriter and a clean sheet of paper.

It took us a year and a half before the first edition was

done and I learned a lot about textbooks.

A textbook, after all, is an orderly presentation of what is known in a given branch of science and is intended to be used for the instruction of students. Note the word 'orderly'. It implies that a textbook must begin at the beginning, proceed through the various stages of the middle, and end at the end. Unfortunately, unless the science concerned is a deductive one such as mathematics or logic, this neat procedure is hampered by the fact that there is no beginning, no middle, and no end.

An inductive science such as biochemistry consists, essentially, of a vast conglomeration of data out of which a number of thinkers have abstracted certain tentative conclusions. It resembles a three-dimensional lacework all knotted together. To expound any portion of biochemistry properly, a certain knowledge of other areas of the science must be assumed. It is, therefore, the task of the writer to decide what one-dimensional order of presentation is least confusing. What subjects can he discuss in the earlier chapters with the best chance of being understood despite the absence of information contained in the later chapters? How often must an author stop to explain at a given point and how often can he get away with a simple reference to a page halfway up the book, or even with a curt 'See Appendix'? (I, by the way, was a devotee of the 'stop and explain' philosophy and I was consequently periodically crushed by the democratic procedure of being outvoted two to one.)

. . . Three collaborators have three different styles. True! Fortunately, by dint of revising each other's work and then beating out the results in triple conference, a reasonably uniform style was achieved with elimination of extremes. Dr Walker, for instance, whose natural style is extremely condensed, was forced to include occasional conjunctions and to allow the existence of a few subordinate clauses. I on the other hand, found that my more passionate outbursts of lyricism were ruthlessly pruned. Many was the gallant rearguard fight by one or another of us in favour of inserting a comma or of deleting it; many the anguished search through the Unabridged in defence of a maligned word.

Though I treat the situation lightly in the above passage, I did not really enjoy collaboration. I was outvoted far too many times and the final product, thought quite a decent and respectable textbook, never really felt, to me, as though it were mine.

To be sure, my two collaborators, Drs Walker and Boyd, were and are wonderful human beings with whom it was a pleasure to be associated, but I am simply not made for collaboration, that's all, where that collaboration extends to my writing.

I was trapped, far more reluctantly, into writing a second text (for student nurses this time) in collaboration, though there the machinery of collaboration was looser. That was it, though. I never did it again and I don't think I ever will. Besides the two texts, four books in my Hundred are collaborations if we go by the title page, but in those four the collaboration was for reasons that did not involve the actual writing. I did all the actual writing.

As it happened, Biochemistry and Human Metabolism *was rather a flop. Oh, the publisher (Williams & Wilkins) didn't lose money on it, but it didn't make much either. And our royalties, considering the time we spent on it were, while not actually beneath contempt, not very far above it.*

The reasons for that are by no means mysterious, either, for shortly after our text appeared, two other texts were published, each of which was longer, more detailed, more thorough and (oh, well) better than ours. So, after the third edition, when Dr Walker left the Medical School for greener pastures and Dr Boyd was too busy with other projects, we just let the book lapse. The publishers were very polite and hid their relief masterfully, but made no perceptible effort to induce us to reconsider.

Still, the first edition of the text has a certain personal

*importance to me since it was the first nonfiction book I
ever wrote. In fact, it was the first professional nonfiction
of any kind that I ever published. Considering that I am
now far more a nonfiction writer than a fiction writer, that
makes it a milestone for me.*

*The first chapter of the text was not mine in any of the
editions. It was written almost entirely by Dr Boyd. The
second chapter, on the other hand, was virtually entirely
mine, in all three editions. Consequently, here is the first
page of Chapter 2 – the first bit of my nonfiction writing,
which now stretches itself over seventy-three of my
Hundred Books:*

from BIOCHEMISTRY AND HUMAN METABOLISM (1952)

In a very real sense, life may be looked upon as a struggle
on the part of the body to maintain the internal structure
of the enormously complex protein molecules of which it
is composed. The difficult nature of such a task may be
judged from the fact that a distinctive property of most
protein molecules is their extreme instability as compared
with other chemical structures. Environmental factors as
mild as the warmth of a human hand or the gentle bubbling of air would suffice, in many cases, to so alter the
properties of a protein solution as to render it biologically
useless.

That life should be built on such fragile, almost evanes-
cent, molecules is not at all surprising. It would seem, upon
reflection, to be inevitable. Life implies change – quick
adjustments to altered conditions. There must be something then in a living organism which can vary with the
absorption of a few quanta of light, with trifling changes in
air pressure, oxygen concentration, temperature, or any
of the other hundreds of variables that beset us every
moment of time. That something is the protein molecule.

It might be tempting for beginning students to equate
complexity of structure with mere size of molecules. Thus,

the beta-lactoglobulin of milk has an empirical formula which is thought to be $C_{1864}H_{3012}N_{468}S_{21}O_{576}$. Here we have a molecule in which we can count almost six thousand individual atoms of five different kinds. The molecular weight is over forty thousand, which means that the molecule is some twenty-three hundred times as heavy as a water molecule and more than two hundred times as heavy as a molecule of the amino acid, tryptophane. And yet beta-lactoglobulin is a protein of comparatively simple structure. Certainly, its molecular weight is well below the average for proteins. Molecular weights in the hundreds of thousands are common and those in the millions are not unknown. There are protein molecules, in other words, which compare with beta-lactoglobulin as that protein compares with tryptophane.

Yet, knowing size, we know comparatively little. There are other types of molecules produced by living organisms which compare with proteins in molecular weight. There is cellulose, for instance, impressive in size, and yet used for nothing more in the living plant than to enclose the cell in a sturdy box. It is a huge molecule, yet so stable that we build houses out of it. Size alone is therefore no guarantee that a molecule will possess the flexibility and instability needed to have within it the potentiality of life.

Through the year and a half that our collaboration on the first edition of the text continued, I grew steadily more chafed and more anxious to try my hand at a book on biochemistry in which I would not be interfered with.

While the book was being written and I was chafing, I attended a lecture by George Wald on the biochemistry of vision, a lecture given at an American Chemical Society meeting at M.I.T.

Wald is the best lecturer on chemistry that I have ever heard, and this particular talk I heard in 1951 was the best and most entertaining one I ever listened to until I heard another talk on the biochemistry of vision given in Wash-

ington, D.C., on December 28, 1966, during the American Association for the Advancement of Science meetings. This 1966 lecture was also given by Wald. (And he won a share of the 1967 Nobel Prize in Physiology and Medicine for his work in this field.)

Wald speaks without notes and with no perceptible hesitation. Without seeming to simplify, he arranges matters so that even those who do not have specialized knowledge of the field can follow. What's more, he makes it seem interesting. And the acid test is this: even if, for some reason, you don't follow the line of argument, it still sounds interesting.

I came out of the lecture in 1951 with an absolutely unbearable desire to write biochemistry for the general public; something that would read as well as Wald's talks sounded. With great enthusiasm I turned out some sample chapters of biochemistry that would serve as a kind of text for the general public.

I tried the result on Doubleday, to whom up to that time I had sold four books. Brad read the manuscript and handed it back with one of the gentlest verbal rejection slips I have ever received. 'Isaac,' he said, very mildly, 'stick to fiction.'

I didn't give in without a struggle. I tried several other publishers. One and all agreed with Brad. Chagrined, I retired the manuscript sample (fortunately, I had never got around to writing the complete book) and returned to fiction.

I might have continued doing so to this day but for a rather unlooked-for accident. My erstwhile collaborator, William C. Boyd, had written an excellent book on genetics (his speciality) for the general public. Mr Henry Schuman, who at that time owned a small publishing firm in New York, had come to visit Bill, hoping he could get him to write a simplified version of the book for teenagers.

Bill, however, was drowned in work and could not undertake the task. Since he is a gentle soul who hated to have Mr Schuman come 200 miles to see him and then have to *leave empty-handed, he introduced him to me, as someone who was longing to write on scientific subjects for the general public.*

I had almost forgotten that, but Bill's reminder had my eyes glistening at once and poor Mr Schuman found himself avalanched in instant response.

It was all different this time. In my previous attempt, I had been trying to rewrite the text in more general terms, but now I threw all that away. I started from scratch and wrote a book for teenagers without any thought of the textbook at all, and that worked. Here, for instance, is how I handled the same subject matter I had discussed in the quoted section of the textbook:

from THE CHEMICALS OF LIFE *(1954)*

What makes proteins so unusual? Well, for one thing, the protein molecule is very large. To show what we mean by that, let's consider the weight of different kinds of atoms and molecules.

Naturally, all atoms are exceedingly light. It takes billions upon billions of them to make up the weight of even the tiniest particle of dust. It is one of the miracles of science that man has been able to weigh atoms despite their minuteness.

Now it turns out that the hydrogen atom is the lightest one that can exist and it is customary to call its weight 1 for convenience. Or, to put it just a little more scientifically, 1 is called the ATOMIC WEIGHT of hydrogen. The carbon atom is 12 times as heavy as the hydrogen atom and carbon's atomic weight is therefore 12. In the same way, we can say that the atomic weight of nitrogen is 14, of oxygen 16, and of sulphur is 32.

In order to find out how much a molecule weighs, it is only necessary to add up the atomic weights of the various atoms it contains. For instance, the hydrogen molecule consists of two hydrogen atoms, each with an atomic weight of 1. The MOLECULAR WEIGHT of hydrogen is therefore 2. Similarly, the nitrogen molecule is made up of two nitrogen atoms which weigh 14 each. The oxygen molecule is made up of two oxygen atoms which weigh 16 each. The molecular weight of nitrogen is therefore 28 and that of oxygen is 32.

The same rule holds where the atoms in a molecule are of different types. The water molecule, with one oxygen and two hydrogen atoms, has a molecular weight of 16 + 1 + 1, or 18.

As we said in the previous section, the water molecule is a rather small one. A molecule of table sugar, by contrast, has 12 carbon atoms, 22 hydrogen atoms, and 11 oxygen atoms. The 12 carbons weigh 144 altogether, the 22 hydrogens weigh 22, and the 11 oxygens weigh 176. Add them all together and the molecular weight of sugar turns out to be 342. This is a more sizeable figure than that for water, but it is by no means tops. A molecule of a typical fat contains as many as 170 atoms and has a molecular weight of nearly 900.

Now we are ready to consider the protein molecule. How does it compare with fat and sugar in this respect? Of course, there are innumerable different kinds of protein molecules, but we can pick a protein that occurs in milk and has been studied quite a bit. *In its molecule are no less than 5,941 atoms.* Of these, 1,864 are carbon, 3,012 are hydrogen, 576 are oxygen, 468 are nitrogen, and 21 are sulphur. The molecular weight, as you can see for yourself, is quite large. It comes to 42,020. The molecule of this protein is thus 45 times as large as a molecule of fat and 120 times as large as a molecule of sugar.

But is this protein a fair example? Actually, it is not, because it is a rather *small* protein. The average protein has a molecular weight of 60,000. Many go much higher. Some of the proteins in clam-blood, for instance, have a molecular weight of 4,000,000. And some of the viruses consist of protein molecules with molecular weights in the tens of millions and even the hundreds of millions.

Now size in itself can be very useful. The body can do things with a protein molecule that it could not do with smaller molecules. It is as though you were given the choice of having a birthday party in the large ballroom of an expensive hotel or in a little one-room tenement flat. Obviously the ballroom would have many more possibilities (provided money were no object).

But is size alone enough? One could imagine a large ballroom with no furniture and no ventilation. It might then be preferable to give the birthday party in the small flat after all.

Actually, there are molecules that are just as large as proteins but that are nevertheless much more limited in their usefulness than proteins. For instance, the chief compound of ordinary wood is CELLULOSE. Its molecule is very large but its only use to the plant is as a stiffening substance in the 'walls' around the living plant cells. Again, the starchlike substance called GLYCOGEN, that occurs in animal livers, has a large molecule and yet is used only as a body fuel. Proteins, on the other hand, have millions and billions of different functions in the body.

Why is this so? Well, the key to the mystery can be found if cellulose or glycogen are treated with certain acids. These acids cause the cellulose or glycogen molecule to break up into smaller pieces. The smaller pieces turn out to be the same in both cases. They are molecules of GLUCOSE, a kind of sugar which is found in blood and which is somewhat simpler than ordinary table sugar.

The cellulose molecule, in other words, seems to resemble a necklace made up of thousands of individual glucose molecules strung together like so many beads. The glycogen molecule is made up of these same glucose molecules strung together in a somewhat different pattern.

Apparently, the fact that cellulose and glycogen are made up of only one type of smaller molecule limits their versatility. This also holds true for other such giant molecules (*with the exception of proteins*) which almost always consist of only one (or sometimes two) sub-units. It is as though you were given the job of making up a language but were only allowed to use a single letter. You could have words like *aa* and *aaaa,* and *aaaaaaaaaaaaaa.* In fact, you could have any number of words, depending on how many *a*'s you wished to string together, but it wouldn't be a satisfactory language. Things would be a little better if you were allowed to use two letters; still better if allowed to use three; and very much better if allowed to use twenty.

The last is exactly the case in proteins. When proteins are exposed to acid, their molecules also break apart into a number of smaller molecules. These smaller molecules are known as AMINO ACIDS, and they are *not all the same.* There are about twenty different amino acids, varying in size from a molecular weight of 90 to one of about 250. They can be strung together to form proteins in every which way. And each time they are strung together in a slightly different way, they make a slightly different protein.

How many different combinations are there possible in a protein molecule? Well, an average protein molecule would contain about 500 amino acids, altogether, but we can start with a much smaller number. Suppose we start with only two different amino acids and call them *a* and *b.* They can be arranged in two different ways: *ab* and *ba.* If we had three different amino acids, *a, b,* and *c,* we could make six combinations: *abc, acb, bac, bca, cab,* and *cba.* With four different amino acids, we could make 24 different combinations. They are easy to figure out and the reader may wish to amuse himself by listing them.

However, the number of possible arrangements shoots up very sharply as the number of amino acids is increased. By the time you get to ten different amino acids, there are more than 3,500,000 possibilities and with twenty amino acids, almost 2,500,000,000,000,000,000 arrangements. (This seems unbelievable, but it is so. If the reader is doubtful let him try listing the different arrangements for only 6 amino acids. He will probably give up long before he has run out of arrangements.)

In the case of our average protein with 500 amino acids, even though the 500 are not all different, the number of possible arrangements is so large that it can only be expressed by a 1 followed by 600 zeros. This is a far, far greater number than the number of all the atoms in the universe. You may understand why this should be if you will imagine taking the 26 letters of the alphabet and counting the number of words you can make out of them. Not only the real words now, but words with any number of letters up to 500, and especially including all the unpronounceable ones.

Remember that each one of these amino-acid arrangements is a slightly different protein. It is no wonder, then, that the body can design different proteins to accomplish different tasks without any danger of ever running out of new varieties. No wonder, too, that out of a type of molecule such as this, life can be built.

Notice that the publisher of The Chemicals of Life *(and of several other books I have quoted from) is Abelard-Schuman. Even while I was writing* The Chemicals of Life, *Henry Schuman merged his publishing firm with Abelard, a publishing firm owned by Mr Lou Schwartz, and it was with Mr Schwartz and the editors who worked for him that I dealt when the book came to be published. – And for the publication of a dozen books after that, too, including the popularization of Dr Boyd's book on genetics.*

It was Henry Schuman, though (who has since died), who started me in the business of popular nonfiction.

One can't help overlapping if one insists on writing many books. For instance, I discussed uranium fission in Inside the Atom, *in* Understanding Physics, *Volume 3, in* The Neutrino, *and in* The Intelligent Man's Guide to Science.

Sometimes, in cases of such multiple repetition, I even use one book as a guide to what I am saying in another book (I do try to use shortcuts, when that turns out to be possible).

The repetition is never total, of course. Each book appeals to a different audience or has the item inserted in a different setting. Thus, Understanding Physics *is narrower and more detailed than* The Intelligent Man's Guide to Science, *so in the former book I can deal with uranium fission in a more leisurely and thorough manner.* The Neutrino *is still more detailed but is aimed somewhat off-centre as far as uranium fission is concerned and is at a somewhat less specialized level. And another book of mine on that subject,* Inside the Atom, *is intended for teenagers and is the simplest of the four.*

In each case, I handle the matter differently and this makes the repetition less dull for me than it might otherwise be. But 'less dull' is not actually 'non-dull' and at the present time if I were asked to write another book in which I had to make a big deal about the discovery and development of the ideas of uranium fission, I would heave a big sigh and try to refuse.

Naturally, then, I try, on occasion, to pick a subject far removed from anything I have previously handled. Not only does this allow me to avoid the feeling of déjà vu, which does come when I go around the same merry-go-round the half-dozenth time, but I can indulge in my continuing penchant for self-education.

After all, it's ridiculous to suppose that I know enough concerning every subject I write books about, to write a book about it. On occasion, I agree to write a book on a subject I know little about. Then I have to learn about it before I can write the book.

This can be very nerve-racking. I can be skimming along happily, learning and teaching simultaneously, so to speak, with the learning process staying one chapter ahead of the teaching – when I suddenly come up against a phase of the subject I have trouble understanding. You get that momentary feeling that a whole book is going to swirl down the drain.

I've never actually had to wash out a book entirely, because of midway failure to learn, but there are places where I have to skate delicately over very thin ice. In Volumes 1 and 3 of Understanding Physics, *for instance, I felt on reasonably firm ground throughout, but in Volume 2 there are a couple of places where I'm not entirely sure I really knew what I was talking about.*

But the risks I take are small compared to the pleasure of diving into new areas –

Thus, in the early days of 1965, Mr Arthur Rosenthal of Basic Books asked me about the importance of the noble gas compounds which had recently been discovered, and which had created quite a sensation. I gave some vague answer, for I had only followed the matter superficially, when an idea struck me full-blown. I said, 'Hey, Arthur, do you want me to write a book about it?'

That, it turned out, had been the idea in his mind all along. It was why he asked me the question in the first place. So I wrote a book about it.

Naturally, as is my wont, I started at the beginning and didn't get to the noble gas compounds till the last chapter, but so what! It was delightful to be breaking new ground and, fortunately, that new ground was solid all the way. Since I had a thorough chemical background, there was no trouble in going through the necessary self-educative project.

And, of course, the greatest fun in such a book are the sidelines you might explore. I concentrated on the noble gases (helium, neon, argon, krypton, xenon, and radon) but the compounds some of them form are usually with fluorine. I stopped, therefore, to give a quick review of the history of chemical knowledge of fluorine, which has its dramatic moments –

from THE NOBLE GASES *(1966)*

This history begins with the miners of early modern times.

In 1529, the German mineralogist George Agricola (1490–1555) described the uses of a certain mineral in ore smelting. The mineral itself melted easily, for a mineral, and, when added to the ore being smelted in a furnace, caused it to melt more easily, thus bringing about a valuable saving of fuel and time.

Agricola called the mineral *fluores* from the Latin word meaning 'to flow', because it liquefied and flowed so easily. In later years, it came to be called *fluorspar*, since *spar* is an old German word for a mineral; a still newer name is *fluorite*, since 'ite' is now the conventional suffix used to denote a mineral.

In 1670, a German glass cutter, Heinrich Schwanhard, found that when he treated fluorspar with strong acid, a vapour was produced that etched his spectacles. This was most unusual, for glass is generally unaffected by chemicals, even by strong ones. Schwanhard took advantage of this property to develop a new art form. He converted portions of glassware with protective varnish and exposed it to the vapour, ending with clear figures on a cloudy background. Naturally, Schwanhard did not know the chemical details of what was happening, but the process of etching was dramatic enough, and the artwork he produced was unusual enough to attract continuing interest.

The Swedish chemist Karl Wilhelm Scheele (1741–1786) was the first to study the vapour of acidified fluorspar in some detail, in 1771. He was able to show, for instance, that the vapour was an acid, and he called it 'fluoric acid'. As a result, Scheele is commonly given credit for having discovered the substance.

It was probably a tragic discovery, for Scheele had a bad habit of sniffing and tasting any new substances he discovered. 'Fluoric acid' was one of several of his discoveries that most definitely should not be treated in this manner. He died at the early age of forty-four, after some years of invalidism; in all probability, his habit of sniffing and sipping unknown chemicals drastically shortened his life. If so, 'fluoric acid' (and other chemicals) had its first famous chemical victim. Scheele was by no means the last.

Once Scheele had established that the vapour produced from acidified fluorspar was an acid, a misconception at once arose as to its structure. The great French chemist Antoine Laurent Lavoisier had decided at just that time that all acids contained oxygen, and it was difficult to break away from that view in the face of so famous a proponent.

In 1810, however, the English chemist Humphry Davy (1778–1829) was able to show that 'muriatic acid', a well-known strong acid, contained no oxygen. He decided that a green gas that could be obtained from muriatic acid was an element; he named it *chlorine* from a Greek word for 'green'. 'Muriatic acid' then was a compound, Davy demonstrated, of hydrogen and chlorine – but no oxygen – and could be called *hydrogen chloride* in its gaseous state, or *hydrochloric acid*, when dissolved in water.

By 1813, Davy was convinced that Scheele's 'fluoric acid' was another example of an acid without oxygen. The French physicist André Marie Ampère suggested that the molecule consisted of hydrogen plus an unknown element. Since 'fluoric acid' had certain similarities to the newly re-named hydrochloric acid, it seemed very likely to both Davy and Ampère that the unknown element was very like chlorine. Indeed, they decided to call it *fluorine*; the first syllable coming from 'fluorspar', while the suffix was chosen to emphasize the similarity of the new element to chlorine. 'Fluoric acid' became *hydrogen fluoride* in its gaseous form, hydrofluoric acid in solution.

What chemists wanted to do, once the existence of fluorine came to be so strongly suspected, was to settle all doubts by isolating the element.

Hydrogen chloride (HCl) could, after all, be treated with oxygen-containing chemicals in such a way that the hydrogen atom was snatched away and attached to oxygen to form water. The chlorine atoms, left behind, combined to form chlorine molecules (Cl_2).

Could not hydrogen fluoride (HF) be similarly treated, so that molecular fluorine (F_2) would be formed? Unfortunately, it could not. As we now know, oxygen is more electronegative than chlorine and can snatch hydrogen's electron (along with the rest of the hydrogen atom) from chlorine. Oxygen is, however, less electronegative than fluorine and is helpless to remove hydrogen from the hydrogen fluoride molecule.

Indeed, as no chemical reactions sufficed to liberate fluorine gas from its compounds, it became clear to nineteenth-century chemists that fluorine atoms held on to the atoms of other elements with record strength. Once free, those same fluorine atoms would recombine with other atoms with immense vigour. It came to be suspected, therefore, that fluorine was the most active of all elements and the most difficult to liberate. That, of course, made the task of liberation all the more of a challenge.

Davy himself had shown that it was not necessary to use chemical reactions in order to liberate a particular element from its compounds. An electric current, passing through a molten compound, can, under proper circumstances, separate the elements composing the compound. He demonstrated this in the case of the alkali metals and alkaline earth metals. The atoms of these elements are the most active in giving up electrons, and they therefore form compounds readily and are released from those compounds only with great difficulty. Prior to Davy's time, these elements had not been isolated, but in 1807 and 1808, using an electric current, Davy isolated and named six metals: sodium, potassium, magnesium, calcium, strontium, and barium.

It seemed natural that fluorine-containing compounds could be split up and free fluorine gas liberated by some electrical method; beginning with Davy, chemist after chemist tried. The attempts were dangerous in the extreme, for hydrogen fluoride is a very poisonous gas and free fluorine, once liberated, is more poisonous still. Davy was badly poisoned by breathing small quantities of hydrogen fluoride and this may have contributed to his later invalidism and his death at the age of only fifty-one.

Other prominent chemists of the time were also poisoned, and their lives made miserable and undoubtedly shortened by the same source. One notable Belgian chemist, Paulin Louyet, was actually killed, as was the French chemist Jérôme Nicklès. And yet the danger of the work seemed but to add to the challenge and excitement of the problem.

The usual starting substance in the attempt to obtain fluorine was fluorspar, which by the nineteenth century was understood to be *calcium fluoride* (CaF_2). To pass an electric current through fluorspar, one had to melt it first and then maintain it at a comparatively high temperature throughout the experiment. Fluorine was more active than ever at such high temperatures.

It was probably formed by the current, but as soon as it was, it promptly attacked everything in sight. It corroded the electrodes through which the electric current entered the fluorspar, even when they were composed of such comparatively inert materials as carbon, silver – even platinum.

A French chemist, Edmond Frémy (1814–1894), a student of the martyred Louyet, repeated the work with fluorspar in 1855, with the usual unsatisfactory results. It occurred to him that it might be preferable to pass an electric current through hydrogen fluoride. Hydrogen fluoride was a liquid at room temperature, and at this lower temperature, fluorine might be easier to handle. Unfortunately, until Frémy's time, hydrogen fluoride was available only in water solution. If there was any water about, fluorine reacted with it at once, tearing the hydrogen atoms out of the water molecule with such force that oxygen was liberated in the energetic form of ozone. One ended with hydrogen fluoride again.

Frémy therefore worked out methods for producing *anhydrous hydrogen fluoride*, that is, hydrogen fluoride that was pure and water-free, by acidifying potassium hydogen fluoride (KHF_2). Unfortunately, he found himself stymied.

Anhydrous hydrogen fluoride would not pass an electric current.

In the end, he, too, gave up. As the 1880s dawned, fluorine was still victor. It had defeated the best efforts of many first-class chemists for three-quarters of a century. (But Frémy, at least, took sufficient care of himself in the course of his experiments to live to be eighty – no mean feat for a fluorine chemist.)

Frémy had a student, Ferdinand Frédéric Henri Moissan, who took up the battle. He tried everything. He formed phosphorus trifluoride and tried to combine it with oxygen. Oxygen and phosphorus held together particularly tightly, and in this case, Moissan felt, the oxygen might be able to compete successfully with fluorine. Not entirely. The battle ended in a draw and Moissan ended with a compound in which phosphorus was combined with both oxygen and fluorine.

He then tried to pass phosphorus trifluoride over red-hot platinum. Platinum combines with fluorine only weakly and it also combines with phosphorus; perhaps it would combine only with the phosphorus and liberate the fluorine. No such luck. Both phosphorus and fluorine combined with the platinum.

Moissan decided to try electrical methods again. He began with arsenic fluoride and abandoned that after beginning to detect in himself signs of arsenic poisoning. He then turned to hydrogen fluoride, and eventually underwent four different episodes of poisoning with that gas, which undoubtedly helped cause his death at the age of fifty-four.

Moissan made use of Frémy's anhydrous hydrogen fluoride, but decided to add something to it to make it possible for it to carry an electric current. He had to add something that would not make it possible for some element other than fluorine to be liberated at the positive electrode. (If any element other than fluorine could be liberated, it would be – fluorine was last in line.) Moissan added potassium hydrogen fluoride to the hydrogen fluoride. The liquid was simply a mixture of fluorides and now it would carry a current.

Furthermore, Moissan made use of equipment built up out of an alloy of platinum and iridium, an alloy that was even more resistant to fluorine than platinum itself. Finally, he brought his entire apparatus to a temperature of $-50°$ C., where even fluorine's activity ought to be subdued.

And yet the experiment failed. Moissan considered and noted that the stoppers that held the electrodes had been corroded. Something was needed for the stopper that would not conduct a current, so that platinum-iridium alloy was eliminated. What else? It occurred to him that fluorspar itself did not carry a current, and could not be attacked by fluorine, either (it already held all the fluorine it could). Moissan carefully carved stoppers out of fluorspar and repeated the experiment.

On June 26, 1886, he obtained a pale yellow-green gas about the positive electrode. Fluorine had finally been isolated, and when Moissan later repeated the experiment in public, his old teacher, Frémy, watched.

Moissan went on, in 1899, to discover a less expensive way of producing fluorine. He made use of copper vessels. Fluorine attacked copper violently, but after the copper was overlaid with copper fluoride, no further attacks need be expected. In 1906, the year before his death, Moissan received the Nobel Prize in chemistry for his feat.

Despite all this, fluorine remained a most ticklish problem for another generation. It could be isolated and used, but not easily and not often. Most of all, it had to be handled with extreme care – and few chemists cared to play with it.

It isn't often one can joke about science. To do so well, one has to know quite thoroughly what it is one is joking about, and in my case, chemistry is the only subject I know so well, I can play games with it.

Back in 1947, when I was working for my Ph.D. I was

making use of catechol in my research. This is a white organic compound which is supplied in tiny feathery crystals. Catechol dissolves very rapidly and the tiny crystals disappear the instant they hit the top of the water. Watching that happen one day, I thought: What if they disappeared just a fraction of a millimetre above the top of the water?

Since the forthcoming write-up of my Ph.D. dissertation was much in my mind, it was the work of a moment to begin a solemn dissertation containing all the stigmata of academic turgidity about a substance which dissolved in water 1.12 seconds before you added the water.

Once it was done, I showed it to John Campbell of Astounding Science Fiction. He laughed and offered to publish it. I cautiously asked him to let me use a pseudonym, as the article might come out before I had my Ph.D. safely tucked away in my inner jacket pocket and the faculty members who met to decide on my fitness might take it amiss if I showed irreverence for the holy name of chemical research.

John promised, but forgot, and the article appeared in the March, 1948, issue of Astounding, not long before my doctor's orals were due, and with my very own personal name blazoned all over it. The article had a mock-solemn title, 'The Endochronic Properties of Resublimated Thiotimoline', a palsied style, and a list of fake references to nonexistent journals.

It was an utter success, and I understand the New York Public Library was pestered for days by eager youngsters trying to find the nonexistent journals so they could read more on the subject.

This did not assuage my agony at all, for I thought I was through. I was sure that I would be tossed out of the oral examination by the united thrust of eight indignant academicians. Fortunately, the Columbia chemistry department was far less stuffy than I imagined and they saw nothing wrong with a little irreverence. Not only did they treat me with kindness in the course of the orals, but when it was drawing to a close and I was half dead with suspense and tension (as doctoral candidates invariably are – doctor's orals being one of the more sadistic rituals of academic life), Professor Ralph S. Halford asked solemnly, 'Asimov, can you tell us something about the endochronic properties of resublimated thiotimoline?'

That broke me up entirely. I was completely unable to say another word, for laughing and gasping, and they led me out in the hall to recover, while they spent twenty minutes swapping dirty jokes and pretending they were discussing my case. (I've been at the other end of doctor's orals since that day in May of 1948, so I know.)

– Oh, I made it, by the way.

There are a number of chemists, to this day, I think, who know nothing about my writings except for thiotimoline. I wrote three articles altogether on this mysterious subject. In the third I abandoned scientific-paper jargon and presented the subject as a pretended speech to a nonexistent scientific society. It appeared in the early years of the space age and that is reflected even in the title: 'Thiotimoline and the Space Age'. I'm presenting it here in full:

'Thiotimoline and the Space Age' *(1960)*

(Transcript of a speech delivered at the 12th annual meeting of the American Chronochemical Society.)

Gentlemen:

I have been called the founder of chronochemistry and in response I cannot resist a certain sense of pride. To have originated a new science is a privilege given to very few.

I can still remember, quite clearly, that day in 1947 when I first dropped a pinch of thiotimoline into water and thought I noticed something odd. To be sure, it dissolved rapidly; but I was used to that. It always seemed to vanish the instant it touched the water.

But I had never handled a sample of thiotimoline quite

as pure as the pinch I had obtained that July day and, as I watched the white powder drop towards the water, I distinctly remember myself thinking: Why, that dissolved *before* it hit the water.

Well, it's an old story to you, I know, though I still like to linger on the thrill of the slow awakening of certainty; of the measurements taken; of the first crude timings by eye; of the more delicate work of the original endochronometer – the same instrument now at the Smithsonian.

The announcement of endochronicity, of the fact that a substance existed which dissolved in water 1.12 seconds *before* the water was added created a stir. You all remember it, I'm sure. And yet, somehow, the impression arose that thiotimoline was a hoax. There was a distinct air of amusement in many of the comments in the learned journals. Private communications reaching me showed a distressing tendency to describe experiments which obviously lacked all scientific validity and which, I could but conclude, were meant as some sort of joke. Perhaps the final proof of the damage this has done is that after twelve years of existence, the American Chronochemical Society can muster an audience of exactly fifteen people to hear this talk.

It has been an expensive joke, gentlemen, one that has cost us our lead in the race for space. For while American researchers have, but with difficulty, obtained grants to continue their investigations of thiotimoline and have been starved into small-scale experiments, while withering under the genial air of disbelief on the part of their colleagues, the Soviet Union has established the town Khruschevsk in the Urals, whose popular nickname of 'Tiotimolingrad' will well describe the nature of the activities that go on behind the walls of the modern and well-equipped scientific laboratories that have been established there.

That the Soviet Union has taken thiotimoline seriously and has done something about it is as sure as can be, and yet we remain sunk in complacency. No important political figure has viewed the matter with alarm. If they have said anything at all for publication, it is simply, 'What's thiotimoline?' I intend now to explain to these nearsighted politicos just what thiotimoline means to our space effort.

Thiotimoline research graduated from what we might now call the 'classic' stage, to the 'modern' with the development of the 'telechronic battery' by Anne McLaren and Donald Michie of the University of Edinburgh. If you have read about it anywhere, you can only be clairvoyant, for the popular press and much of the learned press maintained a stubborn silence. In fact, the original paper appeared only in the small though highly respected *Journal of Irreproducible Results*, edited by that able gentleman Alexander Kohn. Let me describe the telechronic battery.

A simple endochronometer – with which we are all acquainted – is a device which will automatically deliver water into a small tube containing thiotimoline. The thiotimoline will dissolve 1.12 seconds before the water is delivered.

Imagine the endochronometer so connected with a second similar unit that the solution of the thiotimoline in the first activates the water-delivering pipette of the second. The thiotimoline of the second unit will dissolve 1.12 seconds before that water is delivered, and therefore 2.24 seconds before the water is delivered to the first unit.

An indefinite number of endochronometers can thus be hooked up, the thiotimoline of each of the series dissolving 1.12 seconds before the preceding member. A battery consisting of about 77,000 such units would yield a final sample of thiotimoline which dissolved a full day before the initial quantity of water was delivered.

Such batteries have now been developed both at Edinburgh and in my own laboratories in Boston in extremely compact models, through use of printed circuits and advanced miniaturization. A device of not more than a cubic foot in volume can afford a twenty-four hour endochronic interval. There is strong, if indirect, evidence that the Soviet Union possesses even more sophisticated devices and is turning them out in commercial quantities.

The obvious practical application of the telechronic battery is that of weather prediction. In other words, if the first element of a battery is exposed to the air in such a way that rain, if any, will fall upon it, the final element will dissolve the day before and thus offer a foolproof method of predicting rain – or lack of rain – one day ahead.

I trust you will all see, gentlemen, that the telechronic battery can be used for generalized predictions as well.

Suppose, to take a frivolous example, you were interested in a particular horse race. Suppose you intended to place a wager that a particular horse would win that race. Twenty-four hours in advance of the race, you could make up your mind quite firmly that if the horse were to win the next day, you would, immediately upon receiving the news, add water to the first element of a telechronic battery. If it did not win, you would not.

Having made that decision, you need then but observe the last element. If the thiotimoline in that last element dissolves – followed by a chain of solutions all along the battery at 1.12 second intervals, with which you need not be concerned – you will know that the horse will win beyond doubt. You might even, if you were in a flamboyant mood, allow the solution of the final element to activate a flashing light, a fire gong, a charge of explosive; anything that will unmistakably attract your attention.

You laugh, gentlemen, and yet can this system not be applied, without change, to the launching of a satellite?

Suppose that four hours after launching, an automatic device on board the satellite telemeters a signal to the launching base. Suppose, next, that this radio signal is designed to activate the first element of a telechronic battery.

Do you see the consequences? The sending of the signal four hours after launching can only mean that the satellite is safely in orbit. If it were not, it would have plunged to destruction before the four hours had elapsed. If then, the final element of the telechronic battery dissolves today, we can be certain that there will be a successful launching tomorrow and all may proceed.

If the final element does not dissolve, the launching will not be successful and there must, therefore, be something wrong with the satellite assembly. A team of technicians will begin checking the device and at the moment when the defective item is corrected, the telechronic battery will operate. The launching will then be scheduled in the full expectation of success.

Do you still laugh, gentlemen?

Is this not the only feasible explanation for the consistent Soviet successes as compared with our own very spotty record? It is customary, of course, to attribute the appearance of the unfailing success of Soviet launchings to the fact that they have been deliberately hiding many failures, but does this stand up? Have they not, with remarkable consistency, managed to score successes at such time as would most profit themselves?

Sputnik I went up within a month of the hundredth birthday of Tsiolkovsky, the Soviet rocket pioneer. Sputnik II went up to celebrate the fortieth anniversary of the Russian Revolution. Lunik II went up just before Khrushchev's visit to the United States. Lunik III went up on the second anniversary of Sputnik I.

Coincidence? Or did they simply have the foreknowledge of their telechronic batteries? Have they tested a number of possible rocket assemblies and selected that one for which success was forecast? How else can one explain that the United States has not yet succeeded in launching any of their many rockets on some significant day?

Nor, remember, do the Soviets invariably hold their announcements back until they are certain they have achieved success, as some have suggested. In at least one case, they announced an achievement in advance.

When Lunik III was on its way to circle the Moon, the Soviet scientists confidently announced it would take pictures of the hidden side of the Moon as it progressed around that body in its orbit. As far as the orbit of Lunik III was concerned, they were safe. From its motion and from the positions of Earth, Moon, and Lunik, the orbit of Lunik III could be calculated with absolute precision.

How could the Soviet scientists, however, be so sure that the intricacies of the camera assemblage would work to perfection? Could it be that the successful completion of the camera task was set to activate a telechronic battery at the launching base? Could its activation have allowed them to make their announcement a day before the pictures were taken with the full knowledge that success and a prestige victory would result?

I say the answer is: Obviously, yes.

And what of future attempts to send a man into space? Suppose the man were to agree to send a signal, manually, after a certain time had elapsed after firing. A telechronic battery would then tell us, while the astronaut was still on the ground and unlaunched that not only would he be in orbit but that he would be alive and at least well enough to send the message.

If the telechronic battery remains inactive, the man will not be sent up. It is as simple as that. Since it is the chance of harm to an astronaut that is the deciding factor holding back the step of 'man into space', it seems certain that the Soviet Union will achieve this goal first, thanks to our government's obtuseness with respect to thiotimoline.

Presumably, one can extend the principle to all manner of scientific and nonscientific investigations Gigantic mega-batteries can even be built – in theory – to predict the result of an election to be held the following year – but I have laboured the point long enough. Let me, instead, make a few remarks concerning the great dangers as well as the great benefits, which are involved in thiotimoline research.

These begin with the oldest of all paradoxes of thiotimoline – the paradox of fooling. In other words, the chance of having thiotimoline dissolve and then being fooled by a refusal to add the water. The original argument against such a notion, as elucidated in my laboratory, involved the theory of the endochronic atom – which has since been confirmed by half a dozen other investigators. One pair of the bonds of one or more of the carbon atoms in the thiotimoline molecule are forced, through supersteric hindrance, to a point in the temporal plane. One bond extends 1.12 seconds into the past and one extends 1.12 seconds into the future. When the future end of a thiotimoline molecule dissolves and drags the rest of the molecule with it, it is therefore not predicting a possible future event. It is recording an actual future event.

Nevertheless, it has been shown that fooling thiotimoline is possible in theory. Using Heisenberg's principle of uncertainty, it can be demonstrated that one cannot say with certainty that an individual molecule of thiotimoline will dissolve before the water is added and that, in fact, the probability of its not doing so is quite appreciable.

That is undoubtedly true – for an individual molecule. When, however, quintillions of molecules are involved as is the case with even the most microscopic samples of thiotimoline actually used in the individual units of even the most sophisticated telechronic batteries, the chance that all of those quintillions, or even a detectable fraction of them, will fail to dissolve is infinitesimal.

To be sure, in setting up a telechronic battery, in which many thousands of units are involved, the failure of the instrument will depend on the failure to dissolve of any one of those units. The chance of 'Heisenberg failure', as it is called, can be calculated and some estimates at least seem to show that a battery will give a false positive one time out of rather more than a million.

In such a case, the final unit in a telechronic battery will dissolve even though water is not added to the first. Somewhat more often, the converse will be true; that the final unit will not dissolve in advance even though water is added to the first. Naturally the former alternative is more interesting from the theoretical viewpoint, the question arising: Then where did the water come from?

An attempt was made in my laboratories to actually record such a false negative involving solution without subsequent addition of water. The possibility of creation of matter out of nothing existed and this would be of great importance in connection with the Gold–Hoyle theory of the steady-state universe.

The principle involved in the attempt was simple. One of my students would set up a battery adjusted for the manual addition of water the next day, intending in all honesty to allow the experiment to take its course. The final unit would, theoretically, dissolve. I would then place the first student at a different task and put a second student in charge of the battery with instructions not to add water.

Our first great surprise was to find that the final unit actually dissolved, under these circumstances, about once in twenty efforts. This was a far greater incidence than could possibly be explained by 'Heisenberg failure'. But, as it rapidly turned out, the thiotimoline was not 'fooled'. Something, in every case, brought about the addition of water. In the first case, the original student returned to add the water and did so before he could be stopped. In another case, there was accidental spillage. In another, a janitor –

But it would be tedious to describe the manner in which thiotimoline, so to speak, refused to be fooled. Suffice it that we did not have one true case of 'Heisenberg failure'.

With time, of course, we began to guard against ordinary accidents and the incidence of 'pseudofailure' declined. For instance, we placed the battery in closed, desiccated vessels; but, during pseudofailure, these cracked and broke.

In our final experiment we thought that surely we had a 'Heisenberg failure' but in the end, the experiment was not reported in the literature. I tried instead, and without success, to report the implications of it to appropriate officials. Let me describe the experiment to you now.

We placed the battery in a welded steel container after it had registered solution.

And as we waited for the moment when the water should be added but would not, Hurricane Diane struck New England. That was in August of 1955. The hurricane had been predicted, its course had been followed and we were ready for it. There had been several hurricanes in New England in '54 and '55 and we were hardened to it.

At one point, though, the Weather Bureau announced the danger to be passed, the hurricane was blowing out to sea. We all sighed with relief as we waited for zero minute.

However, if any of you were in New England that day you will remember that the Weather Bureau announced later that it had 'lost' the hurricane; that the backlash struck surprisingly; that five inches of rain or more fell in many places within an hour; that rivers rose and extensive flooding began.

I watched that rain; it was a deluge. I watched the small river running across our campus become a torrent and begin to spread up and out across the lawns while the lines of shrubbery seemed to grow out of roiled sheets of water.

I shouted for an axe. One of my students brought one, remarking afterwards that I sounded so wild he was almost afraid I had turned homicidal maniac.

I smashed that steel container. I removed the telechronic battery and in the flickering grey light of that storm-lashed day, I filled a beaker of water and waited for zero minute, ready to douse the battery at the proper moment.

As I did so, the rain slackened, the hurricane moved off.

I do not say we caused the hurricane to return and yet – water had to be added to that battery somehow. If the stainless steel container had to be floated away on a rising flood and smashed by wind and water to have that done, it would be done. The original solution of the final unit predicted that; or else it predicted my deliberate subversion of the experiment. I chose the latter.

As a result of all this, I can envisage what I can only call a 'peace bomb'. Enemy agents working within a particular nation, can assemble telechronic batteries, operate them until a case occurs in which the final unit dissolves. That battery can then be encased in a steel capsule and placed near a stream well above high-water mark. Twenty-four hours later, a disastrous flood is bound to occur, since only so can water reach the container. This will be accompanied by high winds since only so can the container be smashed.

Damage will undoubtedly be as great in its way as would result from an H-Bomb blast and yet the telechronic battery would be a 'peace bomb' for its use will not bring on retaliation and war. There would be no reason to suspect anything but an act of God.

Such a bomb requires little in the way of technology or expense. The smallest nation, the smallest of revolutionary or dissident groups could manage it.

Sometimes in my more morbid moments, I wonder if perhaps Noah's flood – the prototype of which actually has been recorded in Mesopotamian sediments – was not brought about by thiotimoline experiments among the ancient Sumerians.

I tell you, gentlemen, if we have one urgent task ahead of us now it is to convince our government to press for international control of all sources of thiotimoline. It is boundlessly useful when used properly; boundlessly harmful when used improperly.

Not a milligram of it must be allowed to reach irresponsible hands.

Gentlemen, I call you to a crusade for the safety of the world!

By the time 'Thiotimoline and the Space Age' had been written, Astounding Science Fiction *in whose pages so many of my stories had appeared had changed its name to* Analog Science Fact-Fiction. *But the stubbornness of the human heart is strange. The magazine has been* Analog *for a decade but it will always be* Astounding *to me.*

Since I have been talking about my Ph.D., I am re-

minded of the paper I had to write as part of my task in qualifying for the degree. It was elaborate indeed. It eventually made a sixty-seven-page booklet, complete with tedious mathematics and sixty-six equations, seven tables, four graphs, four appendices, a list of references – all the paraphernalia, in short.

It was published in 1948 and copies are buried in Columbia's archives and in my own library and, as far as I know, nowhere else in the world. A shortened version of the dissertation was published in 1950 in the Journal of the American Chemical Society *(Volume 70, page 820, if you're curious enough to check) but that's not the same thing at all.*

You might notice, by the way, that this was published before my textbook, Biochemistry and Human Metabolism, *and so were a few other strictly scientific papers. I don't count these papers as my earliest nonfiction, however, for they weren't written in my capacity as writer. They were a concomitant of my role as scientist, and nothing more – like dropping beakers.*

Yet, my dissertation is the rarest item in my personal library, and I ought to preserve it here. Not the whole thing, of course; even I couldn't endure that. Just the summary – for flavour. And note the title, which is even more ridiculous than the one I plastered on the first thiotimoline article, and quite authentic besides:

from 'The Kinetics of the Reaction Inactivation of Tyrosinase during its Catalysis of the Aerobic Oxidation of Catechol' *(1948)*

1 – The aerobic oxidation of catechol, as catalyzed by the enzyme, tyrosinase, during the first 140 seconds of reaction has been carefully reinvestigated, utilizing buffered enzyme-catechol systems containing limited quantities of ascorbic acid (the chronometric method). It has been found that during that early part of the reaction, the relationship of

total quinone formed (Q) to the observed time of chronometric endpoint (T), is better expressed by the equation:

$$Q = \frac{a(T - M)}{b + T - M}$$

MODIFIED CHRONOMETRIC EQUATION

than by a similar relationship previously used, in which the value, M, was ignored. In this expression, a and b are constants, characteristic of the particular enzyme-substrate system employed. The value of M, here introduced as a necessary correction factor, has been shown to be constant with time for a given set of experimental conditions. Its value varies from one system to another inversely as the degree of agitation of the reaction mixture is varied, and M has been interpreted, therefore, as a measure of the time of mixing. An algebraic method for determining the values of a, b, and M has been described.

2 – It has also been found that during that early part of the reaction (140 seconds) the reaction course is equally well expressed by an equation of the type:

$$Q = a' (1 - e^{(M-T)/b'})$$

MODIFIED FIRST-ORDER EQUATION

where a' equals $0.65a$ and b' equals $0.69b$.

3 – For reaction times greater than 140 seconds, the reaction course has been followed through the utilization of buffered enzyme-catechol systems containing an excess of ascorbic acid; the extent of reaction being measured by determining the residual ascorbic acid at various reaction times. It has been found by this method that the experimentally observed reaction course approximates (within experimental error) that predicted by the Modified Chronometric Equation for periods up to eight minutes, during which 95% of the enzyme is inactivated. The reaction course predicted by the Modified First-Order Equation departs widely from the experimentally observed course after only a little over 2 minutes of reaction.

4 – An analysis of the kinetic implications of the

Chronometric Equation has been presented and the results are consistent with the experimental observation that the half-life of the enzyme is independent of the original enzyme concentration. However, the analysis also indicates that the specific inactivation rate of the enzyme is not constant, but decreases with time. Several possible interpretations of these kinetic implications are inspected and arguments are presented against the possibility that this decrease in specific inactivation rate with time is due to the protective effect of compounds formed during the enzyme reaction or to the existence of a 'reversible inactivation' phenomenon.

5 – A kinetic model is proposed in which tyrosinase is considered as inactivating in stepwise fashion through a series of decreasingly active and increasingly stable intermediates. It is shown that such a model can explain all experimental data reported in this communication, and is not inconsistent with previously known facts concerning the relationship of enzyme stability to types of enzyme activity. A general equation derived from this kinetic model is presented, and it is suggested that the Modified Chronometric Equation is merely an empirical simplification thereof.

PART 6

Biology

One criticism of The Chemicals of Life (*my first non-fiction book for the general public*) *was important and justified. I had made a vital omission.*

The book dealt with proteins and with the smaller molecules that worked along with them and the implication was clear that these were the substances crucial to life. The title said as much. And not once, anywhere in the book, was there any mention of the nucleic acids.

The trouble was that the true significance of nucleic acids, their central importance to life chemistry, was only becoming clear in the early 1950s, and I wasn't sharp enough to get it in time for the book

I had a chance to correct the omission six years later when Mac Talley came to me with a title. It was The Wellsprings of Life *and he wanted a book that would fit. Since he was always excellent at talking me into books, I agreed and talked about all kinds of wellsprings of life. I began, for instance, by discussing it in the most immediate fashion – where did babies come from?*

from THE WELLSPRINGS OF LIFE *(1960)*

The question of the beginning of life almost forces itself on mankind. What child can be so dead to curiosity as not to wonder, on occasion, where he came from, and how? The innocent question is almost traditional. Parents whose children never asked, 'Where do babies come from?' would probably feel uneasy and, I think, rightly so.

Even if a youngster were not dimly aware that he had not always been on the scene and if he were not, therefore, curious (or even apprehensive) concerning his own origin, there would still be the drama of birth all about him. The arrival of a younger brother or sister would be preceded by months of excitement and suspense, the mystery of which he himself would only vaguely share and which would consequently pique and frustrate him. There would be a disquieting and frightening change, both physical and temperamental, in his mother. Finally, there would follow such a revolution in family procedure (usually to his own disadvantage in terms of loss of attention received) that he must brood about it all and, eventually, ask.

And if he remained an only child, there would still be friends who would go through this traumatic experience. A new baby would appear out of nowhere, and the friend would have a possession he himself would not have.

Moreover, this question, 'Where do babies come from?' though traditionally asked and rarely unexpected, is also traditionally embarrassing and difficult to answer. Modern mothers may frequently launch into some bowdlerized version of the biological background of birth, but rarely do they do so with poise. And in most cases, even today, the earliest explanations of the process leave the child with the thought that children are found either under cabbage leaves or under a hospital bed, and that they are brought either by a stork or in a doctor's little black bag.

Such explanations would satisfy all but the most formidable youngster, since he would have no reason to suspect that there is anything inherently improbable in the creation of a baby out of nothing. When, later in life (and, perhaps, thanks to the folk wisdom of the gutter, not very much later in life), he learns that the baby originated as a result of the activities of the father and the mother, this activity is what he may find difficult to believe.

But believe it he must, eventually. The life of the baby, he must finally admit, is the product of the life of the parents; human life arises from human life.

If the child is brought up on a farm, he is apt to gain an accurate insight into the process of baby-making much earlier than the city child, since he will undoubtedly have a chance to observe the behaviour of livestock on the farm.

He will learn soon enough that calves, colts, and chicks are the products of their parents, and he will learn in detail the indispensable (if transient) role of the bull, the stallion, and the rooster in the process.

Then again, the crop that is laboriously grown and triumphantly harvested springs not from the sterile earth, but from the seeds produced by the crops of yesteryear. Life comes only from life in the case of every animal man herds and of every plant man cultivates.

All this, which each child must discover for himself, either through observation or explanation, with greater or lesser trauma, had to be discovered by mankind as a whole at some early stage of culture. Probably the discovery proved no easier for mankind than for the individual child.

The question, 'Where do babies come from?' was often answered by primitive man with tales equivalent to those of the stork and cabbage leaves. In Greek legends, for instance, there are stories of mares which turn their backs to the fructifying east wind and are made pregnant thereby, bearing foals of extraordinary speed. This may have been merely symbolic to later, more sophisticated Greeks, but it may well reflect an early stage where it was actually believed that the wind could be responsible for babies.

The numerous legends of god-born heroes in Greek myths may also reflect the early period when men were honestly uncertain of what brought about pregnancy – perhaps a god, perhaps a ritual prayer, perhaps sitting under a sacred tree. The fertility rites in primitive agricultural societies may have originated, in part, from the same uncertainty.

And the truth, when finally learned, may well have proved as embarrassing for mankind generally as for each child individually. Some people have seen a reflection of this momentous discovery in the biblical legend of the forbidden fruit which Adam and Eve ate and which brought sin and mortality into the world.

Yet, trauma or not, by the time any society had grown sophisticated enough to develop writing (an invention that marks the boundary between the prehistoric and the historic), they had also grown sophisticated enough to know where babies came from. The supernatural and mystic were put aside, and the baby was accepted as the product of the sexual activity of the mother and father. And this, with appropriate modifications, served to explain where lambs, pups, kittens, goslings, and fruit tree saplings came from.

It would seem that, having discovered this about man and having made the extension to various plants and animals, it would be simple and easy to make a further extension to all plants and animals, to suppose that all young of whatever kind were the product of parents.

And yet that next step (which to us, out of the wisdom of hindsight, seems so natural) was not taken until modern times.

After all, if we try to put ourselves in the place of our ancestors, we will notice that there are animals and plants which survive despite the fact that they are not cared for by man. They survive, in fact, despite all man can do to wipe them out.

It is exasperating. Useful domestic animals must be carefully guarded and watched over if they are to remain alive and healthy, yet creatures such as mice, rats, mosquitoes, and flies flourish and multiply, though unrestricted and merciless war is declared on them. The tender grass is nurtured with love and plant food, while dandelions are poisoned and torn up; but it is the grass that perishes and the dandelions that rise triumphant over adversity.

Where do the vermin and weeds come from?

It is only too easy to fall into the exasperated belief that they spring up from the soil itself; that they are formed of mud and corruption; that their birth, in short, is a kind of conspiracy on the part of inanimate nature to spite man by turning itself into noxious forms of life.

Thus, in *Antony and Cleopatra* (Act II, Scene 7) Shakespeare has the Roman, Lepidus, say 'Your serpent of Egypt is bred now of your mud by the operation of your sun; so is your chocodile.'

Lepidus was half-drunk at the time, and even when sober, he was not (as pictured by Shakespeare) a great brain. His drinking companions, Antony and Octavius, who knew better, gravely went along with the gag.

Obviously, Shakespeare himself believed no such thing and introduced the statement as a piece of comedy, but it is quite certain that many in his audience found sufficient humour in the drunken byplay and were quite content, otherwise, to believe that the corrupting mud of the river Nile would indeed bring forth serpents and crocodiles to plague mankind.

The Egyptians themselves (and reasonable foreign observers, such as Herodotus) knew very well that serpents and crocodiles laid eggs and that only from those eggs were new serpents and crocodiles produced.

But then, serpents and crocodiles are sizeable creatures and their eggs are large and easily noticeable. Smaller vermin can be more misleading. Field mice may make their nests in holes burrowed into stores of wheat, and those nests may be lined with scraps of scavenged wool. The farmer, coming across such nests, from which the mother mouse has had to flee, and finding only naked, blind, and tiny infant mice, may come to the most natural conclusion in the world: he has interrupted a process in which mice were being formed from musty wheat and rotting wool.

Which goes to prove that many a false theory is firmly grounded on the best evidence of all: 'I saw it with my own eyes!'

Let meat decay and small wormlike maggots will appear in it. Eventually those maggots become flies. Out of dead meat come live worms and insects. This is no vague theory. This is eyewitness evidence, as any man can prove for himself with nothing more than a piece of decaying meat.

The greatest and clearest mind of the ancient world, that of Aristotle of Stagira, believed this, as indeed he had to, on the evidence he had. He believed in the ability of non-living matter to give rise to certain types of living creatures as a matter of constant and everyday occurrence. This is called the doctrine of *spontaneous generation.*

This doctrine was accepted and taken for granted by all learned men throughout ancient times, throughout the Middle Ages, and into early modern times.

The first crack in the doctrine appeared in 1668, when an Italian physician and poet named Francesco Redi thought he would supplement the evidence of his eyes by arranging an experiment. (By and large, the ancient thinkers were content to observe Nature as it existed and unfolded. They did not try to experiment; that is, to interfere with the natural course of events and thus force Nature to give an answer to some question. This failure to experiment, more than anything else, set narrow bounds to the advance of Greek science.)

Redi noticed that decaying meat not only produced flies but also attracted them. Others before him must have noticed this, too, but Redi was the first to speculate that there might be a connection between the flies before and the flies after; at least he was the first to test such a speculation.

He did this by allowing samples of meat to decay in small vessels. The wide openings of some vessels he left untouched; others he covered with gauze. Flies were attracted to all the samples but could land only on the unprotected ones. Those samples of decaying meat on which flies landed produced maggots. The decaying meat behind the gauze, upon which the foot of fly had never trod, produced no maggots at all, although it decayed just as rapidly and made just as powerful a stench.

Redi's experiments showed plainly that maggots, and flies after them, arose out of eggs laid in decaying meat by an earlier generation of flies. It was just as with serpents and crocodiles, but because the flies' eggs were so small, they went unobserved and so arose the misapprehension.

* * *

But that was just a beginning. I traced the origin of life back in time a few billion years and down to the molecular level as well. That brought in nucleic acids in the last two chapters.

In 1953, you see, Francis Crick and James Watson, working at Cambridge University in England had elucidated the structure of DNA (deoxyribonucleic acid) and showed how it could form replicas of itself over and over again. That was the biochemical analogue of reproduction. But it was in 1953 that I had been writing The Chemicals of Life *and I had missed it.*

Naturally, I put it into The Wellsprings of Life *which I wrote in 1959 and published in 1960. But then in 1961 –*

The next question was how the nucleic acid molecule was connected with protein manufacture. It was the detailed structure of the nucleic acid in the chromosomes which established the particular chemistry of the cell, but it was still the proteins that did the actual chemical work. There had to be some connection.

I advanced one theory as to that connection near the end of The Wellsprings of Life *but it turned out to be an utterly wrong one. And in 1961, the year after the book was published, the correct theory was worked out. Watson and Crick received the Nobel Prize in 1962 for their breakthrough and Marshall Nirenberg who sparked the second received his in 1968.*

So a second time, I was left high and dry with a book that was crucially out-of-date as soon as it was published. You simply have no idea how frustrating that is.

I finally managed to patch up the end of The Wellsprings of Life *to include the genetic code (for that is what the nucleic acid / protein interconnection is called) in the fourth printing of the paperback version, which appeared in 1967, but the hard-cover edition still remains untouched.*

However, all is not bitter. The Wellsprings of Life *brought me my favourite sentence of all the sentences that have appeared in all the reviews of all my books. Professor George G. Simpson of Harvard University reviewed* The

Wellsprings of Life *for* Science, *and in the course of the
review, he said, 'Asimov is one of our natural wonders and
national resources.'*

I have read that sentence and ruminated over it maybe a
thousand times and have enjoyed it every time. I won't go
so far as to say that I agree with it, you understand, but I
will defend with my life Professor Simpson's right to say it.

Anyway, back to my subject. In the midst of my chagrin
over my outdated books, Mac Talley phoned me in early
1962 to ask if I would write a book on the genetic code,
which was now much in the news thanks to Nirenberg's
breakthrough. I said, sorrowfully, that I dared not because
the field was advancing so rapidly that any book I wrote
would be obsolete at once. (I had been bitten twice, and I
did not want to make it thrice.)

Six weeks later, Walter Bradbury, who was then at
Harper's, wrote to ask me the same question. Well, I can
resist once (if I'm lucky) but never twice. When two people
ask me, human flesh and blood must fail.

I explained to Brad, however, that Mac had asked me
first and that if I did do the book I would have to let Mac
get the first crack at it. (I have a very simplistic code of
ethics inflicted upon me by a father trained in the precepts
of the Talmud, and it complicates my life unbearably.)

I suggested that Mac at New American Library sign me
up for the book and do the soft-cover and that Mac then
arrange with Brad to have Harper's do the hard-cover first.
Brad reluctantly demurred; Harper's would not do a hard-
cover by way of a contract with anyone but the author
himself.

I saw Harper's point of view but I was very abashed. I
was very anxious to do a book for Brad (whom I finally
landed three years later with The Neutrino) and yet there
was no way I could argue with the fact that Mac had asked
me first. So I told Brad that I was in a dilemma from which
there was no escape but, alas, not to do the book at all.

Brad asked what the dilemma might be and I explained

my problem as to the Right Thing To Do by my father's lofty principles – and Brad laughed and said he gave me permission to do it with Mac, and he would catch me next time around. So all was well.

I am afraid I get into these inter-publisher complications now and then. I make an honest attempt to please them all and try never to give any of them reasonable cause for grievance – but the more publishers I get and the more books I write, the harder it is.

For instance, at this writing, I haven't yet told Double-day I am doing this book for Houghton Mifflin. It was Houghton Mifflin who suggested doing it, so I can't do it for anyone else; but Doubleday is my oldest publisher and has published more books of mine than any other, and they may well consider that the Hundredth Book ought to have been theirs. And this may occur to them at precisely the time when I ask for formal permission to quote from various Doubleday books in this Houghton Mifflin one.

Well, I shall break the news to them later this month and to keep them happy (I hope) I shall accompany it with a suggestion that may please them and which will restore the balance.

But I digress once again . . .

In the end, The Genetic Code *found a hard-cover publisher in Orion Press, and in it I had the pleasure of going into careful detail on the 1961 breakthrough.*

Since 1962, more has been learned about the details of the genetic code, but there has been no breakthrough like the ill-timed (for me) Watson–Crick breakthrough of 1953 or the Nirenberg breakthrough of 1961. The Genetic Code *can and should be updated but there is nothing in it that sounds medieval.*

Perhaps I shouldn't complain. One advantage of writing a large number of books on a large variety of sometimes-overlapping subjects is that you can correct yourself as you go along and pretty painlessly, too. When readers write to me asking me for more up-to-date information than is contained in one of my books, I can sometimes simply refer them to another of my books.

Thus I took up the question of the origin of life in The Wellsprings of Life *as I understood it in 1960. In* The New Intelligent Man's Guide to Science, *I stretched it to incorporate what scientists had learned by 1965. Then in* Photosynthesis, *which I recently wrote for Basic Books, I could follow it through 1968.*

from PHOTOSYNTHESIS *(1968)*

The first to suggest seriously that life might have had its start in an atmosphere other than the present one was the English biochemist John B. S. Haldane. In the 1920s he pointed out that if life was responsible for the oxygen in the atmosphere, it ought to have started when there was no oxygen in it and when carbon dioxide was present instead . . .

In 1936 a Russian biochemist, Alexander Ivanovich Oparin, published a book called *The Origin of Life*. In it he reasoned that Earth's original atmosphere contained methane and ammonia and suggested that it was in this that life had made its beginning.

In either case, the molecules that served as raw material were small ones. Yet the end result, if life were to be produced, must be enormous molecules of such substances as protein and nucleic acid.

Put in its simplest form, then, the creation of life involved the formation of large molecules out of small ones, and this requires an input of energy.

There are at least four important sources of energy on the primordial Earth: 1) the internal heat of the Earth, 2) the electrical energy of thunderstorms, 3) the radioactive breakdown of certain isotopes in the Earth's crust, and 4) the ultraviolet radiation from the Sun. All four sources were probably present in greater quantity in the distant past than today.

The first who actually tried to imitate primordial conditions in a laboratory experiment was Melvin Calvin. He chose as his raw materials carbon dioxide and water vapour. As his energy source Calvin decided to use the fast-flying particles emitted by radioactive isotopes.

Calvin exposed his mixture of water and carbon dioxide to radiation from radioactive isotopes and, after a while, tested the mixture to see if anything new had formed. He found that some simple organic molecules had appeared, molecules somewhat larger and more complex than the original ones. He found, for instance, molecules of formaldehyde ($HCHO$) and of formic acid ($HCOOH$).

This was a promising beginning. Simple molecules could be made more complicated by energy input of a type available on the primordial Earth . . .

In 1953, Stanley Lloyd Miller placed a mixture of ammonia, methane, and hydrogen in a large glass vessel. In another, he boiled water. The steam that formed passed up a tube connecting the two vessels and into the gas mixture. The gas mixture was pushed by the steam through another tube back into the boiling water. The second tube passed through a surrounding bath of cold water so that the steam condensed into liquid before dripping back into the boiling water. The gas mixture bubbled through the boiling water and around the course again, driven always by freshly formed steam.

Naturally, Miller made very certain that everything he used was completely sterile; that there were no living cells in the system to form complicated compounds. If complicated compounds formed, it would have to be in the utter absence of life.

It would have been reasonable to use ultraviolet light as the energy source, but ultraviolet light is easily absorbed by glass and this raised the problem of getting enough energy through the glass and into the gas mixture. Miller therefore decided to try the use of an electric spark that would serve as an imitation of the kind of energy made available by lightning. Through the gas in one portion of the system, he set up a continuing electric spark.

Things began to happen at once. The water and gases were colourless to begin with, but by the end of one day the water had turned pink. As the days continued to pass, the colour grew darker till it was a deep red.

After a week Miller was ready to subject his mixture to analysis. Like Calvin, he found simple organic molecules in his mixture. One of these was the formic acid which Calvin had detected. Other compounds, related to formic acid, but still more complicated, were also present. These included acetic acid (CH_3COOH), glycolic acid ($HOCH_2$-$COOH$), and lactic acid ($CH_3CHOHCOOH$), all of which were substances that are intimately associated with life.

The presence of ammonia in the starting mixture meant that nitrogen atoms were also available for the buildup of more complex molecules, and Miller found nitrogen-containing compounds too in his final mixture. There were present hydrogen cyanide (HCN), for instance, and urea (NH_2CONH_2).

Most important of all, though, Miller discovered among his products two different amino acids. (Amino acids are the relatively small building blocks out of which the giant protein molecules are built up.) There are nineteen different amino acids that commonly appear, in varying numbers, in protein molecules and the two detected happened to be the two simplest: glycine and alanine.

Miller's experiment was significant in several ways. In the first place, these compounds had formed quickly and in surprisingly large quantity. One-sixth of the methane with which he had started had gone into the formation of more complex organic compounds, yet the experiment had only been in operation for a week.

How must it have been, then, on the primordial Earth, with its vast warm ammoniated ocean stirred by winds of methane, all baking under the Sun's ultraviolet radiation for many millions of years? Uncounted tons of complex compounds would surely have been formed and the oceans must have become a kind of 'warm soup' of them.

Then, too, the kind of organic molecules formed in

Miller's experiments were just those present in living tissue. The path taken by the simple molecules, as they grew more complex, seemed pointed directly towards life. This pointing-towards-life continued consistently in later, more elaborate experiments. At no time were molecules formed in significant quantity that seemed to point in an unfamiliar, non-life direction.

Thus, Philip Hauge Abelson, working at the Carnegie Institution of Washington, followed Miller's work by trying a variety of similar experiments with starting materials made up of different gases in different combinations. It turned out that as long as he began with molecules that included atoms of carbon, hydrogen, oxygen, and nitrogen, amino acids of the kind found normally in proteins were formed.

Nor were electric discharges the only source of energy that would work. In 1959, two German scientists, W. Groth and H. von Weyssenhoff, designed an experiment in which ultraviolet light could be used after all, and they got amino acids also.

It is important to progress further and go beyond the very simplest products. One way of doing so would be to start with larger samples of raw materials and subject them to energy for longer periods. This would produce increasing numbers of more and more complicated products; but the mixtures of these products would become increasingly complex and would be increasingly difficult to analyse.

Instead, chemists began with later stages. The products formed in earlier experiments would be used as new raw materials. Thus, one of Miller's products was hydrogen cyanide. At the University of Houston, the Spanish-born biochemist J. Oro added hydrogen cyanide to the starting mixture in 1961. He obtained a richer mixture of amino acids and even a few compounds consisting of individual amino acids hooked together in short chains in just the same way in which they are hooked together within the protein molecules.

He also formed purines, compounds containing a double-ring system of carbon and nitrogen atoms, and which are found within the various nucleic acid molecules. A particular purine called 'adenine' was obtained, one that is found not only in nucleic acids but in other important compounds associated with life.

In 1962, Oro used formaldehyde as one of his raw materials and produced two five-carbon sugars, ribose and deoxyribose, both of which are essential components of nucleic acids.

In 1963, the Ceylon-born biochemist Cyril Ponnamperuma, at Ames Research Center in California, working with Ruth Mariner and Carl Sagan, began with adenine and ribose as his raw materials and exposed them to ultraviolet light. They linked up to form 'adenosine' in the same fashion in which they are hooked together in nucleic acid molecules.

If phosphates were also included with the starting mixture, they too were added on to the adenosine to form 'adenylic acid', one of the 'nucleotides' that form the building blocks of nucleic acids. Indeed, by 1965, Ponnamperuma was able to announce that he had formed a double nucleotide, a structure in which two nucleotides are combined in exactly the same manner in which they are combined in nucleic acid molecules.

In short, the raw materials of Atmosphere I, exposed to almost any reasonable energy source (particularly to ultraviolet light) built up rapidly into more and more complicated molecules aimed directly at proteins and nucleic acids.

Experimenters in the laboratory have not yet formed natural proteins and nucleic acids in the complete absence of life, but the direction is unmistakable. Eventually, molecules sufficiently complicated to show the properties of life would be formed on the primordial Earth.

Thus, nucleic acids would surely develop finally, possessing molecules sufficiently complex to be capable of bringing about the production of other molecules exactly like themselves out of the raw materials all about. Such nucleic acid molecules maintain and multiply themselves, and this is the minimum one could expect of a living thing. They would represent the first and simplest manifestation that we could call life.

When can all this have happened? Calvin has isolated complex hydrocarbons (molecules made up of carbon and hydrogen atoms only) imprisoned in rocks that are up to three billion years old. These are probably the remnants of very simple living things, living when the rock was first formed.

Considering that the Earth's crust may not be much over three and a half billion years old, this means that the 'chemical evolution' which preceded the actual formation of life may have run its course in as little as half a billion years. This is not too surprising, when we think that small-scale chemical experiments have produced so much in experiments that lasted merely days and weeks.

In fact, 'blind' chemical processes are not so blind. Given certain raw materials and a supply of energy, the changes that take place are just those that are most probable in the light of known chemical and physical laws, and these changes prove to be inevitably in the direction of life. Life is therefore the result of high-probability changes that are next to impossible to avoid if the conditions are right. By this view, life is no 'miracle' at all.

The most ambitious books I ever wrote on biological subjects were a pair of interconnected ones: The Human Body *and* The Human Brain. *These were the first of my books to be handled by the adult division of Houghton Mifflin, as opposed to the juvenile division. The editor was David Harris, who is also editor of this book.*

In the case of The Human Body, *I broke one of my own rules – and I must say it was one of my silliest rules. For some reason, I usually don't let experts (that is, people who happen to know more concerning a particular subject than I do) see my manuscripts. If my publishers wish to check them with such experts, I never object; I am even secretly relieved. But I rarely take that precaution on my own.*

This is not because I can't use such refereeing, because I most certainly can. I have made enormous howlers in my time and a few have even survived into print.

For instance, in The Realm of Numbers, *I casually spoke of an equilateral right triangle (all three sides equal in length) instead of an isosceles right triangle (two sides equal in length). There is no such thing as an equilateral right triangle and I know that very well. The mistake was carelessness rather than ignorance, and somehow that makes it more reprehensible. And what is most reprehensible is that I never caught it in revision, in galley proof, in page proof, or even in the final book. It had to be pointed out to me by numerous young readers.*

The most embarrassing letter of all came from a thirteen-year-old who had an argument with his teacher over the matter and who said, 'If Isaac Asimov says it's so, then it's so,' and sent me a letter demanding I write to his teacher. It stands out in my memory as a really rotten moment when I sat down to write him that when Isaac Asimov says it's so, he sometimes makes an egregious ass of himself.

Perhaps the reason I don't have my manuscripts checked is that I have some dim notion that I am playing some sort of game. I am trying to be accurate and my readers are trying to catch me out in errors, and if I have myself checked, that's cheating. Such an attitude would be quite irrational, of course, but there you are.

Yet in the case of The Human Body, *I didn't dare try to play that game. After all, I was a member of the faculty of a medical school which was crawling with the usual number of anatomists. If I made a dumb mistake in anatomy, I would have them buzzing about my ears like animated stilettos.*

So I handed the manuscript to Dr Elizabeth Moyer, a Junoesque anatomist whose special talent it is to say exactly what is on her mind to dean and freshman alike.

She pointed out quite a few mistakes, which I hastily corrected, and she was very blunt indeed over the fact that I had placed the spleen on the wrong side of the body. The whole school knew about it within forty-eight hours and even now, five years later, when time hangs heavy on her hands, she looks me up and tells me again.

But one thing she said particularly astonished me. She said, 'I was almost afraid to read your chapter on reproduction. I thought you'd be impossible. *But actually I found it the best chapter in the book.'*

Imagine! I admit that in my socializing I tend to notice the existence of the ladies. As a friend of mine once said, I take advantage of the known eccentricity of writers in general and allow ribald nuances to creep into my conversation.

But that's only in life. In my writing, *things are entirely different. Nowhere in my books, fiction or nonfiction, is there a sentence designed (to use a delightful Victorian phrase) to bring the blush of shame to the cheek of innocence.*

Therefore I will resist the impulse to include that chapter on reproduction here, because my readers are as pure as I am. Or, if they are just a shade less pure, they can buy the book.

The Human Body *contains nothing on the brain, nerves, sense organs, or ductless glands. They were the hardest parts so I left them out, promising the publishers I would take care of them in a separate book.*

The publishers calmly went ahead and published the first book on the assumption that I would really do the second. Both Houghton Mifflin and New American Library had had specific experience with the way I started writing one book and made two (or a dozen) out of them.

Deep in my bosom, however, I wasn't at all sure I could do The Human Brain *and I was in high hopes that perhaps the world would suddenly come to an end and I wouldn't have to try.*

The world did not come to an end and eventually, I had

to sit down at the typewriter and begin The Human Brain.
*It turned out to be one of the hardest books I ever had to
write. Like* Understanding Physics, *Volume 2, I skated on
thin ice trying to get the information into my head so
that I could ladle it out for the readers. There were times
when the only relief I could get from the unbearable tension
that resulted was to yell at my children.*

*I managed, I think. At least, after the book was pub-
lished, I got a call from the interviewer on some radio talk
show asking me to come on their programme as a brain
expert and answer questions from the audience. I said,
'Heavens! I'm no brain expert.'*

He said, 'But you wrote a book on the brain.'

*So I said, with artless honesty – as is my way, 'Yes, but
I studied up for the book and put in everything I could
learn. I don't know anything but the exact words in the
book, and I don't think I can remember all those in a
pinch. After all,' I went on, a little aggrieved, 'I've written
books on dozens of subjects. You can't expect me to be
expert on all of them just because I've written books about
them.'*

*He absorbed that and then said with what I thought was
a trace of contempt, 'You mean you're not an expert on
anything?'*

'Well,' I said, 'I'm an expert on one *thing.'*

'Oh?' he said. 'What's that?'

*'On sounding like an expert,' I said, cheerfully. 'Do you
want me to show up on your programme to answer questions on that?'*

– But he didn't.

PART 7

Words

My advance into new writing areas has usually been the result of circumstances, rather than through some deliberate plan on my part. As I said at the start of the book, I never plan anything. As in the case of 'The Man of La Mancha' (whom I suspect I resemble in some ways), I let the wild winds of fortune carry me onward whithersoever they blow.

For instance, writers must be, of necessity, interested in words. These are, after all, the tools of their trade. And a writer, who is also a chemist, ought to be particularly interested in chemical words − in the names of the elements, as an example. Why is there an element named ruthenium? Or praseodymium?

I rarely wonder about such things without deciding to make the matter the subject of some piece of writing or other. In 1956, when this particular gnat began buzzing in my ear, I was writing science articles for Astounding Science Fiction. *Consequently, I wrote a letter to John Campbell, asking if he would like an article on the derivations of the names of the elements.*

By the time I had done that much, though, I was burning with a hard, gemlike flame and could not be headed off. I began the article (which I called 'Names, Names, Names'), without waiting for an answer, on April 29, 1956. By the time I finished, a few days later, I still hadn't received an answer, so I mailed it off.

− You guessed it. A few hours after I mailed the article, I received a letter from John. He didn't like the idea.

Embarrassed at the thought of sending an article where it wasn't wanted, I sent off another letter at once (airmail this time), explaining what had happened, and asking him to place the article into a return envelope without bothering to read it.

On May 17, I called home from school to ask if there were any interesting mail. (I used to do that routinely in the days when I was at the school every day.)

'Yes,' said my wife, 'there's a cheque.'

Now I can't be fooled that way. At any given moment, I know exactly what cheques are on their way or should be on their way and I was expecting nothing particular that day.

So I said, rather sharply, 'For what?'

And my wife answered, knowing very well she was being unresponsive, 'For two hundred twenty-five dollars.'

It turned out to be from John. Before putting my article in the return envelope, he had decided to read it, and then he had decided to buy it. – Passing strange are the ways of editors.

Two months later, I was having lunch with Lillian McClintock of Abelard-Schuman at Locke-Ober's. The question under discussion was my next book for A-S and I was bubbling over with a novel idea. Why not prepare a collection of the science essays I had been writing for Astounding *– I did not then foresee that the day would come when year after year I would be writing science essays for* Fantasy and Science Fiction *and year after year publishing collections of them with Doubleday.*

Lillian was a little dubious at first but my eloquence won her over and it was agreed that I was to send over tear sheets of my articles for a reading by one of the A-S editors.

Naturally, the article I sent over with greatest eagerness was 'Names, Names, Names' which was so fresh it had not yet been published. (I don't know why it is, but it always seems to me that whatever it is that I have last written is best and most exciting. Logic tells me this cannot possibly be true all the time, but I don't try to interfere with this irrational and purely emotional feeling. It keeps me writing in a constant state of high delight at all times.)

By November, it was decided to do the book, which eventually appeared as Only a Trillion *and from which I quoted the introduction earlier in this book. There was one modification, though. Abelard-Schuman did not want 'Names, Names, Names'. They asked me to write other material as replacement, and I did. But my rejected article grew all the dearer to me as I brooded over editorial obtuseness.*

A new chance came a year later. I had met Austin Olney of Houghton Mifflin in connection with the small task of writing an introduction to an English translation of an originally French book on computers.

Once that was out of the way, the conversation swung around, as it somehow often does, to the possibility of my writing a book. On December 26, 1957, I had the first of many such lunch sessions over prospective books.

Austin advanced the notion of my writing a book on mathematics for youngsters – a book which later turned out to be Realm of Numbers *(from which I quoted earlier).*

I was about to agree when an unaccustomed bolt of shrewdness struck my usually artless brain. My eyes narrowed with a kind of transparent cunning and I said, 'I'll do a book for you, Austin, if you'll let me do a book for me.'

Naturally, he wanted to know what I had in mind and I never thought faster in my life. I had to invest a book on the spot that would incorporate the essence of 'Names, Names, Names', so that my hurt brainchild might be healed at last.

I babbled on wildly and what came out was the plan for a book to be entitled Words of Science *in which the background of various scientific terms would be explained in a series of one-page essays, arranged alphabetically, and including, of course, the names of all the elements.*

Austin, good-hearted soul that he is, agreed, and by March 28, 1958, the book was done.

It proved much more successful than I had expected it to be, and was therefore the precursor of others of what I came to call the 'Words' books. Indeed, I have done two more books in the precise format of Words of Science.

These are Words on the Map *and* Words from History. *The titles are self-explanatory, and here are some samples from each:*

from WORDS ON THE MAP *(1962)*

HELIUM

In 1868, a total eclipse was visible in India and, for the first time, the Sun's atmosphere (best observed during eclipses) could be studied by the new technique of spectroscopic analysis. This had been developed only nine years earlier and consisted of passing the light radiated from a white-hot substance through a glass prism. The light is split up into lines of different colours, and each element forms its own characteristic pattern of coloured lines in fixed positions.

The French astronomer Pierre J. C. Janssen allowed the light of the solar atmosphere to pass through the prism during the Indian eclipse and noticed that among the familiar lines of earthly substances, a yellow line was produced which he could not identify. The British astronomer Sir Norman Lockyer compared the position of this line with those of similar lines produced by various elements, and decided that this new line was produced by an element in the Sun that was not present, or had not yet been discovered, on Earth. He called it *helium*, from the Greek word for the Sun, 'helios'.

For decades that was how matters stood. Helium remained an oddly coloured line in sunlight and nothing more. Few chemists took it seriously.

In 1888, the American chemist William F. Hillebrand found that a uranium mineral named uraninite, when treated with strong acid, gave off bubbles of gas. He studied this and decided it was nitrogen. To be sure, some of the gas was nitrogen, but Hillebrand unfortunately ignored the fact that, when heated, some of its spectrum lines were not those of nitrogen.

The Scottish chemist Sir William Ramsay read of this experiment and was dissatisfied. He used another uranium mineral, cleveite, and, in 1895, repeated the experiment. He and Lockyer studied the spectral lines of the gas, and almost at once they realized what they had. Fully twenty-seven years after helium had been discovered in the Sun, it was finally located on Earth.

IDIOT

It is perhaps only human that there are a great many different words used to express mental deficiency, most of them slang; the vocabulary of insult is always great. Psychologists, however, have tried to make objective use of three of them to indicate various grades of mental deficiency.

A *moron* is only mildly deficient. He is capable of doing useful work under supervision. The term was adopted in 1910 by psychologists, and is derived from the Greek 'moros' (stupid).

More seriously retarded is an *imbecile*, who cannot be trusted to do useful work even under supervision, but is capable of connected speech. Whereas *moron* has always applied to mental deficiency, *imbecile* referred originally to physical deficiency since the word is derived from the Latin 'in-' (not) and 'baculum' (staff); that is, it refers to a person too weak to get along without a staff. In the modern meaning, it is the mind that cannot get along without help.

Most seriously retarded is the *idiot*, one who is not capable of connected speech or of guarding himself against the ordinary dangers of life. This word has the oddest history of the three. The ancient Greeks were the most political of people. Concerning oneself with public business was the pet hobby of everyone. The Greek word 'idios' means 'private' so a Greek who, despite all this, was odd enough to concern himself only with his private business rather than with public business was an 'idiotes'. The Greek view concerning such a person is obvious since 'idiotes' and 'idiot' are the same word.

Of the more colloquial words, *fool* comes from the Latin 'follis', meaning 'bellows', obviously implying that a fool is someone whose words, though many and loud, are so much empty air. The slang expression 'windbag' is the exact equivalent. *Stupid* is from the Latin 'stupere' (to be stupefied; to be rendered speechless). Here the implication is of someone without words. Apparently, for one to be intelligent, his words must be neither too few nor too many, and in my opinion that's not a bad way of putting it.

RH NEGATIVE

There is a common Indian monkey, given the name of *rhesus* by the French naturalist Jean Baptiste Audebert in 1797. Audebert insisted that the name was simply made up and meant nothing and yet . . .

In 1900, the Austrian physiologist Karl Landsteiner discovered that human blood might contain one of two substances, or neither (or, as was discovered two years later, both). The substances were called simply A and B so that four blood types – A, B, O, and AB – were possible. Blood also contained antibodies (see ANTIBODY) for the substance or substances it did not possess, so that B blood, for instance, could not be added to A blood or vice versa without causing the blood corpuscles to stick together and grow useless. It was only after Landsteiner's discovery, therefore, that blood *transfusion* (from the Latin 'trans', meaning 'over', and 'fundere', meaning 'to pour') became practical; and physicians knew enough to 'pour over' blood from a well person to a patient that needed blood without killing the patient.

Blood substances not interfering with transfusion also exist. One was discovered in 1940 by Landsteiner and the American physician Alexander S. Wiener in the blood of a rhesus monkey. The new substance was therefore called *Rh* from the first letters. Some eight varieties of this factor are known today. No natural antibodies can exist against

Rh, but in the case of all but one variety, antibodies can be developed artificially. The exceptional variety is called *Rh negative*, the others, *Rh positive*.

It sometimes happens that a mother with Rh negative blood is carrying an unborn child who has inherited Rh positive from the father. Some of the child's Rh positive may filter across to the mother's blood, which may then develop antibodies against it. If these antibodies filter back into the child's blood, they may ruin enough red corpuscles to allow a very sick baby to be born. Physicians then have to replace the baby's blood with fresh blood quickly and, to be prepared for that possibility, expectant mothers are routinely typed for Rh these days, so that at least one third of the made-up name *Rhesus* has become very significant indeed.

from WORDS ON THE MAP (1962)

NEW JERSEY

In 1066, William II, Duke of Normandy, set sail for England, defeated and killed the English king, Harold, and became William I, King of England. His descendants ruled both England and Normandy, plus other sections of France from time to time. Gradually, over the centuries, however, the English-ruled portions of France were taken by the French armies. Finally in 1558, the English lost their last foothold in continental France.

Of the Norman inheritance, however, they retained one last remnant, a few islands off the coast of France. Because they are in the English Channel, they are called the *Channel Islands*.

The largest of these islands was called, in Roman times, 'Caesaria insula' ('Caesar's island'). During the Middle Ages, when the Latin language was garbled by barbarians, 'Caesaria' became tongue-twisted to *Jersey*.

A successful British naval officer of the seventeenth century, George Carteret, was born on the island of

Jersey. During the English Civil War, Carteret was a
Royalist fighting for the king. When Charles I was
beheaded in 1649, Carteret held out in Jersey for two
years before he was forced to retreat to France.

The son of Charles I visited Jersey before the surrender
and, in gratitude, granted Carteret land in America. In
1660, this son regained the throne as Charles II and when,
in 1664, the Dutch possessions in America were captured,
part were given to Carteret in fulfilment of the promise.

Carteret named his territories after the island of his
birth which he had so well defended and it is still known as
New Jersey, though before 1702 it existed in two sections,
West Jersey and *East Jersey*.

New Jersey was one of the thirteen original states of the
United States and was the third to ratify the Constitution.

PHILADELPHIA

After the time of Alexander the Great, there were lines of
Macedonian monarchs over Egypt and Asia who kept
largely to one or two names. For instance, all the Egyptian
kings of the period were called Ptolemy, while the kings of
western Asia were called, for the most part, Seleucus or
Antiochus.

In order to distinguish one monarch from another, the
kings would adopt a second name, which was usually very
flattering. For instance the first Ptolemy was Ptolemy Soter
('preserver'). Next were Ptolemy Philadelphus ('loving his
sister'), Ptolemy Euergetes ('benefactor'), Ptolemy Phi-
lopater ('loving his father'), and so on.

About 260 B.C., Ptolemy Philadelphus rebuilt a city in
Palestine that had suffered in recent wars and renamed it
Philadelphia after himself. It is the modern *Amman*, the
capital of Jordan.

In western Asia Minor, another line of Macedonian
kings were called Attalus. Of these, the second was Attalus
Philadelphus and, about 150 B.C., he founded a city which
he called *Philadelphia* also. This Philadelphia is mentioned

in the Bible, in Chapter 3 of Revelation, as a city that was faithful to Christianity under trying circumstances. Many centuries later, in 1390, it was the last city in Asia Minor to fall to the Turks. It is now called *Alasehir*, from Turkish words meaning 'red city', because of the colour of its soil.

The name of the old Macedonian kings travelled to the Americas in modern times. In 1681, a city was founded in the new colony of Pennsylvania by the pious William Penn. To him, *Philadelphia* seemed perfect on two counts. First, it reminded one of the old city of Asia Minor that was faithful to Christianity, and secondly, the word could be translated 'brotherly love'. So it is that the largest city in Pennsylvania and the fourth largest in the United States is called *Philadelphia*, and is sometimes referred to as the 'City of Brotherly Love'.

VIRGIN ISLANDS

East of Puerto Rico, there is a chain of small islands that curves down to the South American continent. The most northerly of the group were discovered by Columbus in 1493, during his second voyage, and were named by him in honour of Saint Ursula and her companions, who were supposed to have died about 450, defending themselves against the Huns. They were all virgins and the islands are therefore the *Virgin Islands*.

The Virgin Islands have had an unusually mixed history as far as European colonization is concerned. The Dutch, British, Spanish, and French have all, at one time or another, established themselves there. The largest island, a little south of the rest of the group, bears the name of *St Croix* (sant-kroy) or *Santa Cruz* (san'tuh-krooz), both (the former French, the latter Spanish) meaning 'Holy Cross'.

In 1753, Denmark purchased St Croix from the French and also occupied two islands to the north, which bear the names of *St Thomas* and *St John*, after two of the apostles.

This was one of Denmark's very rare excursions into colonization outside the Arctic. These three islands were lumped under the name of *Danish West Indies*.

In 1917, the United States was worried lest Germany might win World War I, then raging, and force weak Denmark to cede the islands, thus gaining a foothold in the western hemisphere. Playing it safe, the United States bought the islands from Denmark. The official title is now the *Virgin Islands of the United States*. (They are usually called simply Virgin Islands, but this is inaccurate because a couple of dozen small islands to their east are also part of the group, but belong to England. Those are called the *British Virgin Islands*.)

Marks of a century and a half of Danish ownership remain on the map of the islands, however. Since the fifteenth century, Denmark has been ruled by kings that have alternately borne the names of Frederik and Christian. Well, the two chief towns on St Croix are *Frederiksted* and *Christiansted*, meaning 'Frederik's town' and 'Christian's town' respectively.

from WORDS FROM HISTORY *(1968)*

BLOODY SHIRT

In 1689, the English overthrew their monarch James II, and put in his place his daughter Mary II, and her husband William III, in a joint reign. This change met the approval of most Englishmen, but the case was different in Scotland. James II was the representative of a Scottish dynasty and within three months of James' ejection, the Scots rose in an unsuccessful revolt.

William tried to placate them and offered to call a truce with every clan that tendered its submission to him before December 31, 1691. There would be no reprisals for earlier acts of rebellion. By that day, all the clans had given their submission except the Macdonalds of Glencoe (in west-central Scotland). Their leader stubbornly waited till the last minute and then it was too late. A sudden snowstorm delayed him and it wasn't till January 5, 1692, that he could find a proper official with whom he could register his submission.

The Campbell clan was the sworn enemy of the Macdonalds, and here was a chance to take advantage of the letter of the law, for the Macdonalds by failing to meet the deadline had become outlaws. The Campbells came to Glencoe, accepted Macdonald hospitality for twelve days, and then at five in the morning, the Campbells (with the king's writ giving them permission) slaughtered all the Macdonalds they could find, and did so with revolting brutality.

After the massacre, so goes the tale, those wives who survived displayed the bloody shirts of their stabbed husbands to arouse compassion and spur on vengeance. This may be the origin of 'to wave the bloody shirt', meaning to rouse, deliberately, a passion for revenge.

This played a role in American history. After the Civil War, the Republicans kept the Democrats out of national power for a quarter of a century by waving the *bloody shirt* of the Civil War, keeping the blame for that carnage fixed firmly upon them.

MOB

It is natural for those who consider themselves among the 'better classes' to look down on the people generally and to have insulting names like 'rabble' for them.

There is often a tinge of fear added to contempt in the aristocrats' view of the people. The common folk, through much of history, have been ignorant and without proper leadership. When they feel uncommonly ill-used, they sometimes rise in blind wrath and destroy anything they can reach. Almost invariably, however, they are beaten down before long by the well-organized forces of government and society and are slaughtered mercilessly in revenge. An example is to be found in the Peasants'

Revolt in Germany in 1524.

What's more, crowds of people can be swayed by clever orators. Once they are ignited, the excitement of the moment and the mutual encouragement of individuals among them can lead them out of control. Shakespeare records in *Julius Caesar* how Mark Antony cleverly turned the people against Caesar's assassins. It is no wonder that Roman writers referred to the 'mobile vulgus' (the 'fickle multitude').

Sometimes the roused people, under capable leadership, can make their rebellion stick, for a while at least. Thus, in Great Britain, the people carried through a rebellion to the point of executing King Charles I in 1649. When Charles II, his son, was reinstated as king in 1660, his supporters felt considerable resentment against the 'fickle multitude', which now cheered the return of the new Charles as loudly as it had cheered the killing of the old.

At the aristocratic Greenribbon Club, there was frequent contemptuous talk of the 'mobile vulgus' until, finally, through frequent use, the term was shortened to its first syllable, *mob*. The word is now used for any dangerous and disorderly crowd of people. More recently, it has been applied to an organized group of gangsters.

POTEMKIN VILLAGE

In 1745, a young German princess, Sophia of Anhalt-Zerbst, married Peter, the nephew of the Russian empress. The 16-year-old bride adopted the Russian religion and took the Russian name of Ekaterina (Catherine). Peter suceeded to the throne in 1762, but was half-mad and was quickly murdered, probably with the connivance of Catherine.

The German princess became the Russian empress Catherine II (also called Catherine the Great), reigned for thirty-four years, and was one of the ablest monarchs Russia ever had.

She was most notorious among her contemporaries

because of her lovers. But then, it was taken for granted that eighteenth-century kings have their mistresses – why should not an eighteenth-century queen do the equivalent?

Her most famous lover was a Russian soldier named Gregory Potemkin. He had distinguished himself in the war fought against Turkey from 1768 to 1774, in which Crimea and other lands in the western and southern Ukraine were absorbed into Russia.

Both Catherine and Potemkin were seriously interested in improving Russia's economy, but this could not be done without more reform than Catherine was willing to see. Potemkin tried to reorganize the Ukraine and carry through a huge colonization venture. Corruption and bad planning spoiled matters and when Catherine demanded to see the results, he had to do considerable faking. In a tour of the south in 1787, he cleverly managed to have Catherine see only what he wanted her to see. He is even supposed to have built false-front villages, carting 'happy villagers' from one to the other just ahead of her.

For that reason, *Potemkin villages* has come to mean a fake with which government officials delude people into thinking all is well. More generally, a Potemkin village is anything which looks good – but on the outside, only.

PART 8

History

Actually, I wrote three other 'Words' books as well, but not in the same format. In Words from the Myths, *for instance, I told, in connected fashion, the tales of the Greek myths and stopped periodically to point out how certain words and phrases in the English language arose from them – words like jovial, hermetic, and Achilles' heel, for instance.*

This, naturally, gave me the idea for a companion book and in December, 1963, I brought in Words from Greek History. *In it, I told Greek history in more or less connected fashion, as I had told the Greek myths, stopping whenever I wanted to point out word derivations (laconic, marathon, philippic, and so on).*

The trouble was it was too long, and Austin handed it back to me and told me that he had very lightly pencilmarked the passages he thought might be cut, without harm to the book. I looked through it with some dismay and said, 'But Austin, you're cutting out all about the words.'

And he said, 'I guess the history parts were more interesting.'

I said, 'Let me take this home and think about it.'

Tumultuous emotions were tumbling about inside me. What Austin didn't know and what no one knew except me, for that matter, was that in college it had been only after some hesitation that I had decided to major in chemistry. There had been a strong impulse to major in history. What finally swung me to chemistry was my feeling that as a history major all I would be able to do in later life would be to teach and engage in library research, whereas chemistry could lead to active experimentation in the laboratory. (It was only in later life that

*I discovered I would rather teach than do lab work and
would rather do library research than either. – And so it
goes.)*

My interest in history stayed on even when I moved into
chemistry. In 1944 and 1945, years before I had published
a single book, I began gathering notes for what was
intended to be a massive history of World War II. It never
came to anything, of course, but I gathered roughly a
million words of notes before the enchantment left me.

Now, nearly twenty years later, here was Austin incau-
tiously telling me that he found the historical portions of a
book interesting. What's more, I remember that Austin
had once said to me as follows, and I quote him precisely:
'Isaac, any time some publishing house asks you to do a
specific book and you feel like doing it, go ahead. But if
you ever write a book strictly because it's your own idea,
bring it to us and we'll publish it.'

I placed Words from Greek History aside, therefore,
and began all over with a completely new book. (Of course,
that did not mean that Words from Greek History remained a total loss. No, indeed, the material within it was
incorporated to a considerable extent in the eventual
Words from History. I try not to let anything go to waste.)

The new book I called The Greeks and it was an overall history of Greece – plain history, no 'words' – from
2,000 B.C to A.D. 1964. I brought it in and said to Austin,
'Here's the revision of Words from Greek History and I
wrote it strictly because it's my own idea. So publish it.'

And Houghton Mifflin published it as my first 'straight
history' book. Of course, it was primarily intended for non-
historians, as my science books are primarily intended for
non-scientists.

from THE GREEKS *(1965)*

THE SPARTAN WAY OF LIFE

The Messenian wars cost Sparta a high price also. A half-century of war, so hard-fought, had ground the military life deep into the Spartan consciousness. It seemed to them they never dared relax, especially when there were so few Spartans and so many helots (slaves). Surely if the Spartans ever relaxed, even slightly, the helots would rise at once.

Furthermore, the Messenian wars had developed the role of the heavily armed foot soldier, or hoplite. Military training had to be particularly hard to inure the soldier to wearing heavy armour and wielding heavy weapons. Fighting was not a trade for weaklings as the Spartans practised it.

For that reason, the Spartans dedicated their lives to warfare. Spartan youngsters were inspected at birth to see if they were physically sound. If they were not, they were abandoned and allowed to die. At the age of seven, they were taken from their mothers and were brought up in barracks.

They were taught to endure cold and hunger, were never allowed to wear fine clothes or eat good food, were trained in all military arts and were taught to endure wariness and pain without complaint.

The Spartan code was to fight hard, follow orders without questions, and to die rather than retreat or surrender. To run away, a soldier had to throw down his heavy shield, which would otherwise slow him down; if he died, he would be carried home, in honour, upon his shield. Therefore, Spartan mothers were supposed to instruct their sons to return from war 'with their shields or on them'.

The Spartan adults ate at a common table, everyone bringing his share, all contributing from the substance produced from his lands by the labour of his helots. (If a Spartan lost his lands for any reason, he was no longer entitled to a place at the table, which was a great disgrace. In later centuries fewer and fewer Spartans were entitled to such a place as land became concentrated in fewer and fewer hands. This was a source of weakness for Sparta but only towards the end of her history did she try to reform the situation.)

The food at the common table was designed to fill a person and keep him alive, but nothing more. Some non-Spartan Greek, having tasted the porridge that Spartans ate in their barracks, is supposed to have said that he no longer wondered why Spartans fought so bravely and without the slightest fear of death. Such porridge made death welcome.

In later centuries, the Spartans maintained that this way of life originated with a man named Lycurgus (ligh-kur′gus) who lived, according to their tradition, sometime about 850 B.C., long before the Messenian wars. However, this is almost certainly not so and it is even doubtful that Lycurgus existed at all.

The proof of this is that down to about 650 B.C. Sparta does not seem to have been very much different from the other Greek states. She had her art, her music, her poetry. During the seventh century, a musician from Lesbos named Terpander (tur-pan′der) came to Sparta and did well there. He is supposed to have improved the lyre and is called the 'Father of Greek music'.

Most famous of all Spartan musicians was Tyrtaeus (turtee′us). By tradition, he was an Athenian but he may well have been a native Spartan. In any case, he lived during the Second Messenian War and his music was said to have inspired the Spartans to new feats of bravery when their ardour flagged.

It was only after the Second Messenian War that the deadly hand of utter militarism completely shut off all that was creative and human in Sparta. Art, music, and literature came to a halt. Even oratory (and all Greeks have loved to talk from ancient times to the present day) was stopped, for Spartans practised speaking very briefly and to the point. The very word 'laconic' (from Laconia) has come to mean the quality of speaking pithily.

By 1964, Austin knew my deplorable habit of making several books grow where one had been planted. When he agreed to publish The Greeks *he said, with commendable editorial caution, 'Look, Isaac, will you do me a favour? Don't write a history of Rome until we see how* The Greeks *does.'*

That was only fair. The Greeks *was published in June, 1965, and on August 2, I visited the Houghton Mifflin offices and asked how the book was doing. 'Pretty well,' Austin said. I asked if the reviews were all right and he said they were.*

So I said, 'Are you willing to risk publishing a history of Rome?'

He said, 'Yes! You can go home and start it, and we'll prepare a contract.'

I said, 'You can prepare a contract, but I don't have to go home. Here is the manuscript.'

What I had done, you see, was gamble that The Greeks *would do reasonably well and had prepared another historical manuscript just in case.*

I did another thing about the history of Rome, too. The Greeks *had proven too long and Austin had gently manoeuvred the cutting of some ten thousand words or so. I was determined to avoid that sort of thing in the future. (It so happens that amputating ten thousand glorious words is a painful operation and, unlike the more ordinary kinds of operations such as the mere hacking off of a right arm, no one has developed an anaesthetic for it.)*

So I only wrote half the history of Rome and thus made sure it wouldn't be too long. I called it The Roman Republic *and it was obvious there would have to be* The Roman Empire *following it – and so there was.*

Of course, I have particular fun when I see something, or think I see something, which is not brought out in the usual history books. There is the case, for instance, of Pompey, a popular Roman general of the first century B.C., *and the Temple at Jerusalem, and here is what I said about that:*

from THE ROMAN REPUBLIC *(1966)*

South of Syria was the land of Judea. A century before,
Judea had revolted against the Seleucid Empire and had
gained its independence under a line of rulers known as
the Maccabees (mak'uh-beez). Judea prospered under
them at first, but eventually its history came to be largely
that of the quarrels among different members of the ruling
family.

When Pompey arrived, two brothers of the Maccabee
family were fighting a civil war. One was Hyrcanus II
(herkay'nus) and the other Aristobulus (uh-ris"toh-
byoo'lus) – both Jews despite their Greek-sounding names.
Each brother tried to win the all-powerful Roman to his
side.

Pompey demanded that all fortresses in Judea be
surrendered to him. This was denied him, and Jerusalem
refused to allow him to enter. For three months Pompey
laid siege to it, and then the always stiff-necked Jews
reluctantly gave in.

Pompey took the city and, out of curiosity, entered the
Holy of Holies of the Temple at Jerusalem – the most
sacred chamber of the Temple which only the High Priest
might enter and then only at the Day of Atonement.

No doubt many Jews must have expected Pompey to die
on the spot as a result of divine displeasure, but he emerged
completely unharmed. Nevertheless, it is an interesting fact
that from that point on, from the time of his violation of
the Temple, Pompey's successes came to an end. The rest
of his life was one long frustrating failure.

*About this time, Austin was promoted into the higher
reaches of the hierarchy (though he remains as accessible
as ever) and I came to be more closely associated with
Walter Lorraine and Mary K. Harmon. This means that
my lunches can be with any of six different combinations
of these three, including an occasional lunch with all three,*

as was true when this book was first planned.

I am now doing history books fairly regularly and am delighted to be doing so. All are put out in uniform design so it is clear they form a series. Houghton Mifflin is just egging me on by doing that, whether they know it or not. It is now my intention, while life and breath hold out, to write history after history, dealing with different periods, different regions, different aspects. With sufficient ingenuity I can manage to do this for decades and produce an indefinite number.

And when I cautiously hint at this to Mary K, who is the sweetest lady editor one could possibly encounter, she says, without batting on eyelash, 'That's fine, Isaac.'

Well, if I'm going to write a million histories, I can't resist quoting a couple of short passages.

from THE EGYPTIANS *(1967)*

Gnosticism was a pre-Christian philosophy that stressed the evil of matter and the world. To the Gnostics, the great abstract God, who was truly real, good, and the omnipotent ruler of all, was a personified Wisdom (or, in Greek, *gnosis*, hence 'Gnosticism').

Wisdom was utterly divorced from the universe – unreachable, unknowable. The universe was created by an inferior god, a 'demiurge' (from a Greek word meaning 'worker for the people' – a practical ruler, an earthly sort of being rather than a divine god above and beyond matter). Because the ability of the demiurge was limited, the world turned out to be evil, as was all in it, including matter itself. The human body was evil, and the human spirit had to turn away from it, and from matter and the world, in an attempt to strive backwards to spirit and Wisdom.

Some Gnostics found themselves attracted to Christianity and vice versa. The outstanding leader of this line of thought was Marcion (mahr'shee-on), a native of Asia

Minor, and supposedly the son of a Christian bishop.

Writing during the reigns of Trajan and Hadrian, Marcion held that it was the God of the Old Testament who was the demiurge – the evil and inferior being who had created the universe, Jesus, on the other hand, was the representative of the true God, of Wisdom. Since Jesus did not partake of the creation of the demiurge, he was pure spirit, and his human shape and experiences were merely a deliberate illusion taken on to accomplish his purposes.

The Gnostic version of Christianity was quite popular in Egypt for a time, since it fitted in well with the anti-Jewish feeling in the land. It made of the Jewish God a demon, and made of the Jewish scriptures something that was demon-inspired.

Gnostic Christianity, however, did not endure long, for the mainstream of Christianity was firmly set against it. Most of the Christian leaders accepted the God of the Jews and the Old Testament as the God spoken of by Jesus in the New Testament. The Old Testament was accepted as inspired scripture and as the necessary preface to the New Testament.

Nevertheless, though Gnosticism passed away, it left behind some dark strains. There remained in Christianity some feeling concerning the evil of the world and of man, and with it an anti-Jewish feeling that was stronger than before.

What's more, the Egyptians themselves never abandoned a kind of Gnostic view with regard to Jesus. They consistently interpreted the nature of Jesus in such a way as to minimize its human aspect. This not only contributed to a continuing debilitating internal struggle among the Christian leaders but was an important factor, as we shall see, in the eventual destruction of Egyptian Christianity.

Another, more joyful, influence of Egyptian ways of thought on Christianity involved the lovely Isis, Queen of Heaven. She was surely one of the most popular goddesses, not only in Egypt but in the Roman Empire, and it was fairly easy to transfer delight in beauty and gentle sympathy from Isis to the Virgin Mary. The important role played by the Virgin in Christian thought lent to the religion a warmly feminine touch that was absent in Judaism, and certainly the existence of the Isis cult made it easier to add that aspect to Christianity.

This was the easier still because Isis was often shown with the infant Horus on her lap. In this aspect Horus, without the hawk head, was known to the Egyptians as Harpechruti ('Horus, the Child'). He had his finger on his lips as a sign of infancy – an approach to sucking his thumb, so to speak. The Greeks mistook the sign as one that asked for quiet, and in their pantheon he became Harpocrates (hahr-pok'ruhteez), god of silence.

The popularity of Isis and Harpocrates, mother and child, was transferred to Christianity, too, and helped make popular the idea of the Virgin and Christ Child that has captured the imagination of millions upon millions in the Christian centuries.

from THE NEAR EAST (1968)

One important factor in Assyria's favour was that its iron supplies increased . . . The Assyrian army was the first to really exploit the new metal in quantity, and it entered a two-century career of conquest that was to make it the terror of the world.

Nor was it only a matter of iron. The Assyrians were the first to make a science of the siege of cities. From very early times, cities had learned that by building walls about themselves they could hold off an enemy most effectively. From the top of the walls it was easy to fire a hail of arrows down upon the enemy, while the enemy in turn could do little damage in shooting arrows up to the tops of the walls.

A siege became an endurance contest, therefore. Those laying siege avoided attempts to fight their way in and

take the city 'by storm'. Instead they were content to
isolate the city and prevent food supplies from entering.
In this way, the city could be starved into surrender. The
city under siege held out as long as possible in the hope
that the besieging army would succumb to boredom,
attrition, and disease. It was generally a long pull and
often, with both sides suffering, some compromise arrangement was made in which the city agreed to pay tribute
but preserved itself intact.

The Assyrians, however, at this period of history, began
to devise methods for beating down the wall. They built
heavy devices that could not be pushed over, placed them
on wheels so that they could be moved easily against the
wall, armoured them to protect the men within, and
equipped them with battering rams to beat down the wall.
Once a breach was made in the wall and the besieging
army poured in, it was usually all over.

This form of siege warfare introduced a new element of
horror. As long as battles were mainly army against army,
bloodshed was limited. A defeated army could run away,
and even fleeing soldiers could turn and defend themselves.
However, when a city was taken by storm, its population
was pinned against its own wall and could not flee. It was
filled with material goods for looting, and with helpless
women and children who might be abused without fear of
reprisal. In the fury of war and the excitement of victory,
the sack of a city involved cruelties beyond description.

*Oddly enough, long before I began to write actual history
books, my interest in history showed up in my fiction. Or,
come to think of it, why should that be odd; isn't it natural
that should be so?*

*In the 1940s, you see, I wrote a series of stories about
the fall of the Galactic Empire, the thousand-year Dark
Age that followed, and the rise of the Second Galactic
Empire. What I had in mind was the fall of the Roman
Empire, of course, and I was very free in making analogies,*

although the imitation was never slavish.

The stories involved the deliberate establishment of two Foundations of scientists towards the end of the days of the First Empire. It seems that the science of 'psycho-history' (an invented term of my own, which deals with the study of quantitative sociology so that the sweeping changes of history can be foreseen in advance and foretold) had been perfected. The Foundations were therefore located in such places and in such fashion as would serve to reduce (according to the predictions of psychohistory) the length and disastrousness of the Dark Age interregnum.

My stories were intended to follow the working out of that plan, but I never finished. How I started the series and why I never finished I outlined a couple of years ago for the fellow members of one of my professional societies, The Science Fiction Writers of America. Here is what I said, in part:

from 'There's Nothing Like a Good Foundation' *(1967)*

The Foundation Series had its origin in 1941, in the course of a subway ride to see John W. Campbell, Jr, editor of *Astounding Science Fiction*. In those days, I visited him frequently and always brought with me the plot of a new s.-f. story. We discussed it and I went home and wrote it. Then he would sometimes accept it and sometimes not.

On this subway ride, I had no story idea to present him with so I tried a trick I still sometimes recommend. I opened a book at random, read a sentence, and concentrated on it till I had an idea. The book was a collection of the Gilbert and Sullivan plays which I just happened to have with me. I opened it to *Iolanthe* and my eye fell on the picture of the fairy queen kneeling before Private Willis of the Grenadier Guards.

I let my mind wander from the Grenadiers, to soldiers in general, to a military society, to feudalism, to the breakup of the Roman Empire. By the time I reached

Campbell I told him that I was planning to write a story about the breakup of the Galactic Empire.

He talked and I talked and he talked and I talked, and when I left I had the Foundation Series in mind. It lasted for seven years, during which I wrote eight stories, ranging in length from a short story to a three-part serial . . .

But there are disadvantages to a series of stories. There is, for one thing, the bugaboo of self-consistency. It is annoying to be hampered, in working out a story, by the fact that some perfectly logical development is ruled out since, three stories before, you had to make such a development impossible because of the needs of the plot of *that* story . . .

Before I could write a new Foundation story I had to sit down and reread all the preceding ones, and by the time I got to the eighth story that meant rereading 150,000 words of very complicated material. Even so, my success was limited. In April, 1966, a fan approached me with a carefully made out list of inconsistencies in dates, names, and events that he had dug out of the series by dint of close reading and cross-reference.

Furthermore, in designing each new Foundation story, I found I had to work within an increasingly constricted area, with progressively fewer and fewer degrees of freedom. I was forced to seize whatever way I could find without worrying about how difficult I might make the next story. Then, when I came to the next story, those difficulties arose and beat me over the head.

Then again, I had to start each story with some indication of what had gone before, for those readers who had never read any of the earlier stories. When I wrote the eighth story, I was forced to begin with a long introduction which I had to disguise as an essay my adolescent girl-heroine was writing for class. It was not at all easy to make such an essay interesting. I had to introduce a number of human-interest touches and interrupt it by action at the first possible opportunity . . .

The eighth story had carried me only one-third of the

way through the original plan of describing one thousand
years of future history. However, to write a ninth story
meant rereading the first eight, starting with a longer
prologue than ever, working in a narrower compass than
ever, and so on. So I quit – permanently . . .

The Foundation Series were first published in book form
in three volumes in the early 1950s [*Foundation, Foundation and Empire, Second Foundation*] and they have never
gone out of print. As book-club selections, in paperback
form, in foreign editions, in hard-cover reissues, and
paperback reissues, they seem to have an indefinite
number of lives . . .

No week passes without some piece of fan mail referring
to the Foundation stories and usually asking for more.
And at the 24th World Science Fiction Convention, held in
Cleveland in 1966, the Foundation Series was awarded
a Hugo as the All-Time Best Series.

What more can I ask for having opened a book in the
subway twenty-five years ago?

*Here's a passage, then, from one of the Foundation stories,
one which was originally called 'The Dead Hand' and
which was eventually included in* Foundation and Empire,
*the middle book of the trilogy. It deals with Cleon II,
Galactic Emperor, and while I wrote it, I had in mind
Roman history. There was a little bit of Justinian and
Belisarius of the sixth century and a little bit of Tiberius
and Sejanus of the first century and so on.*

from 'The Dead Hand' *(1945)*

Cleon II was Lord of the Universe. Cleon II also suffered
from a painful and undiagnosed ailment. By the queer
twists of human affairs, the two statements are not mutually
exclusive, nor even particularly incongruous. There have
been a wearisomely large number of precedents in history.

But Cleon II cared nothing for such precedents. To meditate upon a long list of similar cases would not ameliorate personal suffering an electron's worth. It soothed him as little to think that where his great-grandfather had been the pirate ruler of a dust-speck planet, he himself slept in the pleasure palace of Ammenetick the Great, as heir of a line of Galactic rulers stretching backwards into a tenuous past. It was at present no source of comfort to him that the efforts of his father had cleansed the realm of its leprous patches of rebellion and restored it to the peace and unity it had enjoyed under Stanel VI; that, as a consequence, in the twenty-five years of his reign, not one cloud of revolt had misted his burnished glory.

The Emperor of the Galaxy and the Lord of All whimpered as he lolled his head backwards into the invigorating plane of force about his pillows. It yielded in a softness that did not touch, and at the pleasant tingle, Cleon relaxed a bit. He sat up with difficulty and stared morosely at the distant walls of the grand chamber. It was a bad room to be alone in. It was too big. All the rooms were too big.

But better to be alone during these crippling bouts than to endure the prinking of the courtiers, their lavish sympathy, their soft, condescending dullness. Better to be alone than to watch those insipid masks behind which spun the tortuous speculations on the chances of death and the fortunes of the succession.

His thoughts harried him. There were his three sons; three straight-backed youths full of promise and virtue. Where did they disappear on these bad days? Waiting, no doubt. Each watching the others; and all watching him.

He stirred uneasily. And now Brodrig craved audience. The lowborn faithful Brodrig; faithful because he was hated with a unanimous and cordial hatred that was the only point of agreement between the dozen cliques that divided his court.

Brodrig – the faithful favourite, who had to be faithful, since unless he owned the fastest speed ship in the Galaxy and took to it the day of the Emperor's death, it would be the atom chamber the day after.

Cleon II touched the smooth knob on the arm of his great divan, and the huge door at the end of the room dissolved to transparency.

Brodrig advanced along the crimson carpet and knelt to kiss the Emperor's limp hand.

'Your health, sire?' asked the Privy Secretary in a low tone of becoming anxiety.

'I live,' snapped the Emperor with exasperation, 'if you can call it life where every scoundrel who can read a book of medicine uses me as a blank and receptive field for his feeble experiments. If there is a conceivable remedy; chemical, physical, or atomic, which has not yet been tried; why then, some learned babbler from the far corners of the realm will arrive tomorrow to try it. And still another newly discovered book, or forgery more-like, will be used as authority.

'By my father's memory,' he rumbled savagely, 'it seems there is not a biped extant who can study a disease before his eyes with those same eyes. There is not one who can count a pulsebeat without a book of the ancients before him. I'm sick and they call it "unknown". The fools! If in the course of millennia, human bodies learn new methods of falling askew, it remains uncovered by the studies of the ancients and uncurable forevermore. The ancients should be alive now, or I then.'

The Emperor ran down to a low-breathed curse while Brodrig waited dutifully. Cleon II said peevishly, 'How many are waiting outside?'

He jerked his head in the direction of the door.

Brodrig said patiently, 'The Great Hall holds the usual number.'

'Well, let them wait. State matters occupy me. Have the Captain of the Guard announce it. Or wait, forget the state matters. Just have it announced I hold no audience, and let the Captain of the Guard look doleful. The jackals among them may betray themselves.' The Emperor sneered nastily.

'There is a rumour, sire,' said Brodrig, smoothly, 'that it is your heart that troubles you.'

The Emperor's smile was little removed from the previous sneer. 'It will hurt others more than myself if any act prematurely on that rumour. But what is it *you* want? Let's have this over.'

Brodrig rose from his kneeling posture at a gesture of permission and said, 'It concerns General Bel Riose, the Military Governor of Siwenna.'

'Riose?' Cleon II frowned heavily. 'I don't place him. Wait, is he the one who sent that quixotic message some months back? Yes, I remember. He panted for permission to enter a career of conquest for the glory of the Empire and Emperor.'

'Exactly, sire.'

The Emperor laughed shortly. 'Did you think I had such generals left me, Brodrig? He seems to be a curious atavism. What was the answer? I believe you took care of it.'

'I did, sire. He was instructed to forward additional information and to take no steps involving naval action without further orders from the Imperium.'

'Hmp. Safe enough. Who is this Riose? Was he ever at court?'

Brodrig nodded and his mouth twisted ever so little. 'He began his career as a cadet in the Guards ten years back. He had part in that affair off the Lemul Cluster.'

'The Lemul Cluster? You know, my memory isn't quite – Was that the time a young soldier saved two ships of the line from a head-on collision by . . . uh . . . something or other?' He waved a hand impatiently. 'I don't remember the details. It was something heroic.'

'Riose was that soldier. He received a promotion for it,' Brodrig said dryly, 'and an appointment to field duty as captain of a ship.'

'And now Military Governor of a border system and still young. Capable man, Brodrig!'

'Unsafe, sire. He lives in the past. He is a dreamer of ancient times, or rather, of the myths of what ancient times used to be. Such men are harmless in themselves, but their queer lack of realism makes them tools for others.' He added, 'His men, I understand, are completely under his control. He is one of your *popular* generals.'

'Is he?' the Emperor mused. 'Well, come, Brodrig, I would not wish to be served entirely by incompetents. They certainly set no enviable standard for faithfulness themselves.'

'An incompetent traitor is no danger. It is rather the capable men who must be watched.'

'You among them, Brodrig?' Cleon II laughed and then grimaced with pain. 'Well, then, you may forget the lecture for the while. What new development is there in the matter of this young conqueror? I hope you haven't come merely to reminisce.'

'Another message, sire, has been received from General Riose.'

'Oh? And to what effect?'

'He has spied out the land of these barbarians and advocates an expedition in force. His arguments are long and fairly tedious. It is not worth annoying your Imperial Majesty with it at present, during your indisposition. Particularly since it will be discussed at length during the session of the Council of Lords.' He glanced sidewise at the Emperor.

Cleon II frowned. 'The Lords? Is it a question for them, Brodrig? It will mean further demands for a broader interpretation of the Charter. It always comes to that.'

'It can't be avoided, sire. It might have been better if your august father could have beat down the last rebellion without granting the Charter. But since it is here, we must endure it for the while.'

'You're right, I suppose. Then the Lords it must be. But why all this solemnity, man? It is, after all, a minor point.

Success on a remote border with limited troops is scarcely a state affair.'

Brodrig smiled narrowly. He said coolly, 'It is an affair of a romantic idiot; but even a romantic idiot can be a deadly weapon when an unromantic rebel uses him as a tool. Sire, the man was popular here and is popular there. He is young. If he annexes a vagrant barbarian planet or two, he will become a conqueror. Now a young conqueror who has proven his ability to rouse the enthusiasm of pilots, miners, tradesmen, and such-like rabble is dangerous at any time. Even if he lacked the desire to do to you as your august father did to the usurper, Ricker, then one of our loyal Lords of the Domain may decide to use him as his weapon.'

Cleon II moved an arm hastily and stiffened with the pain. Slowly he relaxed, but his smile was weak, and his voice a whisper. 'You are a valuable subject, Brodrig. You always suspect far more than is necessary, and I have but to take half your suggested precautions to be utterly safe. We'll put it up to the Lords. We shall see what they say and take our measures accordingly. The young man, I suppose, has made no hostile moves yet.'

'He reports none. But already he asks for reinforcements.'

'Reinforcements!' The emperor's eyes narrowed with wonder. 'What force has he?'

'Ten ships of the line, sire, with a full complement of auxiliary vessels. Two of the ships are equipped with motors salvaged from the old Grand Fleet, and one has a battery of power artillery from the same source. The other ships are new ones of the last fifty years, but are serviceable, nevertheless.'

'Ten ships would seem adequate for any reasonable undertaking. Why, with less than ten ships my father won his first victories against the usurper. Who *are* these barbarians he's fighting?'

The Privy Secretary raised a pair of supercilious eyebrows. 'He refers to them as "the Foundation".'

PART 9

The Bible

In a way, none of my books has done badly. By that I mean that none has lost money for its publisher and none has had to be remaindered.

On the other hand, not one of my Hundred Books has ever hit the best-seller lists or even come close to doing so. Nor do I expect any of my future books to do so. I'm rather resigned to that. After all, my books don't contain those little items that have a broad general appeal: no sex to speak of, very little violence and, indeed, not much sensationalism of any sort.

I don't mean to sound aggrieved, or to give the impression that I feel I am maintaining integrity and virtue against difficulties. Not at all. It never occurs to me to add sensationalism of any sort, and if I tried to do so I almost certainly couldn't do it convincingly and would merely ruin the book. What's more, to do everyone justice, not one editor of the many with whom I have dealt, has ever once by as much as a word indicated and I ought to stick in a little sex or violence for the sake of additional sales.

Despite all this resignation and contentment, I will admit that I get a little rattled when one of my books manages to get into the black with a narrower margin than usual. Two of my 'words' books didn't do as well as the rest, for instance. These were Words in Genesis *and* Words from the Exodus, *which, together, covered the first five books of the Bible and searched out their contribution to English vocabulary.*

This was particularly frustrating, for I had hoped to continue all the way through the Bible in similar fashion, and now I was too abashed to do so.

Yet the matter of the Bible nagged at me and nagged at

*me until some time in 1965 I wondered if I might not do
a big book on the whole Bible. It would be a book that
dealt with the historical background to the events of the
Bible rather than merely with word derivations, for I had
begun my history series by then and I was all of a history-
fire. Then, too, I thought of doing it at the adult level
rather than aiming it at youngsters primarily.*

As it happened, I had done a big book, Asimov's
Biographical Encyclopedia of Science and Technology *the
year before for Doubleday and it was doing considerably
better than, in my heart of hearts, I had thought it would.
It seemed to me that Doubleday might be receptive to
another book.*

*They were! In no time at all, I was sending samples to
Lawrence P. Ashmead, the Doubleday editor with whom
I am currently working most closely. He is a young man
of incredible industry, gentleness, and charm, and I am
delighted with him.*

*Eventually the book was all done, all 400,000 words of it,
stretching from Genesis to Revelation, and Doubleday decided to put it out in two volumes, published in successive
Octobers. The first volume dealt with the Old Testament
and the second volume with – but you've guessed it.*

*My greatest difficulty with the book was the title.
Generally, I make up a direct and simple title, and it stays,
like* The Neutrino *or* Photosynthesis. *Or the editor makes
one up either to begin with or as an alternative and that
stays, as* The Wellsprings of Life *or* The Intelligent Man's
Guide to Science.

*Not so in the case of my Bible book. My working title
when I first broached the subject to Doubleday was* It's
Mentioned in the Bible. *That was vetoed at once.*

*So I worked along with the manuscript under the work-
ing title of* Background to the Bible. *Once the manuscript
began to go through the publishing mills, Larry called me
up to say that he didn't think* Background to the Bible *had
enough oomph, and he suggested* The Intelligent Man's
Guide to the Bible.

I was intrigued at the thought of the book as a companion piece for The Intelligent Man's Guide to Science *but said at once that we would have to get permission from Basic Books. Titles are pretty much up for grabs and there are countless books that duplicate some other books' titles. Indeed* The Intelligent Man's Guide to Science *itself bears an uncomfortable similarity to George Bernard Shaw's* The Intelligent Woman's Guide to Socialism. *Still, there's my fetish for playing it square with all my publishers and Larry Ashmead is naïve enough to share my views on ethics anyway.*

So we asked Basic Books, certain that was merely the formality of the courteous approach, and to our discomfort, Basic Books vetoed the notion very firmly.

That was it! I at once abandoned that title, to make Basic Books happy, and tried to think of a still better title for Doubleday to make them happy. I pointed out to Larry, therefore, that science might be for intelligent men, but that the Bible was supposed to be for everybody. Why not name the book, then, Everyman's Guide to the Bible? *Larry thought that was fine and the galley proofs came out with that title.*

But then the Doubleday salesmen got into the act. There was an 'Everyman's Library' put out by another publishing house and besides, Asimov's Biographical Encyclopedia of Science and Technology *was, as I said earlier, doing better than expected. Why not, then,* Asimov's Guide to the Bible?

I objected that it would sound like egregious arrogance on my part whereupon the editorial staff of Doubleday united in a soothing effort designed to assure me that my reputation for modesty was worldwide and nobody would object to my name in the title. So I let myself be soothed.

I'm not sure, though, that my reputation for modesty is really worldwide because there is a well-known story at Doubleday that goes as follows: Time *magazine printed two very complimentary columns on me in their July 7, 1967, issue and one Doubleday editor came running to*

*Larry Ashmead when the issue came out, asking if he had
seen it and volunteering the information that it was full of
'delightful Asimovian immodesties'.*

*Anyway, I thought I would test them. When the book
came out, the book jacket was tasteful, conservative, and
yet interestingly designed. Across the top is 'Isaac Asimov'
in pale blue. Underneath, 'Asimov's Guide to the' still in
pale blue, and finally 'Bible' in larger letters (with a
particularly large 'B') in a subdued red.*

*I took one look at it and said with a perfectly straight
face, 'How come the Bible gets top billing?*

*You think they all laughed, knowing that Asimov, with
his worldwide reputation for modesty, was just kidding?*

*Not at all. They began to assure me that my name
appeared twice and that that more than made up for the
fact that 'Bible' was in large letters.*

*But never mind. A good part of the fun in the Bible
book was my chance to discuss a million and one items at
will. For instance, when Balaam is trying to curse the
children of Israel immediately before their invasion of
Canaan, he refers to the unicorn. So I got a chance to talk
about the unicorn:*

from ASIMOV'S GUIDE TO THE BIBLE (1968)

Balaam's inability to curse continued at all stations. From
Mount Pisgah, Balaam praised God, saying:

> Numbers 23:22. *God brought them out of Egypt; he*
> [Israel] *hath as it were the strength of an unicorn.*

The Bible mentions the unicorn on several other occasions, notably in the Book of Job:

> Job 39:9. *Will the unicorn be willing to serve thee,
> or abide by thy crib?*

The Hebrew word represented in the King James
Version by 'unicorn' is *re'em*, which undoubtedly refers to

the wild ox (*urus* or aurochs) ancestral to the domesticated cattle of today. The *re'em* still flourished in early historical times and a few existed into modern times although it is now extinct. It was a dangerous creature of great strength and was similar in form and temperament to the Asian buffaloes.

The Revised Standard Version translates *re'em* always as 'wild ox'. The verse in Numbers is translated as 'they have as it were the horns of the wild ox', while the one in Job is translated 'Is the wild ox willing to serve you?' The Anchor Bible translates the verse in Job as 'Will the buffalo deign to serve you?'

The wild ox was a favourite prey of the hunt-loving Assyrian monarchs (the animal was called *rumu* in Assyrian, essentially the same word as *re'em*) and was displayed in their large bas-reliefs. Here the wild ox was invariably shown in profile and only one horn was visible. One can well imagine that the animal represented in this fashion would come to be called 'one-horn' as a familiar nickname much as we might refer to 'longhorns' in speaking of a certain breed of cattle.

As the animal itself grew less common under the pressure of increasing human population and the depredations of the hunt, it might come to be forgotten that there was a second horn hidden behind the first in the sculptures and 'one-horn' might come to be considered a literal description of the animal.

When the first Greek translation of the Bible was prepared about 250 B.C. the animal was already rare in the long-settled areas of the Near East, and the Greeks, who had had no direct experience with it, had no word for it. They used a translation of 'one-horn' instead and it became *monokeros*. In Latin and in English it became the Latin word for 'one-horn'; that is, 'unicorn'.

The Biblical writers could scarcely have had the intention of implying that the wild ox literally had one horn. There is one Biblical quotation, in fact, that clearly contradicts that notion. In the Book of Deuteronomy, when Moses is giving his final blessing to each tribe, he speaks of the tribe of Joseph (Ephraim and Manasseh) as follows:

> Deuteronomy 33:17. *His glory is like the firstling of his bullock, and his horns are like the horns of unicorns* . . .

Here the word unicorn is placed in the plural since the thought of a 'one-horn's' single horn seems to make the phrase 'horns of a unicorn' self-contradictory. Still, the original Hebrew has the word in the singular so that we must speak of the 'horns of a unicorn', which makes it clear that a unicorn has more than one horn. In addition, the parallelism used in Hebrew poetry makes it natural to equate 'unicorn' and 'bullock', showing that the unicorn is something very much resembling a young bull. The Revised Standard Version has, in this verse, the phrase 'the horns of a wild ox'.

And yet the fact that the Bible speaks of a unicorn seemed, through most of history, to place the seal of divine assurance upon the fact that a one-horned animal existed. The unicorn is therefore commonplace in legends and stories.

This is especially so since travellers in Greek times spoke of a one-horned beast that existed in India, and assigned great powers to the single horn of that animal. For instance, a cup made out of the horn of such a beast rendered harmless any poisonous liquid that might be poured into it.

There is, indeed, a one-horned beast in India (as well as in Malaya, Sumatra and Africa) and this is the rhinoceros (from Greek words meaning 'nose-horn'). The horn on its snout is not a true horn but is a concretion of hair; nevertheless, the concretion looks like a horn and fulfils the purpose of one. It is very likely that the rhinoceros is the Greek unicorn, although its horn scarcely possesses the magic qualities attributed to it in legend.

Since the rhinoceros is one of the largest land animals

still alive, and is possessed of enormous strength, it might be thought to fit the description in the Bible. Some Latin translations of the Bible therefore convert the Greek *monokeros* into 'rhinoceros'. But this is farfetched. It is very unlikely that the Biblical writers knew of the rhinoceros and they certainly knew of the wild ox.

The unicorn entered European legend without reference to the rhinoceros, which was as unknown to the medieval Westerner as to the Biblical Israelite. The shape of the unicorn was, to the European, whatever fancy pleased to make it, and it is most familiar to us now as a rather horselike creature with a single long horn on its forehead. In this shape, two unicorns were depicted as supporting the royal arms of Scotland. When Scotland and England were combined under the House of Stuart in 1603, the Scottish unicorns joined the English lions on the coat of arms of what now became Great Britain.

The old enmity between the two nations is reflected in the nursery rhyme 'The lion and the unicorn were fighting for the crown'. The fact that it is an English rhyme and that England usually won the wars, though never conclusively, is signified by the second line, 'The lion beat the unicorn all around the town'.

The most distinctive feature of this modern unicorn is its horn, which is long, thin, slowly tapering, and a straight helix. It has precisely the shape and dimensions, in fact, of the single tooth of the male of a species of whale called the narwhal. This tooth takes the shape of a tusk, sometimes twenty feet long.

Undoubtedly, sailors occasionally obtained such tusks and then sold them to landlubbers for great sums by claiming each to be the horn of a unicorn with all the magical virtue of that object.

Getting involved in the Bible leads me to alter my other fields of writing perceptibly. For instance, I couldn't resist using my increased familiarity with Biblical details as a background to one of my F & SF *articles:*

'Twelve Point Three Six Nine' *(1967)*

Once in junior high school, my English teacher gave the class the assignment of reading and pondering Leigh Hunt's poem 'Abou ben Adhem'. Perhaps you remember it.

Abou ben Adhem awoke one night from a deep dream of peace and found an angel making a list of the names of those who loved God. Ben Adhem naturally wanted to know if he was included and was told he wasn't. Humbly he asked to be included as one who loved his fellow men, at least.

The next night the angel reappeared 'And show'd the names whom love of God had bless'd/And lo! Ben Adhem's name led all the rest.'

I knew the poem and had a pretty good notion as to the course of the class discussion planned for the next day by the teacher. There would be little homilies about how to love God meant to love mankind and vice versa. I agreed with that, but thought it would be rather dull to spend time on so self-evident a proposition. Could not some alternate meaning be wrenched out of the miserably unsubtle poem? I could find none.

The next day, our English teacher, with a kindly smile, asked, 'Now, class, who will volunteer to tell me why Abou ben Adhem's name led all the rest?'

Blinding inspiration struck me. I raised my hand violently and when the teacher nodded at me, I said, with a beatific smile, 'Alphabetical order, sir!'

I didn't really expect him to be grateful for this new light I was shedding on Leigh Hunt's poem, so I wasn't surprised when he pointed his thumb quietly at the door I left (knowing the way, for I had been ejected for obstreperous behaviour on several previous occasions) and the class discussion went on without me.

But, as I discovered afterwards, Abou ben Adhem had been effectively punctured and the teacher had gone on to discuss other matters, so I suppose I won out.

If I get weary of the lack of subtlety in 'Abou ben Adhem' you can imagine how desperate I get at those who maintain the entire Universe to be equally unsubtle.

Naturally I get most desperate when the unsubtlety is of a sort to which I feel myself to be (in secret) deeply attracted. For instance, there are those who, having noted some simple and hackneyed relationships between numbers or between geometrical figures, promptly suppose that the structure of the Universe is designed merely to show off those relationships. (And, to my self-disgust, I always find this sort of thing interesting.)

Mystics have been guilty of such simple-mindedness, I am sure, in every society complicated enough to have invented arithmetic, but the best early examples known today are to be found among the Greeks.

For instance, Pythagoras of Samos, about 525 B.C., plucked taut strings and listened to the notes that were produced. He observed that pleasant-sounding combinations of notes were heard when strings were of lengths that bore a simple arithmetical ratio to one other: 1 to 2 or 3 to 4 to 5. It was that, perhaps, which led him and his followers to believe that the physical world was governed by numerical relationships, and simple numerical relationships at that.

It is true, of course, that numerical relationships are of importance in the Universe, but they are not always simple by any means. For instance, a fact of apparently fundamental importance is the ratio of the mass of the proton to the electron – which is 1836.11. Why 1836.11? No one knows.

But we can't blame the Pythagoreans for their lack of knowledge of modern physics. Let us rather consider with astonishment a pupil of Pythagoras by the name of Philolaus of Tarentum. As far as we know, he was the first man in history (about 480 B.C.) to suggest that the Earth moved through space.

Let's try to trace his reasoning. As the Greeks could see, the starry heavens revolved about the Earth. However, seven particular heavenly objects – the Sun, the Moon, Mercury, Venus, Mars, Jupiter, and Saturn – moved independently of the fixed stars and of each other. One might suppose, therefore, that there were eight concentric (and transparent) spheres in the heaven, revolving about the Earth. The innermost contained the Moon affixed to itself, the next Mercury, then Venus, then the Sun, then Mars, Jupiter, Saturn. The eighth and outermost contained the host of stars.

Philolaus was not content with this arrangement. He suggested that the eight spheres did not move about the Earth but about some 'central fire'. This central fire was invisible, but its reflection could be seen as the Sun. Furthermore, the Earth itself was also fixed in a sphere that revolved about the central fire. And, in addition, there was still *another* body, the 'counter-Earth', which we never saw because it stayed always on the side of the Sun opposite ourselves, and that counter-Earth was in still another sphere that revolved about the central fire.

So a total of ten revolving spheres are allowed for in Philolaus' system: the eight ordinary ones, plus a ninth for the Earth, and a tenth for the counter-Earth.

However did Philolaus arrive at that? To be sure, two centuries after his time, Aristarchus of Samos also suggested the Earth moved – but he insisted it moved around the Sun. This was considered absurd at the time but at least Aristarchus made use of bodies perceptible to the senses. Why did Philolaus invent an invisible central fire and an invisible counter-Earth?

The probable answer rests with the *number* of spheres. If the Earth revolved about the Sun, you would have to add a sphere for the Earth, but subtract one for the now stationary Sun and the total would still be eight. If you keep both Earth and Sun moving about an invisible centre and added a counter-Earth, you would have ten.

And why ten spheres? Well, the Pythagoreans thought ten was a particularly satisfactory number because $1 + 2 + 3 + 4 = 10$, something which lent itself to involved reasoning that ended in ten as a perfect number. If, then, we argue that the Universe has to be perfect and that its notion of perfection had to agree with that of the Pythagoreans, and if it were further granted that the Universe had no reason for existence but to exhibit that perfection – then the total number of spheres has to be ten (even though two of the spheres have to be kept secret for some arcane reason).

Unfortunately the trouble with all such irrefutable arguments based on the mystical properties of numbers is that no two people can ever quite bring themselves to believe in the same mystique. The Pythagorean notion went out of the window and astronomers contented themselves with eight spheres. Indeed, since the starry sphere was dismissed as mere background, the magic number became seven.

Arguments concerning the structure of the Universe, based on simple arithmetic (and worse) did not die out with the Greeks, by any means.

In 1610 Galileo, using the telescope, discovered that Jupiter had four lesser bodies circling it. This meant that there were eleven bodies (excluding the fixed stars themselves) that circled the Earth according to the old Greek system – or eleven bodies circling the Sun, according to the newfangled Copernican system.

Great was the opposition to this new discovery, and the arguments against it by one adversary will live forever in the history of human folly.

It was not necessary, explained the learned scholar, to look through the telescope. The new bodies could not be there, since there could only be seven bodies circling the Earth (or Sun) and no more. If the additional bodies were seen, it had to be because of a defect in the telescope, because the new bodies *could* not be there.

And how could one be sure they could not be there? Easy! As there are seven openings in the head – two eyes, two ears, two nostrils, and a mouth – so there must be seven planetary bodies in the heavens.

Thus, it seemed, it was necessary to so order the entire Universe as to make some sort of permanent record in the heavens as to the number of openings in the human head. It was as though God needed crib notes that would enable him to keep the figure in mind so that he wouldn't create Man with the wrong number of openings. (I'm sorry if that sounds blasphemous, for I don't mean it to be so. The blasphemy is on the part of those men, past and present, who try to make it appear that God is a kinder-garten infant, playing with number blocks.)

Such folly dies hard. In fact, it never dies.

Astronomers, having accepted the Copernican notion of bodies circling the Sun rather than the Earth, now recognized two classes of bodies in the Solar System.

There were bodies that revolved directly about the Sun; these were the planets and in 1655, six were recognized – Mercury, Venus, Earth, Mars, Jupiter, and Saturn. Then, there were bodies that revolved not about the Sun directly, but about one of the planets. These were the satellites and there were five of them recognized at the time: our own Moon and the four satellites of Jupiter, which Galileo had discovered (Io, Europa, Ganymede, and Callisto).

But in 1655 the Dutch astronomer Christian Huygens discovered a satellite of Saturn which he named Titan. That meant the Solar System consisted of six planets and six satellites. Huygens was a first-class scientist and a great figure in the history of astronomy and physics, but he wasn't proof against the symmetry of six and six. He announced that the total was complete. No more bodies remained to be found.

Alas, in 1671 the Italian-French astronomer Giovanni D. Cassini discovered another satellite of Saturn and spoiled the symmetry. Huygens lived to see it, too. Indeed, he lived to see Cassini discover three more satellites of Saturn.

Then we have Johann Kepler, who was not content with merely working out the number of heavenly bodies on the basis of simple arithmetic. He went a step further and tried to work out the relationships among the distances of those bodies from the Sun by interconnection with simple geometry.

There are five and only five regular solids (solids with all faces equal and all angles equal – as is true, for instance, of the cube, the most familiar of the five).

Why not reason as follows, then? The regular solids are perfect and so is the Universe. There are just five regular solids and, since there are six planets, there are just five interplanetary gaps.

Kepler therefore attempted to nest the five regular solids in such a way that the six planets moved along the various boundaries in the proper relationship of distances. Kepler spent a lot of time trying to adjust his solids and failed. (The acid test, that makes Kepler a great deal more than a crackpot, is that, having failed, he promptly dropped the notion.)

During the last week of 1966, however, I discovered something about Kepler I had not known before.

I was attending a meeting of the American Association for the Advancement of Science and was listening to papers on the history of astronomy. One particularly interesting paper included the statement that Kepler had felt that there ought to be just 360 days in a year. The Earth was rotating faster than it should have been, which was what made the number of days in the year $365\frac{1}{4}$. (If the day were 24 hours and 21 minutes long, there would be just 360 days in the year.)

This too-fast rotation of the Earth, in Kepler's view, somehow carried over to the Moon, forcing it to revolve a bit too quickly about the Earth. Obviously the Moon should be revolving about the Earth in just $1/12$ of a year; that is, in about $30^2/_5$ days. Instead, it revolved in only about $29\frac{1}{2}$ days.

If the Earth revolved about the Sun in 360 days of $24\frac{1}{3}$ hours apiece (naturally, the hours and its subdivisions would be slightly lengthened to make just 24 hours to the slightly longer day), how convenient that would be. After all, 360 is such a pleasant number, being exactly divisible by 2, 3, 4, 5, 6, 8, 9, 10, 12, 15, 18, 20, 24, 30, 36, 40, 45, 60, 72, 90, 120, and 180. No other number approximating its size is evenly divisible in so many different ways.

And if each lunar month were equal to 30 days of a little over 24 hours each, there would be exactly 12 lunar months in a year. The number 12 is evenly divisible by 2, 3, 4, and 6; and 30 by 2, 3, 5, 6, 10, and 15.

Nor is it just a matter of tricks of numbers. With 30 days to the lunar month and 12 lunar months to the year, a beautifully simple calendar could be devised.

Instead, what do we have? About $29\frac{1}{2}$ days to a lunar month, about $365\frac{1}{4}$ days to a year, and about $12\frac{3}{8}$ lunar months to the year. And the result of this farrago of fractions? Nearly five thousand years of fiddling with calendars that has ended with one that is *still* inconvenient.

My thoughts might have ended there, but the lecturer at the AAAS meeting gave the number of lunar months in the year in decimal form rather than fractions. He said, 'Instead of 12 lunar months to a year, there are 12.369.' *

My eyebrows raised in astonishment at once. Indeed? Are there really 12.369 lunar months in a year? My mind began fitting notions together and at the conclusion of the lecture I raised my hand to ask a question. I wanted to know if Kepler had tried to draw a certain simple deduction from that figure. No, said the lecturer, it sounds like something Kepler might have done, but he didn't.

* Actually, this is wrong, I think. According to the best figures I can find, the number of lunar months in a year is closer to 12.368. It is 12.36827, to be exact. But let's not spoil my chapter.

Excellent! Excellent! That left me free to indulge in a little mysticism of my own. After all, everyone knows I am in love with figures, and I could easily design the Universe in order to show off first-grade arithmetic. What's more, I happen to be interested in the Bible, so why not show that the design of the Universe is connected with certain elementary statistics involving the Bible?

(I am not without precedent here. Isaac Newton was an indefatigable Biblical student who produced nothing worthy of note; and the Scottish mathematician John Napier, who first worked out logarithms, also worked out a completely worthless system for interpreting the Book of Revelation.)

Let me, therefore, go along with Kepler. Let us suppose that the whole purpose of the rate of Earth's rotation about its axis, the Moon's revolution about the Earth, and the revolution of the Earth/Moon system about the Sun, is to present mankind with pretty numbers and a symmetrical calendar.

What, then, went wrong? Surely God knew what he was doing and would not make a careless mistake. If the year were more than 360 days long there would have to be a reason for it; an exact reason. The error would be no error but would be something designed to instruct mankind in the simple-minded manner that mystics seem to like to consider characteristic of God.

There are $365\frac{1}{4}$ days in a year so that the excess over 360 (the 'right' number) is $5\frac{1}{4}$ or, in decimal form, 5.25. You must admit now that 5.25 is an interesting number since 25 is the square of 5.

Let's reason like a mystic. Can 5.25 be a coincidence? Of course not. It must have meaning and that meaning must be in the Bible. (After all, God is the centre about which the Bible revolves as the Sun is the centre about which the Earth revolves. What is more natural than to find in the revolving Bible the reasons for the details of the revolving Earth.)

The Old Testament, according to tradition, is divided into three parts: the Law, the Prophets, and the Writings. All are holy and inspired, but the Law is the most sacred portion and that is made up of the first five books of the Bible: Genesis, Exodus, Leviticus, Numbers and Deuteronomy.

Why, then, are there five days beyond the 'proper' 360? Surely in order to mark the five books of the Law in the very motions of the Earth. And why the extra quarter day beyond the five? Why, to make the excess not merely 5 but 5.25. By squaring the 5 and emphasizing it in that fashion, the Law is demonstrated to be not only holy, but particularly holy.

Of course, there is a catch. The length of the year is not really precisely 365.25 days. It is a bit short of that, and is 365.2422 days long. (To be even more precise it is 365.242197 days long, but 365.2422 is close enough, surely.)

Does that mean that the whole scheme falls to the ground? If you think so, you don't know how the mind of a mystic works. The Bible is so large and complex a book that almost any conceivable number can be made to have a Biblical significance. The only limit is the ingenuity of the human mind.

Let's, for instance, take a look at 365.2422. The excess over the 'proper' 360 is 5.2422. The figures to the right of the decimal point can be broken up into 24 and 22 and the average is 23. What, then, is the significance of the 23?

We have settled that the 5 represents the five books of the Law. That leaves the Prophets and the Writings. How many books are contained in those? The answer is 34.*

That doesn't seem to get us anywhere – but wait. Twelve

---

* At least according to Jews and Protestants. The Roman Catholic version of the Bible includes eight additional books considered apocryphal by Jews and Protestants.

of the books are relatively short prophetic works: Hosea, Joel, Amos, Obadiah, Jonah, Micah, Nahum, Habakkuk, Zephaniah, Haggai, Zechariah and Malachi. For convenience, in ancient times, these were often included in a single roll which was referred to as the Book of the Twelve.

Thus, in the apocryphal book of Ecclesiasticus (accepted as canonical by the Catholics) the author – writing about 180 B.C. – lists the great men of Biblical history. After mentioning the major prophets individually, he lumps the minor prophets together:

> Ecclesiasticus 49:10. *And of the twelve prophets let the memorial be blessed . . .*

Well, then, if the twelve minor prophets be included as a single book – as there is ample precedent for doing – how many books are there in the Prophets and Writings together by the Jewish/Protestant count? Why, 23.

We can therefore say that of the number of days in the year (365.2422), 360 days represent the 'correct' figure, 5 days represent the Law, and 0.2422 represent the Prophets and the Writings. The days of the year thus become a memorial to the Old Testament.

That takes us to the number of lunar months in the year, which is 12.369, the number that first attracted my attention.

If the days in the year represent the Old Testament, then surely the lunar months in the year must represent the New Testament. Any mystic will tell you that this is self-evident.

Well, then, what can we say would be a central difference between the Old Testament and the New Testament? We might try this: In the Old Testament, God is treated as a single entity while in the New Testament, He is revealed as a Trinity. Consequently if this is so, and if the number of lunar months in a year represents the New Testament, that number should somehow be related to the number 3.

And if we look at 12.369, we see that it is neatly divisible by 3. Hurrah! We are on the right track, as any fool can plainly see (provided he *is* a fool, of course).

Let us, then, divide 12.369 by 3, and we come out with 4.123. Surely that is a highly significant number, consisting, as it does, of the first four integers.

And what connection do the first four integers have with the New Testament? Why the answer is obvious and springs to the mind at once.

The four gospels, of course! The four separate biographies of Jesus by Matthew, Mark, Luke and John.

It so happens that Gospels 1, 2 and 3 – Matthew, Mark and Luke – give essentially the same view of Jesus. Many of the incidents found in one are found in the others and the general trend of events is virtually identical in all. These are the 'synoptic Gospels', the word 'synoptic' meaning 'with one eye'. Gospels 1, 2 and 3 all see Jesus with the same eye, so to speak.

Gospel 4, that of John, is quite different from the other three; differing, in fact, on almost every point, even quite basic ones.

Therefore, if we are going to have the number of lunar months in the year signify the Gospels, would it not be right to group 1, 2 and 3 together and keep 4 separate? And is this not precisely what is done in a number like 4.123?

If you had doubts before, would you not admit we were on the right track now?

We can say then that of the number of lunar months in a year, 12.369, the 12 represents the Gospel of John (4 times 3, for the Trinity) and the 0.369 represent the Synoptic Gospels (123 times 3).

But why is the Fourth Gospel first? Why is a third of the number of lunar months in a year 4.123, rather than 123.4?

This is a good and legitimate question and I have an answer. If the central fact of the New Testament is the Trinity, we must ask how the matter of the Trinity is handled in the various Gospels.

The first evidence of the existence of all three aspects

of God together is at the time of Jesus' baptism by John the Baptist (who, of course, is *not* the John who wrote the Fourth Gospel). In Mark, the oldest of the Gospels, the incident at the baptism is described as follows:

Mark 1:10. *And . . . he* [Jesus] *saw the heavens opened, and the Spirit like a dove descending upon him:*
Mark 1:11. *And there came a voice from heaven, saying, Thou art my beloved Son, in whom I am well pleased.*

Here Father, Son and Holy Spirit are all present at once. Nothing in this account, however, would make us necessarily think that this manifestation was apparent to anyone outside the Trinity. There is nothing to make us suppose, for instance (if Mark only is considered), that John the Baptist, who was present at that moment, was also aware of the descent of the Spirit, or heard the voice from heaven.

Similar accounts are given in Matthew 3:16–17, and in Luke 3:22. Neither in Matthew nor in Luke is it stated that anyone outside the Trinity was aware of what was happening.

In John's Gospel, however, the Fourth, the account of the descent of the Spirit is placed in the mouth of John the Baptist.

John 1:32. *And John bare record, saying, I saw the Spirit descending from heaven like a dove, and it abode upon him.*

Since, in Gospel 4, the first manifestation of the Trinity is described as clearly apparent to man, something that is not so in Gospels 1, 2 and 3, then obviously the number *ought* to be 4.123, rather than 123.4.

What more can anyone want?

Now let me emphasize something I hope has been quite apparent to everyone. I am merely playing with numbers.

What I have presented here in connection with the days and months in the year has been made up out of my head, and I am no more serious about it than I was, once long ago, about the alphabeticity of Abou ben Adhem.

And yet I would not be in the least surprised to find that some people were tempted to think there was something to all this nonsense. They might wonder if I had accidentally stumbled on a great truth without knowing it, even while I was imagining myself to be doing nothing more than playing silly games.

And I suppose that some people (maybe even the same people) would say: 'Hey, I'll bet Abou ben Adhem's name led all the rest because the list *was* in alphabetical order.'

PART 10

Short-Shorts

You can well imagine that my writing very largely fills up my life.

Still when the large chunks; books, major articles, longish stories; are all put together, there are little chinks left in the interstices. I suppose I could use those little chinks to give me time to sit back and let my eyes glaze over, but I find it more restful to write small items. You might almost call them fillers.

For instance, every month I write a little 500-word article for Science Digest, *answering some question asked by a reader. It is placed in a department called 'Isaac Asimov Explains'. Since no limits are set on the questions (except for those imposed by my own finite knowledge and my own finite ingenuity in devising an answer that will fit into 500 words) I am sometimes forced to set myself some unusual and, therefore, interesting tasks.*

I have explained the meaning of relativity, for instance, also the significance of parity, the nature of time, and so on – and done each in 500 words. What's more, a question is angled at me, sometimes, that is clearly elicited by the fact that I am known to be a science-fiction writer. Here is one of them, as an example:

from 'Isaac Asimov Explains' *(1968)*

In many science-fiction stories I read about 'force fields' and 'hyperspace'. What are these and do they really exist?

Every sub-atomic particle gives rise to one or more of four different kinds of influences. These are the gravitational, electromagnetic, weak nuclear, and strong nuclear. Each influence spreads out from its source of origin as a 'field' that, in theory, pervades the entire universe. Similar fields from large numbers of particles can add their separate influences and produce terrifically intense resultant fields. Thus, the gravitational field is by far the weakest of the four, but the gravitational field of the Sun, a body made up of so vast a number of particles, is enormous.

Two particles within such a field may be made to move towards each other or away from each other, depending on the nature of the particles and of the field and with an acceleration depending on how far apart they are. Such accelerations are usually interpreted as caused by 'forces', so we speak of 'force fields'. In this sense, they really exist.

The force fields we know, however, always have matter as their source and don't exist in the absence of matter. In science-fiction stories, on the other hand, it is often useful to imagine the construction of strong force fields without matter. One can then have a section of vacuum which will serve as a barrier to particles and radiation just as though it were a solid piece of steel six feet thick. It would have all the inter-atomic forces but none of the atoms that give rise to those forces. Such 'matter-free force fields' are a convenient science-fictional device but, alas, have no basis in the science we know today.

'Hyperspace' is another convenient science-fictional device; one intended to get around the speed-of-light barrier.

To see how it works, think of a large, flat sheet of paper on which there are two dots six feet apart. Next, imagine an extremely slow snail that can only travel a foot an hour. Clearly, it will take him six hours to travel from one dot to the other.

But suppose we bend the essentially two-dimensional sheet of paper through the third dimension, so as to bring the two dots close together. If they are now only a tenth of an inch apart and if the snail can somehow cross the air gap between the two ends of the piece of paper which have been curved towards each other in this fashion, he can go from one dot to the other in just a half a minute.

Now for the analogy. If two stars are fifty light-years apart, then a spaceship going at maximum speed, that of light, will take fifty years to go from one to the other (relative to someone in either one of these star systems). This creates a great many complications, and science-fiction writers find they can simplify their plots if they pretend that the essentially three-dimensional structure of space can be folded through a fourth spatial dimension so that the stars are separated by only a small fourth-dimensional gap. The ship then crosses this gap and goes from one star to the other in a very short period of time.

It is customary for mathematicians to speak of objects with four dimensions by referring to analogous three-dimensional objects and adding the prefix 'hyper', a Greek expression meaning 'above', 'over', or 'beyond'. An object whose surface is equally distant from the centre in all four dimensions is a 'hypersphere'. Similarly, we can have a 'hypertetrahedron', 'hypercube', and a 'hyper-ellipsoid'. Using this convention, we can speak of the four-dimensional gap between the stars as 'hyperspace'.

But, alas, however convenient hyperspace may be to the science-fiction writer, there is nothing in the science we know to show that it exists as anything but a mathematical abstraction.

Since I have the final choice in answering questions, I sometimes elect to answer one not because it is important but because of some utterly extraneous reason.

For instance, on February 14, 1942, I met the young lady who was later to become my wife. (Yes, it was Valentine's Day, but that was thoroughly coincidental.) At the time I was quite young and totally impecunious. I had neither money, looks, presence, style, or any of the obvious qualities that would be expected to attract a girl who was the precise image of Olivia de Havilland.

I had to depend rather strongly on my possession of a high IQ. I felt, after all, that there might be two or three girls on Earth who would feel the stirrings of mad passion at a vision of intellect and – who knows – this might be one of them.

I therefore dropped casual hints to the effect that I was working towards my Ph.D., that I was writing and selling science fiction, and so on. It seemed to make little impact.

But once, on a rather unusually balmy April evening in 1942, when we were walking down Fifth Avenue, she asked me, 'What happens if an irresistible force meets an immovable body?'

She may just have been making idle conversation or perhaps may have felt a perverse impulse to squelch my intellectual arrogance. However, I answered her without hesitation and she said, 'I never dreamed there was a sensible answer to that.'

We were married on July 26, 1942.

Naturally, when the question arose again in connection with 'Isaac Asimov Explains', I fell all over myself to write an answer:

from 'Isaac Asimov Explains' *(1968)*

What would happen if an irresistible force met an immovable body?

This is a classic 'puzzler' over which uncounted millions of arguments must have rolled their wordy way.

Before I give you my solution, however, let's make a few things clear. The game of exploring the universe by rational techniques, like any other game, must be played according to the rules. If two people are going to talk meaningfully together, they must agree on what the symbols they use (words or otherwise) are to be taken as meaning, and their comments must make sense in terms of that meaning.

All questions that do not make sense in terms of the definitions agreed upon are thrown out of court. There is no answer because the question must not be asked.

For instance, suppose I asked the question, 'How much does justice weigh?' (I might be thinking, perhaps, of the figure of a blinded Justice with scales in her hand.)

But weight is a property of mass and only material things have mass. (Indeed, matter may be most simply defined as 'That which has mass'.)

Justice is not a material thing, but an abstraction. By definition, mass is not one of its properties, so that to ask the weight of justice is to pose a meaningless question. It requires no answer.

Again, it is possible, by a series of very simple algebraic manipulations, to show that $1 = 2$. The only trouble is that in the course of this demonstration, we must divide by zero. In order to avoid such an inconvenient equality (to say nothing of a number of other demonstrations that would destroy the usefulness of mathematics) mathematicians have decided to make division by zero inadmissible in any mathematical manipulation. The question then: 'What is the value of the fraction $2/0$?' violates the rules of the game and is meaningless. It requires no answer.

Now we are ready for our irresistible force and our immovable body.

An 'irresistible force' is, by definition (if words are to have any meaning at all), a force that cannot be resisted; a force that will move or destroy any body it encounters, *however great*, without being perceptibly weakened or deflected. In any universe which contains an irresistible force, there can be no such thing as an immovable body, since we have just defined an irresistible force as capable of moving *anything*.

An 'immovable body' is, by definition (if words are to have any meaning at all), a body that cannot be moved; a body that will absorb any force it encounters, *however great*, without being perceptibly changed or damaged by the encounter. In any universe which contains an immovable body, there can be no such thing as an irresistible force, since we have just defined an immovable body as capable of resisting *any* force.

If we ask a question that implies the simultaneous existence of both an irresistible force and an immovable body, we are violating the definitions implied by the phrases themselves. This is not allowed by the rules of the game of reason. The question, 'What would happen if an irresistible force met an immovable body?' is therefore meaningless and requires no answer.

You might wonder if definitions can be so carefully made that no unanswerable questions can ever be asked. The answer, surprisingly enough, is 'No!' Mathematicians have shown that it is impossible to devise any mathematical system that will not permit unanswerable questions. But that is another story.

Another category of brief in-betweens arises in connection with the introductions I write to other people's books. I get involved, usually, because someone asks me who is a friend of mine, or the friend of a friend, or the friend of a relative, or the relative of a friend. Apparently, these groups include nearly all the population of the globe and I've never worked out an efficient way to refuse friends, relatives, and their adjuncts.

I make up for it by trying to think up an introduction in which I manage to say something that strikes me as interesting. After all, I have to read the stuff as it comes out of the typewriter and I can't very well toss off something inconsequential and tepid as the least-effort way of fulfilling a commitment. I hate reading things that are inconsequential and tepid and, while a reader of a book can always skip the introduction, the writer of that introduction can't.

Here's one, for instance, that was placed in a science-fiction anthology entitled Future Tense, *edited by Richard Curtis:*

'On Prediction' *(1968)*

The matter of prediction is full of pitfalls.

For instance, if a new scientific theory is to prove a useful one, it ought to predict phenomena that are unexpected or even downright 'impossible' by older theories. If the prediction is found to be accurate then that is a great point in favour of the new theory.

But is the prediction sufficient in itself to 'prove' the new theory? – Not at all. Not if other aspects remain unacceptable.

For instance, I hereby propose a new theory to the effect that nylon is repelled by gravitational force and that anything made out of nylon will therefore fall upwards. In line with this theory, I will predict that if you make a parachute of nylon and connect yourself to it by a harness and then jump from a plane, you will fall very slowly because gravitational repulsion will be pushing up against the nylon.

If you care to try the experiment you will find that this prediction is absolutely correct and goes flatly against old Galileo's statement that all objects fall at the same rate. Does that mean that nylon is *really* repelled by gravitation?

Of course not. What Galileo really said was that all objects fall at the same rate *in a vacuum* and, by taking air resistance into account, we can explain the parachute effect without postulating gravitational repulsion. Besides the one prediction that comes true is balanced by others that emphatically do not. A nylon object left to itself will *not* fall upwards.

Or take the predictions of Immanuel Velikovsky. He advanced a theory that at the time of the Biblical Exodus, Jupiter expelled a comet which passed close to the Earth, caused the plagues of Egypt, stopped the Earth's rotation, affected its orbit, and did many more things before settling down to become the planet Venus. In line with all this, Velikovsky predicted that Venus would be found to be hotter than astronomers suspected and, by golly, he was right.

Does that mean that because of this correct prediction, we must accept the whole of Velikovsky's theories? Of course not. There remain many aspects of it (very many) which are extremely dubious in the light of modern theory. Astronomers will therefore try to explain Venus' temperature in various non-absurd ways before accepting Velikovsky, and it is my calm prediction that they will succeed.

But then if Velikovsky's theory is not correct, how did he know Venus was hot? Well, I know it's very frustrating, but coincidences can take place and if an intelligent, imaginative man makes many predictions, some of them are bound to be close enough to the truth (usually in a very primitive way), to cause innocents to suspect that all the other predictions are true, too.

For instance, the alchemists thought lead could be transmuted to gold and nineteenth-century chemists laughed at the whole idea. Twentieth-century chemists, however, succeeded in carrying through numerous transmutations of one element into another.

Aha!!! Can we not deduce from that that those old alchemists were smart cookies; that they knew what they were doing; that they had access to ancient secrets we have lost?

But how about telling the whole story. Alchemists thought lead could be transmuted to gold by ordinary chemical procedures like heating and distilling and mixing and muttering spells. We do it now by particle accelerators and nuclear reactors. The two sets of methods bear no relationship and merely to dream of a goal is no sign of preternatural knowledge of the eventually discovered methods of reaching that goal.

And so it is with predictions in fiction.

One can find lots of 'predictions' in fiction if one looks assiduously enough and trustingly enough.

In the Greek myths, Daedalus invented feathered wings held together by wax, with which he and his son, Icarus, could fly through the air. Was that not a prediction of modern aeroplanes? Admittedly, we use metal and welding instead of feathers and wax but isn't the principle the same?

Again, in the Norse myths, the world was foreseen as coming to an end in the great Twilight of the Gods. And now science tells us that the world will come to an end when the Sun enters its red giant phase about eight billion years hence.

May we assume from that that the shaggy Norsemen of old had somehow figured out modern astrophysics?

Will anyone who believes that raise his hand?

And if we go through the fairy tales, we will come across flying carpets (helicopters?), seven-league boots (railroads?), magic (electronic instruments), oracles (computers?), wicked demons (Nazis?), and anything else you want.

But, you know, the fantasts and mythmakers of the past were not trying for predictions. They were allegorizing or wishing.

Nowadays, though, we have science fiction, and what makes science fiction different from all previous types of fantasy literature, is that the science-fiction writer disciplines his imagination. Anything does *not* go. Only that goes that fits science as we know it today or as that science can be plausibly extrapolated. With that in mind, prediction really becomes prediction and not accident.

To be sure, it is not the first duty of the science-fiction writer to predict the future. His first duty is to write an entertaining story, which matches the structure of science or, at the very least, does not betray an ignorance of the structure of science.

In doing so, though, it is almost impossible for him not to draw a picture which is the equivalent of a prediction of some facet of future technology or sociology. And if an intelligent writer, with a competent understanding of science, does this, then, every once in a while, the prediction hews so close to the eventual course of history, as to come true.

This anthology is a sampling of stories in which the

cloudy crystal ball cleared for a moment to allow a writer to look ahead and see what was to be – tanks, atomic bombs, television, communications satellites.

And as we read we must ask ourselves: What inventions or social phenomena being discussed in science fiction right now will come true a generation from now? Care to guess?

Still another grouping of short pieces comes under the heading of book reviews, a form of writing I never do willingly. There are three reasons for my reluctance, one of which is rather discreditable to myself. In the interests of frankness, I shall give all three, including the discreditable one.

First, I don't believe that a review should be written on the basis of what is said in the flap material or on what appears in the first five pages. I have read too many reviews of my own books which arrive at their inspiration in this way. I feel cheated in such cases and I feel prospective readers are cheated as well. This means that when I myself get a book for review, I must read the whole thing, and with reasonable care, too, and this means spending considerable time which I can often ill afford.

Second, I have some serious question as to the ethics of book reviewing. (I told you I have a troublesome and simple-minded set of ethics.) I quite understand that it is useful to warn the book-buying public in advance as to the contents and purposes of a book and even, in the opinion of the reviewer, its quality. (A review that tells certain readers enough about my books to let them know in advance they won't like them does me a favour. A reader who is conned into buying one of my books and hating it, not only will never buy another but he will be a constant source of word-of-mouth adverse opinion. Better not to make the sale in the first place.)

However, reviews of specialized books are often handed out to other individuals who specialize in the field. (Who

*else, after all, is competent to review?) When that happens,
a reviewer finds himself compelled to speak either good
or evil of a friend or rival. Can he ever be sure of
objectivity? Will he be trying to do a friend a favour or a
rival an injury? Will he lean over backwards into reverse
prejudice?*

*I'm as confident of my own integrity as it is reasonably
possible to be but I see no reason to put it to unnecessary
tests. For that reason, I have always refused to review
science-fiction books, all of which are written by people
who are simultaneously friends and rivals. Non-fiction I do
review when pushed into it, but always with a twinge.*

*The third reason is the discreditable one. When I review
a book favourably, passages from that review are often
used in the promotional material for the book. And when
that happens I get to feeling sorry for myself, since it
seems unfair to me that I am boosting other people's books
when my own are so very rarely reviewed under conditions
of the slightest prominence.*

*This is thoroughly foolish of me, for since I turn out
six to eight books a year I can scarcely expect to get the
treatment accorded to someone whose book is an 'event'.
I strongly suspect that most book-review editors have
grown so calloused through watching my books come out
every other month that they no longer see them. Besides,
my books sell with nice regularity even without prominent
reviews, so what is hurt except my own self-love?*

*Unfortunately, self-love is immune to rational arguments
and I still get to feeling sorry for myself. About the only
thing I can do to counter it is to write book reviews on
occasion anyway on the principle that it is permissible to
have silly weaknesses, but that it is not permissible to give
in to them.*

*Naturally, though, I do try to pick books which I think
will mean something to me so that when I review it I can
also speak my mind, as, for instance, in the following
review:*

'An Uncompromising View' *(1968)*

Mechanical Man, The Physical Basis of Intelligent Life.
Dean E. Wooldridge. McGraw-Hill Book Co., New York.
1968. 212 pp. $8.95.

This book is comparatively brief, not because it covers
little ground, but because it covers a great deal with
remarkable conciseness.

Its thesis rests in the proper interpretation of the
ambiguous title. It deals not with the construction or
theory of robots, but with the view that man himself –
you, for instance – is a machine.

To make this point, Dr. Wooldridge moves systemati-
cally through the field of biology, passing from the abandoned outposts of vitalism, inward, ever inward, to the
very heart of its still staunchly-manned core-fortress.

Addressing himself to the educated layman, he begins
with proteins and nucleic acids and the great, if recent,
victory over the genetic code. Having taken care of the
molecules, he moves on to the cellular level and discusses
the nervous system. From there, in unfaltering strides, he
gives us a fascinating section at the organ level, for he
takes up the brain. And in doing so, he takes up the
computer, too, recognizing no fundamental difference
between what the brain does and what the computer does
(granting different levels of complexity *at present*). Then,
on to the whole organism and its feeling of 'consciousness',
and to the final goal of society where such philosophical
and sociological questions as free will and religion are
considered.

The details are not new and at no point is the account
so deep and detailed that one may feel educated in that
particular aspect of biology. To present details or a
biological education is clearly not the intent of the author.

What he is putting across, rather, is an attitude; and one
that needs presentation, all the more so because it still
rouses primitive fears and antagonisms.

The history of the intellectual progress of mankind can very nearly be made into an account of the slow abandonment of anthropocentrism. In astronomy, there is the successive abandonment of the Earth, then the Sun, as the centre of the universe; in biology, there is the tardy realization that the plant and animal kingdoms were not primarily created for the service of man; in geology, there is the reluctant understanding that the physical Earth did not begin concurrently with human civilization; and so on, and so on, and so on.

Yet one harsh centric area remains. No matter how we gain knowledge concerning tropisms and reflexes – conditioning and imprinting – most of us persist in thinking that even if lower animals such as worms and insects can be considered as acting in mechanical fashion and as though they were being directed by (admittedly very complicated and successful miniaturized) computers – this is not so in the case of the higher animals, and it is particularly not so in the case of man.

We have free will; *we* have consciousness; *we* decide what to do of our own volition; *we* choose and select and consider and ponder and create. It is almost an article of faith that this goes beyond the purely mechanical fulfilment of blindly interlocking atoms and molecules and that no machine can therefore be made into a man.

And yet the brain is made up of atoms and molecules and nothing more. There is nothing in the most magnificent human brain but the matter it contains. If there is something called a 'mind' or 'personality' or even 'soul', it is but a subjective interpretation of the consequences of the working of that matter, and we can learn about these mysterious words only by studying the matter.

At the 1967 AAAS meetings there was a ponderous symposium discussing whether the human brain could be understood in terms of the laws of physics and chemistry, and the consensus was that it could not. This was an appalling surrender to long-standing prejudice and, in my view, represented a 'failure of nerve'. The coming century,

I trust, will demonstrate this, and Dr Wooldridge's book – cool, concise, and absolutely uncompromising in its material view of man's mind – reinforces that trust.

Even in my fiction writing, I sometimes write a very short piece to fill a scrap of time. I have written an occasional 'vignette' 500 words long or less. Such tiny pieces consist entirely of endings, to be sure, building up to the final shock in the last line.

I myself am a devotee of the pun as final shock. This penchant for punning and wordplay which I have induces considerable unpopularity for myself at social gatherings, you can well imagine. It was only two nights ago that I told some friends of mine, Mr and Mrs Mamber, that if they had a daughter they ought to name her Rebekah. Naturally, they asked why, and I said that she would be known by the nickname, 'Ree', and would then be 'Ree Mamber'.

I was ostracized for the rest of the evening.

Anyway, the first vignette I wrote depended for its effect on a perfectly deplorable pun in the last line, and one which makes its maximum impact on devotees of old-fashioned science fiction. I wrote in such a way that the last line was by itself at the top of the final page of the manuscript, so that Anthony Boucher (who was then editor of F & SF and who was an outstanding devotee of bad puns and campy science fiction) would not see it in advance and find its impact deadened.

It worked perfectly. He turned to the last page, not seeing what I was getting at, and the pun hit him dead centre. Here is the vignette, in full:

'Dreamworld' *(1955)*

At thirteen, Edward Keller had been a science-fiction devotee for four years. He bubbled with Galactic enthusiasm.

His Aunt Clara, who had brought him up by rule and rod in pious memory of her deceased sister, wavered between toleration and exasperation. It appalled her to watch him grow so immersed in fantasy.

'Face reality, Eddie,' she would say, angrily.

He would nod, but go on, 'And I dreamed Martians were chasing me, see? I had a special death ray, but the atomic power unit was pretty low and –'

Every other breakfast consisted of eggs, toast, milk, and some such dream.

Aunt Clara said, severely, 'Now, Eddie, one of these nights you won't be able to wake up out of your dream. You'll be trapped! Then what?'

She lowered her angular face close to his and glared.

Eddie was strangely impressed by his aunt's warning. He lay in bed, staring into the darkness. He wouldn't like to be trapped in a dream. It was always nice to wake up before it was too late. Like the time the dinosaurs were after him –

Suddenly, he was out of bed, out of the house, out on the lawn, and he knew it was another dream.

The thought was broken by a vague thunder and a shadow that blotted the sun. He looked upwards in astonishment and he could make out the human face that touched the clouds.

It was his Aunt Clara! Monstrously tall, she bent towards him in admonition, mastlike forefinger upraised, voice too guttural to be made out.

Eddie turned and ran in panic. Another Aunt Clara monster loomed up before him, voice rumbling.

He turned again, stumbling, panting, heading outwards, outwards.

He reached the top of the hill and stopped in horror. Off in the distance a hundred towering Aunt Claras were marching by. As the column passed, each one of the Aunt Claras turned her head sharply towards him and the thunderous bass rumbling coalesced into words:

'Face reality, Eddie. Face reality, Eddie.'

Eddie threw himself sobbing to the ground. Please wake up, he begged himself. Don't be caught in this dream.

For unless he woke up, the worst science-fiction doom of all would have overtaken him. He would be trapped, *trapped*, in a world of giant aunts.

PART 11

Humour

In some ways, my most unexpected excursion (to myself, anyway) is into the realm of humour.

For many years, my writings were singularly free of humour, to my own astonishment and rather to that of others as well, for in my social life I am well known as an authentically funny fellow.

Good sense tells me not to say this myself, but I may as well indulge in one of my 'delightful Asimovian immodesties' – one more won't kill me any deader than I am by now. The thing is that I am offhandedly witty, I am perfectly capable of telling jokes all evening without repeating myself (clean jokes, yet) and I can give an extemporaneous talk on any subject before any audience and have them in the aisles.

In fact, on those few occasions when I have addressed a scientific convention and given a legitimate scientific talk of the kind that later gets published in a solemn scientific journal – I still have them laughing.

So why is my writing so sober?

I'm not sure. Lack of self-confidence, perhaps. Every once in a while I did write what I considered to be a humorous science-fiction story. I invariably loved it and died laughing when I reread it. In each case I managed to sell it, and in each case a kind of solemn silence swallowed it up and it was never heard of again.

Fortunately, a turning point came in 1962, and it happened after this fashion:

It seems that every year at the annual World Science Fiction Convention, awards are handed out for a variety of categories, in imitation of the well-known Oscar awards of the movie industry. The science-fiction awards are called Hugos after Hugo Gernsback, the editor of the first magazine to be devoted entirely to science fiction. (It was Amazing Stories *and its first issue was April, 1926.)*

It occurred to Bob Mills, who had earlier been editor of F & SF, succeeding Tony Boucher, and who was now an author's agent, that an anthology of Hugo-winning short stories and novelettes ought to be prepared. As editor of that anthology, he felt, someone should be chosen who had never won a Hugo. The obvious candidate was myself since I had never won a Hugo and yet I was a perennial toastmaster at these Conventions (I told you I am a funny fellow) and had handed out more Hugos to other people than anyone else in the business.

Timothy Seldes, who was then my editor at Doubleday (he was Larry Ashmead's predecessor), was all for it and the proposal was put to me.

I was dubious for a very silly reason. I was already thinking of *My Hundredth Book* and was almost halfway to the goal. All the books I had written so far were really mine, for even when I published one as a collaboration, most or all of the writing chore was mine (except for the first edition of the biochemistry textbook). An anthology, however, would be primarily the work of others. Could I count a collection of other people's writings as a book of mine just because I had my name on it as editor?

Ordinarily, I might be able to argue that I had had to do a lot of reading and judging and that the book was my creation in that I had selected the stories and arranged them to make an organic whole. I couldn't even say that much in this case, however, since the stories which had won the Hugo were fixed and since they were to appear in chronological order.

So I agreed only on condition that I be able to write a longish introduction to each story and to the book as a whole and give it a kind of atmosphere that would make me feel justified in considering the book – to at least a certain extent – as a creation of my own.

And when I started working on these introductions, why, somehow, they turned out to be funny.

This time (aha!) it worked. At least I received a surprising number of letters from readers who flattered me by telling me that they thought the introductions were the best part of the book.

You can bet that was all the encouragement I needed. Prior to 1962, collections of my own stories appeared bare, with no editorial comment. After 1962, collections of my stories tended to be surrounded by chatter, usually not-very-serious chatter, and this tendency has increased until it has reached an extreme (for now) in the very volume you are holding.

So – Does this mean I can write a humorous science-fiction story after all? I decided to try again.

It came about because Esquire *magazine was planning a special issue and asked me to contribute. I suggested a satirical piece (you see, it was beginning to go to my head) and they agreed, but when I sat down to write the article, it turned into a science-fiction story.*

(I can't help it. I tell anyone who listens that there is a little man inside me that does the writing, that he is quite beyond my control, and that I just sit there at the typewriter and read what comes out in utter fascination.)

When I reread what I had written this time, however, I realized that it was a satire on The Double Helix, *that excellent book written by James D. Watson, which tells the history of the discovery of the structure of DNA in utterly human terms.*

The humour in my story depends partly on the reader having read The Double Helix *or at least having read about* The Double Helix, *but so what? Anyone who is sufficiently interested in science fiction or in me to buy this rather heterogeneous mish-mash of a book you are now holding is bound to know about* The Double Helix.

But when I sent the story to Esquire, *it turned out that either they had never heard of* The Double Helix *or feared their readers hadn't – so they rejected it. (See, I even get rejects in the year 1968! I'm human!)*

I didn't care. I sent it to Fred Pohl, and he took it for

his magazine, **If.**

At least, he took it after a little hesitation. He wrote and said that he would like to cut it in half. (He must have had some obscure reason for that, but who knows what evil lurks in the hearts of editors.)

I wrote back, rather humbly, and said I didn't want to sound like Harlan Ellison (a tremendously talented science-fiction writer who is known throughout the field for his trigger-temper and his refusal to take any lip from any editor), but the story had to be published in toto for two reasons: (1) It was a satire on The Double Helix and the satirical point would be killed if it were cut, and (2) it was the only story I had ever written in which I wrote as ribaldly as I talk, and I might never do it again, so I didn't want to lose one precious paragraph.

Consequently, said I, if he felt he had to cut it, would he return the manuscript instead?

Whereupon Fred answered and said he would print it in full and I did, too, sound like Harlan Ellison.

Which was a terrible thing to say.

Anyway, here's the story, which concludes the book in symmetrical fashion. The first inclusion was a piece of the very first science-fiction story I managed to write and sell; and the last inclusion is the very latest (so far) science-fiction story I managed to write and sell – thirty years later.

'The Holmes-Ginsbook Device' *(1968)*

I have never seen Myron Ginsbook in a modest mood.

But then, why should I have? Mike – we all call him Mike, although he is Dr Ginsbook, Nobel Laureate, to a reverential world – is a typical product of the twenty-first century. He is self-confident, as so many of us are, and by right should be.

He knows the worth of mankind, of society, and most of all of himself.

He was born on January 1, 2001, so he is as old as the century exactly. I am ten years younger, that much further removed from the unmentionable twentieth.

Oh, I mentioned it sometimes. All youngsters have their quirks and mine had been a kind of curiosity about mankind's earlier history, concerning which so little is known and so little, I admit, ought to be known. But I was curious.

It was Mike who rescued me in those days. 'Don't,' he would say, leering at the girls as they passed in their bikini business suits, and leaning over at intervals to feel the material judiciously, 'don't play with the past. Oh, anicent history isn't bad, nor medieval times, but as soon as we reach the birth of technology, forget it. From then on it's scatology; just filth and perversion. You're a creature of the twenty-first. Be free! Breathe deeply of our century's clean air! It will do wonders for you. Look at what it's doing for that remarkable girl to your left.'

And it was true. Her deep breathing was delightful. Ah, those were great days, when science was pulsing and we two were young, carefree and eager to grab the world by the tail.

Mike was sure he was going to advance science enormously and I felt the same. It was the great dream of all of us in this glorious century, still youthful. It was as though some great voice were crying: *Onward! Onward! Not a glance behind!*

I picked up that attitude from Paul Derrick, the California wizard. He's dead now, but a great man in his time, quite worthy of being mentioned in the same breath with myself.

I was one of his graduate students and it was hard at first. In college, I had carefully selected those courses which had had the least mathematics and the most girls and had therefore learned how to hemstitch with surpassing skill but had, I admit, left myself weak in physics.

After considerable thought, I realized that hemstitching was not going to help me make further advances in our great twenty-first-century technology. The demand for improvements in hemstitching was meagre and I could see clearly that my expertise would not lead me to the coveted Nobel Prize. So I pinched the girls good-bye and joined Derrick's seminars.

I understood little at first but I did my best to ask questions designed to help Derrick demonstrate his brilliance and rapidly advanced to the head of the class in consequence. I was even the occasion for Derrick's greatest discovery.

He was smoking at the time. He was an inveterate smoker and proud of it, always taking his cigarette out and looking at it lovingly between puffs. They were girlie-cigarettes, with fetching nudes on the clear white paper – always a favourite with scientists.

'Imagine,' he would say in the course of his famous lectures on Twenty-first-Century Technological Concepts, 'how we have advanced on the Dark Ages in the matter of cigarettes alone. Rumours reach us that in the ill-famed twentieth century, cigarettes were a source of disease and air-pollution. The details are not known, of course, and no one, I imagine, would care to find out, yet the rumours are convincing. Now, however, a cigarette liberates air-purifying ingredients into the atmosphere, fills it with a pleasant aroma, and strengthens the health of the smoker. It has, in fact, only one drawback.'

Of course, we all knew what it was. I had frequently seen Derrick with a blistered lip, and he had a fresh blister that day. It impeded his speech somewhat.

Like all thoughtful scientists, he was easily distracted by passing girls, and on those occasions he would frequently place his cigarette in his mouth wrong-end-in. He would inhale deeply and the cigarette would spontaneously ignite, with the lit end in his mouth.

I don't know how many learned professors I had seen, in those days, interrupt their intimate conversations with secretaries to yell in agony as another blister was added to tongue or lip.

On this occasion, I said in jest, 'Professor Derrick, why don't you remove the igno-tip before putting the cigarette in your mouth?' It was a mild witticism and actually, if I remember correctly, I was the only who laughed. Yet the picture brought up by the remark was a funny one. Imagine a cigarette without its ignitable tip! How could one smoke it?

But Derrick's eyes narrowed. 'Why not?' he said. 'Observe!'

In front of the class, Derrick whipped out a cigarette, observed it carefully – his particular brand presented its girlies in lifelike tints – then pinched off the igno-tip.

He held it up between two fingers of his left hand and said again, 'Observe!' He placed the unignitable residue of the cigarette in his mouth. A thrill went through us all as we observed from the position of the girlie that he had deliberately placed the cigarette in his mouth wrong-end-in. He inhaled sharply and nothing, of course, happened.

'The unblistering cigarette,' he said.

I said, 'But you can't light it.'

'Can't you?' he said and, with a flourish, brought the igno-tip up against the cigarette. We all caught our breath. It was a sheer stroke of genius, for the igno-tip would light the safe outside end of the cigarette, *whichever end it was.*

Derrick inhaled sharply and the igno-tip flared into life, igniting the outer tip of the cigarette – and the tip of Derrick's thumb and forefinger. With a howl, he dropped it and naturally, the entire class laughed with great cheerfulness this time.

It was a stroke of misfortune for me. Since I had suggested the miserable demonstration, he kicked me out of his class forever.

This was, of course, unfair, since I had made it possible for him to win the Nobel Prize, though neither of us realized it at the time.

You see, the laughter had driven Derrick to frenzy. He

was determined to solve the problem of the unblisterable cigarette. To do so, he bent his giant mind to the problem full time, cutting down his evenings with the girls to five a week – almost unheard of in a scientist, but he was a notorious ascetic.

In less than a year, he had solved the problem. Now that it is over, of course, it seems obvious to all of us, but at the time, I assure you, it dumbfounded the world of science.

The trick was to separate the igno-tip from the cigarette and then devise some way of manipulating the igno-tip safely. For months, Derrick experimented with different shapes and sizes of handles.

Finally, he decided on a thin shaft of wood as ideal for the purpose. Since it was difficult to balance a cigarette tip on the wood, he discarded the tobacco and paper and made use of the chemicals with which the cigarette tip had been impregnated. These chemicals he coated on the tip of the shaft.

At first, he lost considerable time trying to make the shaft hollow so that it could be sucked or blown through to ignite the chemicals. The resulting fire might then be applied to the cigarette. This, however, revived the original problem. What if one put the wrong end of the shaft in the hand?

Derrick then got his crowning idea. It would only be necessary to increase the temperature of the chemicals by friction, by rubbing the tip of the wood against a rough surface. This was absolutely safe for if, in the course of bestowing a fatherly kiss on the lips of a girl student intent on an A in her course at any hazard – a typical event in every scientist's life – one should rub the wrong end of the wood on a rough surface, nothing at all would happen. It was a perfect fail-safe mechanism.

The discovery swept the world. Who, today, is without his package of igno-splints, which can be lit at any time in perfect safety, so that the day of the blistered lip is gone forever? Surely this great invention is a match for any other this great century has seen; so much a match, in fact, that some wags have suggested the igno-splints be called 'matches'. Actually, that name is catching on.

Derrick received his Nobel Prize in physics almost at once and the world applauded.

I returned then and tried to re-enrol in his class, pointing out that but for me he would never have earned that Nobel Prize. He kicked me out with harsh expletives, threatening to apply an igno-splint to my nose.

After that my one ambition was to win a Nobel Prize of my own, one that would drown out Derrick's achievement. I, John Holmes, would show him.

But how? How?

I managed to get a grant that would take me to England in order to study Lancashire hemstitching, but I had no sooner got there than I pulled every string I could to get into Cambridge, with its famous covey of girl students and its almost equally famous Chumley-Maudlin (pronounced Cholmondeley-Magdalen) Technological Institute.

The girl students were warm and exotic and I spent many an evening stitching hems with them. Many of the Cantabrigian scientists were struck with the usefulness of the pursuit, not having discerned earlier this particular advantage of sewing. Some of them tried to get me to teach them to hemstitch but I followed that old First Law of Scientific Motivation: 'What's in it for me?' I didn't teach them a thing.

Mike Ginsbook, however, having watched me from a distance, quickly picked up the intricate finger-manipulations of hemstitching and joined me.

'It's my talent,' he said with charming immodesty. 'I have a natural aptitude at manipulation.'

He was my man! I recognized at that moment that he would help me to the Nobel Prize. There remained only to choose the field of activity that would get it for us.

For a year our association produced nothing except for a sultry brunette or two; and then one day I said to him

lazily, 'I can't help but notice, Mike, that your eyes are
extraordinarily limpid. You're the only one on campus
who doesn't have bloodshot sclera.'

He said, 'But the answer is simple. I never view microfilms. They are a curse.'

'Oh?'

'I've never told you?' A sombre look crossed his face
and a clear stab of pain furrowed his brow. I had clearly
activated a memory almost too sharp to bear. He said,
'I was once viewing a microfilm with my head completely
enclosed in the viewer, naturally. While I was doing that,
a gorgeous girl passed by – a girl who won the title of
Miss Teacher's Pet the next two years running, I might
say – and I never noticed her. I was told about it afterwards by Tancred Hull, the gynaecologist. He spent three
nights with her, the cad, explaining that he was giving her a
physical checkup. Had pictures taken to prove it that were
the talk of Cambridge.'

Mike's lips were quivering. 'From that time on,' he said
in a low, suffering voice, 'I have vowed never to view a
film again.'

I was almost faint with the sudden inspiration that struck
me. 'Mike,' I said, 'might there not be some way in which
microfilms can be viewed more simply? Look, films are
covered with microscopic print. That print has to be
enlarged for us to see it. That means bending over an
immobile screen or encasing the head in a viewer.

'But –' and I could hardly breathe with the excitement
of it – 'what if the material on the film were enlarged until
it could be seen with the naked eye and then a photograph
of the enlarged print were taken? You could carry the
photograph with you, looking at it at your leisure whenever
you chose. Why, Mike, if you were looking at such a photo
and a girl passed by, it would be the work of a moment
to lift your head. The photo would not take up your
attention as a viewer would.'

'Hmm,' said Mike, thoughtfully. I could see his giant

mind spinning over every ramification of the subject. 'It really might not interfere with girl-watching; less important, it might prevent bloodshot eyes. Oh, but wait, all you would have would be about five or six hundred words and you would be bound to read that through before the day was over. Then what?'

It was amazing to watch him pick unerringly the flaw in the project.

For a moment, I was daunted. I hadn't thought of that. Then I said, 'Perhaps you could make a large series of small photographs and paste them together in order. Of couse, that might be more difficult to carry.'

'Let's see –' Mike's mind continued to work. He leaned back in his chair, closed his eyes, straightened suddenly and looked piercingly about in every direction to make sure there were no girls in the vicinity, then closed them again.

He said, 'There's no question but that magnification is possible; photography is possible. If all of a typical micro-film is expanded and photographed, however, so that it could be read with the unaided eye, the resultant series of photographs would cover an area of –' Here he whipped out his famous girlie slide rule, designed by himself, with the hairline neatly and stimulatingly bisecting a buxom blonde. He manipulated it caressingly. '– An area of one hundred fifty square feet in area at least. We would have to use a sheet of paper ten feet by fifteen feet and crawl around on it.'

'That would be possible,' I muttered.

'Too undignified for a scientist unless, of course, he were pointing out something to a girl student. And even then she might get interested in reading whatever it was he was pointing out and that would kill everything.'

We were both down in the dumps at that. We recognized that we had Nobel material here. Films had the virtue of being compact, but that was their only virtue.

Oh, if only you could fold a ten-foot-by-fifteen-foot piece of paper in your hand. You would require no electronic or photonic equipment to read it. You could read any part of it at will. You could go backwards or forwards without having to manipulate any controls. You would merely shift your eyes.

The whole thought was incredibly exciting. The technological advance involved in using eye muscles in place of expensive equipment was enormous. Mike pointed out at once that glancing back and forth over a large sheet of paper would exercise the eye muscles and equip a scientist better for the important task of not failing to observe the feminine parade.

It remained only to determine how best to make a large sheet of paper portable and manipulable.

I took a course in topology in order to learn folding techniques and many was the evening my girl friend of the day and I would design some order of folding. Beginning at opposite ends of the sheet of paper, we would come closer and closer as we folded according to some intricate formula, until we were face to face, panting and flushed with the mental and physical exertion. The results were enormously exciting but the folding procedures were never any good.

How I wished I had studied more mathematics. I even approached Prunella Plug, our harsh-voiced laundress, who folded bed sheets with aplomb and dignity. She was not about to let me into the secret, however.

I might have explained what I wanted the folding for, but I wasn't going to let *her* in on it. I meant to share the Nobel Prize with as few people as possible. The famous phrase of the great scientist Lord Clinchmore – I'm not in science for my health, you know' – rang through my mind.

One morning I thought I had it. Oh, the excitement of it! I had to find Mike, for only his keen analytical mind would tell me if there were flaws in the notion. I tracked him down to a hotel room at last but found him deeply involved with a young lady – or popsie, to use the scientific term.

I banged away at the locked door until he came out, rather in a bad humour for some reason. He said, 'Darn it, Jack, you can't interrupt research like that.' Mike was a dedicated scientist.

I said, 'Listen. We've been thinking in terms of two dimensions. What about *one* dimension?'

'How do you mean, one dimension?'

'Take the photos,' I said, 'and make them follow one after the other in a single line!'

'It would be yards and yards long.' He worked out the figures with his finger on his colleague's abdomen, while I watched closely to make sure that he made no mistakes. He said, 'It could easily be two-hundred feet long. That's ungainly.'

'But you don't have to fold,' I said. 'You roll. You place one end on one plastic rod, and the other end on another. You roll them together!'

'Great Scott,' said Mike, shocked into profanity by the thought. 'Maybe you have it.'

It was that very day, however, that the blow struck. A visiting professor from California had news. Paul Derrick, he said, was rumoured to be working on the problem of a non-electronic film. He didn't seem to know what that meant, but we did and our hearts sank again.

I said, 'He must have heard of what we're doing here. We've *got* to beat him.'

And how we tried! We took the photographs ourselves, pasted them side by side, rolled them on rods. It was a job of unimaginable complexity and delicacy that might well have used skilled artisans, but we were intent on allowing no outsider to see what we were doing.

It worked, but Mike was uncertain. He said, 'I don't think it's really practical. If you want to find a particular place in the film, you have to roll and roll and roll, one way or another. It is very hard on the wrists.'

But it was all we had. I wanted to publish, but Mike held back. 'Let's see what Derrick has worked out,' he said.

'But if he has this, he will have anticipated us.'

Mike shook his head, 'If this is all he's got, it doesn't matter. This isn't going to win the Nobel Prize. It isn't good enough – I just feel it, here.'

He placed his hand on the girlie stitched on his shirt pocket so sincerely that I did not argue. Mike was a great scientist and a great scientist just knows what will get a Nobel Prize and what will not. That's what makes a scientist great.

Derrick did announce his discovery – and it had a flaw in it that an average high-school student would have spotted at once.

His non-electronic film was simply our old two-dimensional sheets, but without even our efforts to fold them. It just hung down the side of a large wall. A movable ladder was supplied that was attached to a runner near the ceiling. One of Derrick's students climbed the ladder and read aloud into the microphones.

Everyone ooh-ed and ah-ed at the sight of someone reading with the unaided eye, but Mike, watching on television, slapped his thigh in amusement.

'The idiot,' he said. 'What about people with acrophobia?'

Of course! It leaped to the eye when Mike pointed it out. Anyone afraid of heights couldn't read under the Derrick system.

But I seized Mike's wrist and said, 'Now wait awhile, Mike. They're going to laugh at Derrick and that's dangerous. As soon as this point about acrophobia comes out, Derrick will feel humiliated and he will turn with every fibre of his magnificent brain to the project. He will then solve it in weeks. We've got to get there first.'

Mike sobered up at once. 'You are right, Jack,' he said simply. 'Let's go out on the town. A girl or two apiece will help us think.'

It did, too, and then the next morning we thought about other things and got back to work.

I remember I was walking back and forth, muttering, 'We've tried two dimensions; we've tried one dimension; what's left?' And then my eye fell upon Mike's girlie shirt with the nude on the breast pocket so cleverly hemstitched that strategic areas were distinctly raised.

'Heavens,' I said, 'we haven't tried *three* dimensions.'

I went screaming for Mike. This time I was sure I had it and I could hardly breathe waiting for his judgment. He looked at me, eyes luminous. 'We have it,' he said.

It's so simple, looking back on it. We simply piled the photographs in a heap.

The heaps could be kept in place in any number of ways. They could be stapled, for instance. Then Mike got the idea of placing them between stiff cardboard covers to protect individual photographs from damage.

Within a month, we had published. The world rang with the discovery and everyone knew that the next Nobel Prize in physics would be ours.

Derrick, to do him justice, congratulated us and said, 'Now the world can read without electronics and by the use of the unaided eyes, thanks to the Holmes-Ginsbook device. I congratulate those two dirty rats on their discovery.'

That handsome acknowledgment was Science at its best.

The Holmes-Ginsbook device is now a household item. The popularity of the device is such that its name has been shortened to the final syllable and increasing numbers of people are calling them simply 'books'.

This eliminates my name, but I have my Nobel Prize and a contract to write a book on the intimate details surrounding the discovery for a quarter-million-dollar advance. Surely that is enough. Scientists are simple souls and once they have fame, wealth and girls, that's all they ask.

And that's it. You now have a more or less general once-over as far as my writing career is concerned, at the

milestone of *My Hundredth Book*, and I must say that
going through it all has given me a serious attack of
vertigo.

It's an awful lot of typewriter-banging in an awful lot
of different directions considering that at the time this
book appears, I will still be on the sunny side of fifty.

Nor, frankly, do I intend to stop.

I've got a huge book on Shakespeare in the works, and
a history of the Byzantine Empire, and a book on sex for
teenagers (honest!), and a number of other things.

Am I going to be aiming at *My Two Hundredth Book*
now?

Oh, I don't know. No one lives forever, after all. But I
can say this – as long as I do live, I intend to keep writing.

Charles Dickens died as he was working on The Mystery
of Edwin Drood *with his pen trailing a mark along the
page and his head slumped over the manuscript – and that
is the only way a writer would want to go.*

APPENDIX

My First Hundred Books

NOTE All dates are those of original American publication. Where books have been separately published and are still in print in Britain the name of the British publisher is given, preceded by the abbreviation Br. In all other cases the publisher given is the original American publisher.

TITLE	PUBLISHER	DATE
1 Pebble in the Sky	Br. Sidgwick & Jackson	1950
2 I, Robot	Br. Dennis Dobson	1950
3 The Stars Like Dust –	Br. Panther	1951
4 Foundation	Br. Panther	1951
5 David Starr: Space Ranger	Doubleday	1952
6 Foundation and Empire	Br. Panther	1952
7 The Currents of Space	Br. Panther	1952
8 Biochemistry and Human Metabolism	Williams & Wilkins	1952
9 Second Foundation	Br. Panther	1953
10 Lucky Starr and the Pirates of the Asteroids	Doubleday	1953
11 The Caves of Steel	Br. Panther	1954
12 Lucky Starr and the Oceans of Venus	Doubleday	1954
13 The Chemicals of Life	Br. Signet Books	1954
14 The Martian Way and Other Stories	Br. Dennis Dobson	1955
15 The End of Eternity	Br. Abelard-Schuman	1955
16 Races and People	Abelard-Schuman	1955

52	Fifty Short Science Fiction Tales	Collier Books	1963
53	View from a Height	Doubleday	1963
54	The Kite That Won the Revolution	Houghton Mifflin	1963
55	The Human Brain	Houghton Mifflin	1964
56	A Short History of Biology	Doubleday	1964
57	Quick and Easy Math	Houghton Mifflin	1964
58	Adding a Dimension	Br. Dennis Dobson	1964
59	Planets for Man	Random House	1964
60	The Rest of the Robots	Br. Dennis Dobson	1964
61	Asimov's Biographical Encyclopedia of Science and Technology	Doubleday	1964
62	A Short History of Chemistry	Doubleday	1965
63	The Greeks	Houghton Mifflin	1965
64	Of Time and Space and Other Things	Doubleday	1965
65	The New Intelligent Man's Guide to Science	Basic Books	1965
66	An Easy Introduction to the Slide Rule	Houghton Mifflin	1965
67	Fantastic Voyage	Br. Dennis Dobson	1966
68	The Noble Gases	Basic Books	1966
69	Inside the Atom (3rd revision)	Abelard-Schuman	1966
70	The Neutrino	Br. Dennis Dobson	1966
71	The Roman Republic	Houghton Mifflin	1966
72	Understanding Physics, Volume 1	Br. Signet Books	1966
73	Understanding Physics, Volume 2	Br. Signet Books	1966
74	Understanding Physics, Volume 3	Br. Signet Books	1966
75	The Genetic Effects of Radiation	Atomic Energy Commission	1966
76	Tomorrow's Children	Br. Compton Russell	1966
77	The Universe	Br. Penguin	1966
78	From Earth to Heaven	Doubleday	1966
79	The Moon	Follett	1967
80	Environment Out There	Scholastic	1967
81	The Roman Empire	Houghton Mifflin	1967

OPUS 200

Contents

Introduction

In October 1969, Houghton Mifflin published my book *Opus 100*. It wasn't named at random. It was the hundredth book of mine to be published.

That hundredth book took its time coming, of course. It wasn't till I was eighteen, after all, that I became a professional writer. (To be specific, my first sale took place on October 21, 1938.) Then, for eleven years after that, my only sales were to the science fiction magazines, so that I became a well-known and successful writer (within the highly specialized and non-numerous ranks of the science fiction world, anyway) without having a single book to my name.*

Then, on January 19, 1950, just after I had turned thirty, I finally published my first book, *Pebble in the Sky*. It was a science fiction novel.

After that, first slowly (two books in 1950 and two more in 1951) and then more rapidly (eight books in 1960 and twelve books in 1966), I began to pile them up.

What with one thing and another, I finally managed to reach the hundredth book not quite twenty years after I had published the first one. That's an average of five books a year, which isn't bad, at least as far as quantity is concerned.

With regard to quality, it is perhaps harder to judge, but even if we disregard my own personal opinion that

---

* In later years, these early stories were included in various books, so they didn't go to waste forever, you may be sure.

my books are great, it remains fair to assume that publishers are reasonably sane and would not have published so many of my books if they didn't think they were good.

Once a hundred books had come boiling out of my typewriter ribbons, I could have been forgiven if I had then retired. I might have considered a hundred books a reasonable life's work and spent the rest of my existence doing other things – having a good time, for instance.

There was a catch, though; two catches, in fact.

In the first place, when my hundredth book came out I was still ten weeks on the sunny side of fifty (which may not be much of a sunny side, but where age is concerned, I'll snatch at a hair's breadth), and I didn't feel old enough to retire.

In the second place, I was *already* having a good time and, if I retired, the only thing I would really want to do in retirement would be to write. So why retire only to do what I was already doing?

So I kept on working; and to such good effect – for one gets better (or at least faster) with practice – that in a surprisingly brief period of time I found I was reaching my two hundredth book.

The second hundred was completed by 1979, so that it had only taken me ten years to turn them out, which is an average of ten books a year.

Naturally, Houghton Mifflin (stifling who-knows-how-many sighs) feels honour-bound to publish *Opus 200* now, and I'm perfectly content to let them do so.

Let me emphasize now that, in publishing first *Opus 100* and then *Opus 200*, neither I nor Houghton Mifflin is in any way celebrating the matter of quantity. My two hundred books are far from being a record.

According to *The Guinness Book of World Records*, an Englishman named Charles Hamilton and an American named Charles Andrews each published about 100,000,000 words in their lifetimes, whereas my published output so far comes to perhaps 15,000,000 words.

Even supposing I live out a reasonably long life and continue writing at a reasonably fast clip, I don't think I can possibly surpass 25,000,000 published words at most.

Furthermore, Charles Andrews, according to the *Book of Records*, wrote 100,000 words a week when at his peak, and I think I do well if I manage a measly 15,000 words of finished material in one week.

Then, too, the British novelist John Creasey and the Belgian novelist Georges Simenon each published over 500 books in the course of their careers, and I don't see that it is at all likely that even a long and continually busy life is going to lift me past the 400 mark.

Nevertheless, I do not labour under any sense of failure because of this. Those authors who surpass me in quantity have (as far as I know) an only limited range. Their domain is fiction, and usually but one or two kinds of fiction, so that they attain speed by rolling down well-oiled tracks.

I, on the other hand, write not only fiction but non-fiction. I write different kinds of non-fiction for different kinds of audiences, and that is the purpose of my *Opus* books – to celebrate that variety.

For *Opus 100* I took passages from my first hundred books and carefully divided them into categories. For *Opus 200* I've taken passages from my second hundred books and divided them into the same categories – plus several additional ones.

Nobody who reads my writings, after all, is very likely to have read all my books, or even most of them, and many people who do read and are, presumably, fond of some of my books are not aware of some of the other kinds of writing I do.

In these *Opus* books, then, the average reader will get a chance to sample the variety to a fuller extent than he would otherwise have a chance to do. If he already likes part of what I write, he may find he also likes, or is at least curious about, some other parts of what I write. It might give him additional pleasure to read those other parts *in toto*, and that would then certainly please me.

And if he doesn't already like part of what I write . . . then he might not buy this book in the first place, which would be a shame, but there's no law against it.

PART 1

Astronomy

To anyone who got his start writing science fiction in the days before World War II, astronomy was the science. No one envisioned space travel outside science fiction (except for a very few people working on rockets, who were considered by all the 'hardheaded' people around them to be but a half-step removed from science fiction writers). That meant that some facets of astronomy used to be the exclusive domain of those who wrote and read science fiction. For instance, where but in science fiction could one describe the surface of the Moon as seen from the surface of the Moon? Astronomy lost some of its exclusivity, where science fiction writers were concerned, by the time my second hundred books began to be written in the late 1960s. Astronauts strove to reach the Moon, and in 1969, the year in which Opus 100 *was published, they succeeded. We know the surface of the Moon in great detail now and science fiction has had to come to terms with that.*

But we have only reached the Moon; no one has yet actually lived on it. Therefore, the description of a working and viable settlement on the Moon still lies within the province of fiction.

For instance, in 1972 (by which time several spaceships had landed on the Moon and returned safely), my science fiction novel The Gods Themselves *(Book 121) was published by Doubleday. It won both the Nebula (the award of the Science Fiction Writers of America) and the Hugo (the award of the fans gathered in a world convention).* The third part of the novel is set on the Moon, which is pictured as an elaborate human settlement. Here is a passage in which Selene, the young woman born and bred on the Moon, teaches Ben, who arrived from Earth*

---

* I mention this for no reason other than that it gives me pleasure to do so.

but a month before, how to manoeuvre on the Moon's surface.

from THE GODS THEMSELVES *(1972)*

Selene laughed, and the sound was metallic in Denison's earpiece. Her figure was lost in the spacesuit she wore.

She said, 'Now come, Ben, there's no reason to be afraid. You're an old hand by now – you've been here a month.'

'Twenty-eight days,' mumbled Denison. He felt smothered in his own suit.

'A month,' insisted Selene. 'It was well past half-Earth when you came; it is well past half-Earth now.' She pointed to the brilliant curve of the Earth in the southern sky.

'Well, but wait. I'm not as brave out here as I am underground. What if I fall?'

'What if you do? The gravity is weak by your standards, the slope is gentle, your suit is strong. If you fall, just let yourself slide and roll. It's almost as much fun that way, anyhow.'

Denison looked about doubtfully. The Moon lay beautiful in the cold light of the Earth. It was black and white; a mild and delicate white as compared with the sunlit views he had seen when he had taken a trip a week before to inspect the solar batteries that stretched from horizon to horizon along the floor of Mare Imbrium. And the black was somehow softer, too, through lack of the blazing contrast of true day. The stars were supernally bright and the Earth – the Earth was infinitely inviting with its swirls of white on blue, and its peeping glimpse of tan.

'Well,' he said, 'do you mind if I hang on to you?'

'Of course not. And we won't go all the way up. It will be the beginners' slope for you. Just try to keep in time with me. I'll move slowly.'

Her steps were long, slow, and swinging, and he tried to keep in synchronization. The up-sloping ground beneath them was dusty and with each step he kicked up a fine powder that settled quickly in the airlessness. He matched her stride for stride, but with an effort.

'Good,' said Selene, her arm locked in his, steadying him. 'You're very good for an Earthie – no, I ought to say Immie.'

'Thank you.'

'That's not much better, I suppose. Immie for Immigrant is as insulting as Earthie for Earthman. Shall I just say you're simply very good for a man your age?'

'*No!* That's much worse.' Denison was gasping a little and he could feel his forehead moistening.

Selene said, 'Each time you reach the point where you're about to put your foot down, give a little push with your other foot. That will lengthen your stride and make it all the easier. No, no – watch me.'

Denison paused thankfully and watched Selene take off with low, effortless leaps. Somehow, despite the grotesquery of the suit, she appeared slim and graceful when she moved. She returned and knelt at his feet.

'Now you take a slow step, Ben, and I'll hit your foot when I want it to shove.'

They tried several times, and Denison said, 'That's worse than running on Earth. I better rest.'

'All right. It's just that your muscles aren't used to the proper co-ordination. It's yourself you're fighting, you know, not gravity... Well, sit down and catch your breath. I won't take you up much further.'

Denison said, 'Will I do any damage to the pack if I lie down on my back?'

'No, of course not, but it's not a good idea. Not on the bare ground. It's only at 120 degrees absolute – 150 degrees below zero, if you prefer – and the smaller the area of contact the better. I'd sit down.'

'All right.' Gingerly, Denison sat down with a grunt. Deliberately, he faced northward, away from the Earth. 'Look at those stars!'

Selene sat perpendicular to him. He could see her face

dimly through the faceplate now and then when the Earthlight caught it at the proper angle.

She said, 'Don't you see the stars on Earth?'

'Not like this. Even when there are no clouds, the air on Earth absorbs some of the light. Temperature differences in the atmosphere make them twinkle, and city lights, even distant city lights, wash them out.'

'Sounds disgusting.'

'Do you like it out here, Selene? On the surface?'

'I'm not crazy about it really, but I don't mind it too much, now and then. It's part of my job to bring tourists out here, of course.'

'And now you have to do it for me.'

'Can't I convince you it's not the same thing at all, Ben? We've got a set route for the tourists. It's very tame, very uninteresting. You don't think we'd take them out here to the slide, do you? This is for Lunarites – and Immies. Mostly Immies, actually.'

'It can't be very popular. There's no one here but ourselves.'

'Oh, well, there are particular days for this sort of thing. You should see this place on race days. You wouldn't like it then, though.'

'I'm not sure I like it *now*. Is gliding a sport for Immies in particular?'

'Rather. Lunarites don't like the surface generally.'

'How about Dr Neville?'

'You mean, how he feels about the surface?'

'Yes.'

'Frankly, I don't think he's ever been up here. He's a real city boy. Why do you ask?'

'Well, when I asked permission to go along on the routine servicing of the solar batteries, he was perfectly willing to have me go, but he wouldn't go himself. I rather asked him to, I think, so I could have someone answer my questions, if there were any, but his refusal was rather strong.'

'I hope there was someone else to answer your questions.'

'Oh, yes. He was an Immie, too, come to think of it. Maybe that explains Dr Neville's attitude towards the electron pump.'

'What do you mean?'

'Well –' Denison leaned back and kicked his legs up alternately, watching them rise and fall slowly with a certain lazy pleasure. 'Hey, that's not bad. Look, Selene, what I mean is that Neville is so intent on developing a pump station on the Moon when the solar batteries are perfectly adequate for the job. We couldn't use solar batteries on Earth, where the Sun is never as unfailing, as prolonged, as bright, as radiant in all wave lengths. There's not a single planetary body in the solar system, no body of any size, that is more suitable for the use of the batteries than the Moon is. Even Mercury is too hot. But the use does tie you to the surface, and if you don't like the surface –'

Selene rose to her feet suddenly and said, 'All right, Ben, you've rested enough. Up! Up!'

He struggled to his feet and said, 'A pump station, however, would mean that no Lunarite would ever have to come out on the surface if he didn't want to.'

'Uphill we go, Ben. We'll go to that ridge up ahead. See it, where the Earthlight cuts off in a horizontal line?'

They made their way up the final stretch silently. Denison was aware of the smoother area at their side – a wide swath of slope from which most of the dust had been brushed.

'That's too smooth for a beginner to work up,' Selene said, answering his thoughts. 'Don't get too ambitious or you'll want me to teach you the kangaroo-hop next.'

She made a kangaroo-hop as she spoke, turned about-face almost before landing, and said, 'Right here. Sit down and I'll adjust –'

Denison did, facing downhill. He looked down the slope uncertainly. 'Can you really glide on it?'

'Of course. The gravity is weaker on the Moon than on Earth, so you press against the ground much less strongly, and that means there is much less friction. Everything is more slippery on the Moon than on the Earth. That's why the floors in our corridors and apartments seemed unfinished to you. Would you like to hear me give my little lecture on the subject? The one I give the tourists?'

'No, Selene.'

'Besides, we're going to use gliders, of course.' She had a small cartridge in her hand. Clamps and a pair of thin tubes were attached to it.

'What is that?' asked Ben.

'Just a small liquid-gas reservoir. It will emit a jet of vapour just under your boots. The thin gas layer between boots and ground will reduce friction virtually to zero. You'll move as though you were in clear space.'

Denison said uneasily, 'I disapprove. Surely it's wasteful to use gas in this fashion on the Moon.'

'Oh, now. What gas do you think we use in these gliders? Carbon dioxide? Oxygen? This is waste gas to begin with. It's argon. It comes out of the Moon's soil in ton lots, formed by billions of years of the breakdown of potassium-40 ... That's part of my lecture, too, Ben ... The argon has only a few specialized uses on the Moon. We could use it for gliding for a million years without exhausting the supply ... All right. Your gliders are on. Now wait till I put mine on.'

'How do they work?'

'It's quite automatic. You just start sliding and that will trip the contact and start the vapour. You've only got a few minutes' supply, but that's all you'll need.'

She stood up and helped him to his feet. 'Face downhill ... Come on, Ben, this is a gentle slope. Look at it. It looks perfectly level.'

'No, it doesn't,' said Denison sulkily. 'It looks like a cliff to me.'

'Nonsense. Now listen to me and remember what I told you. Keep your feet about six inches apart and one just a few inches ahead of the other. It doesn't matter which one is ahead. Keep your knees bent. Don't lean into the wind because there isn't any. Don't try to look up or back, but you can look from side to side if you have to. Most of all, when you finally hit level, don't try to stop too soon; you'll be going faster than you think. Just let the glider expire and then friction will bring you to a slow halt.'

'I'll never remember all that.'

'Yes, you will. And I'll be right at your side to help. And if you do fall and I don't catch you, don't try to do anything. Just relax and let yourself tumble or slide. There are no boulders anywhere that you can collide with.'

Denison swallowed and looked ahead. The southward slide was gleaming in Earthlight. Minute unevennesses caught more than their share of light, leaving tiny uphill patches in darkness so that there was a vague mottling of the surface. The bulging half-circle of Earth rode the black sky almost directly ahead.

'Ready?' said Selene. Her gauntleted hand was between his shoulders.

'Ready,' said Denison faintly.

'Then off you go,' she said. She pushed and Denison felt himself begin to move. He moved quite slowly at first. He turned towards her, wobbling, and she said, 'Don't worry. I'm right at your side.'

He could feel the ground beneath his feet – and then he couldn't. The glider had been activated.

For a moment he felt as though he were standing still. There was no push of air against his body, no feel of anything sliding past his feet. But when he turned towards Selene again, he noticed that the lights and shadows to one side were moving backwards at a slowly increasing speed.

'Keep your eyes on the Earth,' Selene's voice said in his ear, 'till you build up speed. The faster you go, the more stable you'll be. Keep your knees bent . . . You're doing very well, Ben.'

'For an Immie,' gasped Denison.

'How does it feel?'

'Like flying,' he said. The pattern of light and dark on
either side was moving backwards in a blur. He looked
briefly to one side, then the other, trying to convert the
sensation of a backward flight of the surroundings into
one of a forward flight of his own. Then, as soon as he
succeeded, he found he had to look forward hastily at the
Earth to regain his sense of balance. 'I suppose that's not
a good comparison to use to you. You have no experience
of flying on the Moon.'

'Now I know, though. Flying must be like gliding – I
know what *that* is.'

She was keeping up with him easily.

Denison was going fast enough now so that he got the
sensation of motion even when he looked ahead. The
Moonscape ahead was opening before him and flowing
past on either side. He said, 'How fast do you get to go
in a glide?'

'A good Moon-race,' said Selene, 'has been clocked at
speeds in excess of a hundred miles an hour – on steeper
slopes than this one, of course. You'll probably reach a
top of thirty-five.'

'It feels a lot faster than that somehow.'

'Well, it isn't. We're leaving off now, Ben, and you
haven't fallen. Now just hang on; the glider will die off
and you'll feel friction. Don't do anything to help it. Just
keep going.'

Selene had barely completed her remarks when Denison
felt the beginning of pressure under his boots. There was
at once an overwhelming sensation of speed and he
clenched his fists hard to keep from throwing his arms up
in an almost reflex gesture against the collision that wasn't
going to happen. He knew that if he threw up his arms,
he would go over backwards.

He narrowed his eyes, held his breath till he thought
his lungs would explode, and then Selene said, 'Perfect,
Ben, perfect. I've never known an Immie to go through
his first slide without a fall, so if you do fall, there'll be
nothing wrong. No disgrace.'

'I don't intend to fall,' whispered Denison. He caught a large, ragged breath, and opened his eyes wide. The Earth was as serene as ever, as uncaring. He was moving more slowly now – more slowly – more slowly –

'Am I standing still now, Selene?' he asked. 'I'm not sure.'

'You're standing still. Now don't move. You've got to rest before we make the trip back to town . . . Damn it, I left it somewhere around here when we came up.'

Denison watched her with disbelief. She had climbed up with him, had glided down with him. Yet he was half-dead with weariness and tension, and she was in the air with long kangaroo-leaps. She seemed a hundred yards away when she said, 'Here it is!' and her voice was as loud in his ears as when she was next to him.

She was back in a moment with a folded, paunchy sheet of plastic under her arm.

'Remember,' she said cheerily, 'when you asked on our way up what it was, and I said we'd be using it before we came down?' She unfolded it and spread it on the dusty surface of the Moon.

'A lunar lounge is its full name,' she said, 'but we just call it a lounge. We take the adjective for granted here on this world.' She inserted a cartridge and tripped a lever.

It began to fill. Somehow Denison had expected a hissing noise, but of course there was no air to carry sound.

'Before you question our conservation policies again,' said Selene, 'this is argon also.'

It blossomed into a mattress on six stubby legs. 'It will hold you,' she said. 'It makes very little actual contact with the ground and the vacuum all around will conserve its heat.'

'Don't tell me it's hot,' said Denison, amazed.

'The argon is heated as it pours in, but only relatively. It ends up at 270 degrees absolute, almost warm enough to melt ice, and quite warm enough to keep your insulated suit from losing heat faster than you can manufacture it.

Go ahead. Lie down.'

Denison did so, with a sensation of enormous luxury. 'Great!' he said with a long sigh.

'Mamma Selene thinks of everything,' she said.

She came from behind him now, gliding around him, her feet placed heel to heel as though she were on skates, and then let them fly out from under her, as she came down gracefully on hip and elbow on the ground just beside him.

Denison whistled. 'How did you do that?'

'Lots of practice! And don't you try it. You'll break your elbow.'

Some of the real findings on the Moon tended to destroy a few of the more interesting science fictional notions. For instance, to the best of our knowledge, there have always been not more than small traces of water on the Moon, and even these are vanishing. Our study of the Moon rocks has shown that. Yet, in the science fiction written before we reached the Moon, it was often assumed that there was some water on the Moon that might be frozen under the soil or chemically combined with the molecules of the crustal rock.

Even as late as 1972 I held on to the hope that this might be so despite the negative findings of the first astronauts on the Moon. Thus, here is another scene from The Gods Themselves. *This time Selene and Ben are inside the settlement.*

Denison tried to beat down his self-consciousness. Time and again, he made a groping motion as though to hitch upwards the trousers he wasn't wearing. He wore only sandals and the barest of briefs, which were uncomfortably tight. And, of course, he carried the blanket.

Selene, who was similarly accoutred, laughed. 'Now Ben, there's nothing wrong with your bare body, barring a certain flabbiness. It's perfectly in fashion here. In fact, take off your briefs if they're binding you.'

'No!' muttered Denison. He shifted the blanket so that it draped over his abdomen and she snatched it from him.

She said, 'Now give me that thing. What kind of a Lunarite will you make if you bring your Earth puritanism here? You *know* that prudery is only the other side of prurience. The words are even on the same page in the dictionary.'

'I have to get used to it, Selene.'

'You might start by looking at me once in a while without having your glance slide off me as though I were coated with oil. You look at other women quite efficiently, I notice.'

'If I look at you –'

'Then you'll seem too interested and you'll be embarrassed. But if you look hard, you'll get used to it, and you'll stop noticing. Look, I'll stand still and you stare. I'll take off my briefs.'

Denison groaned. 'Selene, there are people all around and you're making intolerable fun of me. Please keep walking and let me get used to the situation.'

'All right, but I hope you notice the people who pass us don't look at us.'

'They don't look at *you*. They look at me all right. They've probably never seen so old-looking and ill-shaped a person.'

'They probably haven't,' agreed Selene cheerfully, 'but they'll just have to get used to it.'

Denison walked on in misery, conscious of every grey hair on his chest and of every quiver of his paunch. It was only when the passageway thinned out and the people passing them were fewer in number that he began to feel a certain relief.

He looked about him curiously now, not as aware of Selene's conical breasts as he had been, nor of her smooth thighs. The corridor seemed endless.

'How far have we come?' he asked.

'Are you tired?' Selene was contrite. 'We could have taken a scooter. I forget you're from Earth.'

'I should hope you do. Isn't that the ideal for an immigrant? I'm not the least bit tired. Hardly the least bit tired at any rate. What I am is a little cold.'

'Purely your imagination, Ben,' said Selene firmly. 'You just think you ought to feel cold because so much of you is bare. Put it out of your head.'

'Easy to say,' he sighed. 'I'm walking well, I hope.'

'Very well. I'll have you kangarooing yet.'

'And participating in glider races down the surface slopes. Remember, I'm moderately advanced in years. But really, how far have we come?'

'Two miles, I should judge.'

'Good Lord! How many miles of corridors are there altogether?'

'I'm afraid I don't know. The residential corridors make up comparatively little of the total. There are the mining corridors, the geological ones, the industrial, the mycological . . . I'm sure there must be several hundred miles altogether.'

'Do you have maps?'

'Of course there are maps. We can't work blind.'

'I mean you, personally.'

'Well, no, not with me, but I don't need maps for this area; it's quite familiar to me. I used to wander about here as a child. These are old corridors. Most of the new corridors – and we average two or three miles of new corridors a year, I think – are in the north. I couldn't work my way through them, without a map, for untold sums. Maybe not even with a map.'

'Where are we heading?'

'I promised you an unusual sight – no, not me, so don't say it – and you'll have it. It's the Moon's most unusual mine and it's completely off the ordinary tourist trails.'

'Don't tell me you've got diamonds on the Moon?'

'Better than that.'

The corridor walls were unfinished here – grey rock,

dimly but adequately lit by patches of electroluminescence. The temperature was comfortable and at a steady mildness, with ventilation so gently effective there was no sensation of wind. It was hard to tell here that a couple of hundred feet above was a surface subjected to alternate frying and freezing as the Sun came and went on its grand bi-weekly swing from horizon to horizon and then underneath and back.

'Is all this airtight?' asked Denison, suddenly uncomfortably aware that he was not far below the bottom of an ocean of vacuum that extended upwards through infinity.

'Oh, yes. Those walls are impervious. They're all booby-trapped, too. If the air pressure drops as much as ten per cent in any section of the corridors there is a hooting and howling from sirens such as you've never heard and a flashing of arrows and blazing of signs directing you to safety such as you've never seen.'

'How often does this happen?'

'Not often. I don't think anyone has been killed through air-lack in at least five years.' Then, with sudden defensiveness, 'You have natural catastrophes on Earth. A big quake or a tidal wave can kill thousands.'

'No argument, Selene.' He threw up his hands. 'I surrender.'

'All right,' she said. 'I didn't mean to get excited . . . Do you hear that?'

She stopped in an attitude of listening.

Denison listened, too, and shook his head. Suddenly, he looked around. 'It's so quiet. Where is everybody? Are you sure we're not lost?'

'This isn't a natural cavern with unknown passageways. You have those on Earth, haven't you? I've seen photographs.'

'Yes, most of them are limestone caves formed by water. That certainly can't be the case on the Moon, can it?'

'So we can't be lost,' said Selene, smiling. 'If we're alone, put it down to superstition.'

'To what?' Denison looked startled and his face creased

in an expression of disbelief.

'Don't do that,' she said. 'You get all lined. That's right. Smooth out. You look much better than you did when you first arrived, you know. That's low gravity and exercise.'

'And trying to keep up with nude young ladies who have an uncommon amount of time off and an uncommon lack of better things to do than to go on busmen's holidays.'

'Now you're treating me like a tourist guide again, and I'm not nude,' Selene retorted.

'At that, even nudity is less frightening than Intuitionism . . . But what's this about superstition?'

'Not really superstition, I suppose, but most of the people of the city tend to stay away from this part of the corridor complex.'

'But why?'

'Because of what I'm going to show you.' They were walking again. 'Hear it now?'

She stopped and Denison listened anxiously. He said, 'You mean that small tapping sound? *Tap – tap*. Is that what you mean?'

She loped ahead with the slow-motion movement of the Lunarite in unhurried flight. He followed her, attempting to ape the gait.

'Here – here –'

Denison's eye followed Selene's eagerly pointing finger. 'Good Lord,' he said. 'Where's it coming from?'

There was a drip of what was clearly water; a slow dripping, with each drip striking a small ceramic trough that led into the rock wall.

'From the rocks. We do have water on the moon, you know. Most of it we can bake out of gypsum; enough for our purposes, since we conserve it pretty well.'

'I know. I know. I've never yet been able to manage one complete shower. How you people manage to stay clean I don't know.'

'I *told* you. First, wet yourself. Then turn off the water

and smear just a little detergent on you. You rub it – Oh, Ben, I'm not going through it yet again. And there's nothing on the Moon to get you all that dirty anyway . . . But that's not what we're talking about. In one or two places there are actually water deposits, usually in the form of ice near the surface in the shadow of a mountain. If we locate it, it drips out. This one has been dripping since the corridor was first driven through, and that was eight years ago.'

'But why the superstition?'

'Well, obviously, water is the great material resource on which the Moon depends. We drink it, wash with it, grow our food with it, make our oxygen with it, keep everything going with it. Free water can't help but get a lot of respect. Once this drip was discovered, plans to extend the tunnels in this direction were abandoned till it stopped. The corridor walls were even left unfinished.'

'That sounds like superstition right there.'

'Well – a kind of awe, maybe. It wasn't expected to last for more than a few months; such drips never do. But after this one had passed its first anniversary, it began to seem eternal. In fact, that's what it's called: The Eternal. You'll even find it marked that way on the maps. Naturally people have come to attach importance to it, a feeling that if it stops it will mean some sort of bad fortune.'

Denison laughed.

Selene said warmly, 'No one *really* believes it, but everyone part-believes it. You see, it's not really eternal; it must stop sometime. As a matter of fact, the rate of drip is only about a third of what it was when it was first discovered, so that it is slowly drying. I imagine people feel that if it happened to stop when they were actually here, they would share in the bad fortune. At least, that's the rational way of explaining their reluctance to come here.'

'I take it that you don't believe this.'

'Whether I believe it or not isn't the point. You see, I'm quite certain that it won't stop sharply enough for anyone to be able to take the blame. It will just drip slower and slower and slower and no one will ever be able to pinpoint the exact time when it stopped. So why worry?'

'I agree with you.'

At the start, my writing consisted almost entirely of science fiction. Of my first hundred books, nearly one third is science fiction. That fell off with time, however. Of my second hundred books, only thirteen can be considered science fiction under even the most liberal interpretation.

That did not end my concern with astronomy, however, for I continued to deal with it in my non-fiction and for every age level.

I wrote some picture books for Walker & Company, for instance, at the suggestion of Beth Walker. They were ABC books, actually, in which two words were defined for each letter of the alphabet. The idea was that an eight-year-old could read the definitions (or, at least, have an adult read it to him) and then be fascinated by the pictures.

The first and most successful of these was ABC's of Space (Book 101), which was published in 1969. Here, for instance, are the definitions of the two words under O:

from ABC'S OF SPACE *(1969)*

O is for *Ocean of Storms*

a dark, smooth area on the Moon where the first unmanned spaceship landed in 1966. It is not really an ocean, because there is probably no water on the Moon. There are no storms either, but we still use the name.

o is for *orbit*

the path a small world takes around a larger one. The

Moon moves in an orbit around the Earth. The Earth moves in an orbit around the Sun. Both orbits are almost like circles. An orbit is also the path a spaceship takes around the Earth or Moon.

I was not particularly fond of the ABC books, of which three others were published by Walker by 1972. These were ABC's of the Ocean (Book 107), ABC's of the Earth (Book 117), and ABC's of Ecology (Book 124). The ABC format didn't leave me enough scope.

I did, however, start another series of books for Walker & Company with which I had a good deal more fun.

The title of each book in the series, which was originally suggested by my editor, Millicent Selsam, was to begin How Did We Find Out. *They were to deal with science history on a junior high school level.*

The first one of these was How Did We Find Out the Earth Is Round? *(Book 133), which Walker published in 1973. Writing the book was sheer pleasure, and I knew I had something I would continue. Indeed, of my second hundred books, no fewer than thirteen are members of the* How Did We Find Out *series.*

One of the things that made the series pleasurable for me was that the books varied widely in subject matter. Three of them dealt with astronomy, four with physics, two with biology, one with mathematics, one with chemistry, one with geology, and one with anthropology.

One of the 'astronomicals' was How Did We Find Out About Comets? *(Book 162), which was published in 1975. Millie requested that topic during the hullabaloo concerning the then forthcoming comet Kohoutek. Though, alas, the comet fizzled, the book certainly remained valid. Here's how I handled the way in which cometary orbits were finally worked out.*

from HOW DID WE FIND OUT ABOUT COMETS (1975)

A German astronomer, Johannes Kepler, who had been one of Tycho's assistants, disagreed with part of Copernicus's theory. After studying the motions of the planets in the sky, Kepler said, in 1609, that the planets moved around the sun in orbits that were not circles. Each planet moved around the sun in an 'ellipse'.

An ellipse looks like a flattened circle. It can be so slightly flattened that you cannot tell it from a circle. It can be more flattened, so that you can see at a glance that it is not a circle. Or it can be very flattened, so that it looks long and thin, something like a cigar.

The orbit of the earth around the sun is an ellipse that is only very slightly flattened. It is almost circular. The moon's orbit around the earth is more flattened, and Mercury's orbit around the sun is still more flattened. Even Mercury's orbit, which is more flattened than that of any other planet known in Kepler's time, is not *very* flattened. Its orbit still looks like a circle.

The sun is not at the very centre of the elliptical orbits of the planets around it. The flatter the ellipse, the closer one end of it is to the sun.

When the earth moves around the sun, it is only 91,500,000 miles from the sun at one end of its orbit, but 94,500,000 miles from the sun at the other end. The further distance is less than 4 per cent greater than the nearer distance.

Mercury's orbit around the sun is more elliptical, so there is a bigger difference. When Mercury is at the end of the ellipse nearer the sun, it is only 28,000,000 miles away. At the other end, it is 44,000,000 miles from the sun. The further distance is about 50 per cent greater than the nearer distance.

Kepler was able to work out elliptical orbits for all the planets, but what about the comets? If they were heavenly bodies, did that mean they had orbits, too?

Kepler carefully studied the reports he had about the

changing positions of comets in the sky. Finally, he decided that comets must move in straight lines. He thought they came from far out in space, passed near the sun, then travelled onward far out in space in the other direction.

They could only be seen when they were close to the sun and reflected its light. Before they came close enough to the sun, they could not be seen. After they moved far enough from the sun, they again could not be seen. According to Kepler's view, comets were not part of the solar system. Each comet just passed through the solar system once and was never seen again.

An Italian astronomer, Giovanni Alfonso Borelli, carefully studied the positions of a comet that appeared in the sky in 1664. He found he had to disagree with Kepler.

The only way to make sense out of the path the comet took across the sky, Borelli said, was to suppose that it changed direction as it passed the sun. It came closer and closer to the sun, along a line that was nearly straight. Then it moved around the sun, and left along a line that was again nearly straight but had changed direction.

The way Borelli explained this was to point out that ellipses could be very flattened indeed. They could be so flattened that they would resemble a very long, thin cigar. In fact, if you imagined an ellipse that was more and more flattened, and longer and longer, you could eventually imagine one that was so flattened it just went on and on forever. Such an ellipse would be closed only at one end. In the other direction, it would never be closed, but would just go on and on. A one-ended ellipse that goes on and on forever is called a 'parabola'.

Borelli decided that a comet's orbit was a parabola, with the sun very near the closed end. The comet came in at one side of the parabola, went whizzing around the sun, and then moved outwards along the other side of the parabola.

Borelli's view was like that of Kepler, except that the orbit he conceived was not a straight line. Like Kepler,

Borelli thought a comet was originally so far away it could not be seen. As it came closer and closer to the sun, it grew bright enough to be seen, and then as it went further and further from the sun, it once more became too dim to be seen. In Borelli's view, as in Kepler's, the comets were not members of the solar system. Each comet just passed through the solar system once and never returned.

Kepler's notion of elliptical orbits worked very well for the planets, but there were lots of questions left. Why did the planets go around the sun in ellipses instead of circles (or some other curve)? Why did planets move faster when they were nearer the sun than when they were further away?

These questions and many others were answered by the English scientist Isaac Newton. In 1687, he published a book in which he described his theory of universal gravitation. According to this theory, every body in the universe attracted every other body. The strength of the attraction between two particular bodies depended on the 'mass' of each body (how much matter it contained) and on how far apart the two bodies were. The strength of the attraction could be calculated by a simple mathematical equation.

Newton showed how to use the equation to work out the exact orbit of the moon around the earth and of the planets around the sun.

The same equation explained why each planet moved quickly at some times and slowly at other times, and why some planets moved faster than others. It explained little changes in the motion of the planets that were produced by the tiny pulls of one planet on another even as all were caught in the gigantic pull of the much larger sun. It explained the tides on the earth and many other things, too.

But comets were the one set of heavenly bodies that remained puzzling. If comets travelled in orbits that were parabolas, Newton's theory could account for that fact.

Suppose, though, the orbits were not quite parabolas. Suppose the orbits were just very long ellipses and were closed at the other end.

We can only observe the comet at the end of the orbit near the sun. The shape of that small part of the enormous orbit would be a narrow curve if the ellipse were very long. The shape would be slightly wider, if the ellipse were even longer, and still wider if the ellipse never closed at all and were a parabola.

The differences in the shapes of the small bit of orbit we could see, as predicted by Newton's theory, were so tiny that astronomers in Newton's time could not tell them apart. They couldn't really say whether the orbit of a comet was a very long ellipse or whether it was a parabola.

It made a difference. If a comet's orbit were a parabola, it would visit the solar system once and would never be seen again. If the orbit were a very, very long ellipse, then eventually the comet would come to the other end of the ellipse, turn around, and begin to approach the sun again. The comet would return.

In fact, if astronomers could calculate the exact length of the orbit, they could even predict *when* the comet would return. That would be a big victory for Newton's theory.

Newton had a young friend, Edmund Halley, who had helped Newton publish his book and who was interested in the comet problem.

In 1682, a comet appeared and Halley very carefully studied its positions and the way it moved across the sky. From the part of the orbit he could see, he couldn't tell whether it would ever return.

It seemed to him, though, that if a comet did return it should do so at regular periods – every so many years – and that it should always trace the same curve across the sky. He therefore began to collect all the reports on the positions of earlier comets that he could find. By 1705, he had collected good reports on two dozen comets of the past and began to compare them.

He noticed that the comet of 1682, which he had himself observed, followed the same curve across the sky that the comet of 1607 had. The same curve had also been followed by the comet of 1532 (which Fracastoro and Apian had studied) and the comet of 1456.

These comets had come at seventy-five- or seventy-six-year periods. Could it be that it was a single comet that returned every seventy-five years or so? Could it be that it was a 'periodic comet'?

Halley worked out the orbit for a comet that returned every seventy-five years and followed the same curve in the sky that the comet of 1682 had followed.

The results were quite amazing. Saturn, the planet furthest from the sun (as far as was known in Halley's time) was never further from the sun than 930,000,000 miles. The comet of 1682, however, moved out as far as 3,200,000,000 miles from the sun before it reached the other end of its elliptical orbit and began moving inwards again. The comet moved over three times as far away from the sun as Saturn ever moved.

On the other hand, when the comet passed along the end of the ellipse that was near the sun, it came as close as 54,000,000 miles from the sun. This was only about half of earth's distance from the sun.

After Halley had calculated the orbit, he announced that the comet of 1682 would return some time in 1758 and would follow a particular path across the sky.

Halley did not live long enough to see the comet's return. He was eighty-six years old when he died in 1742, but that was much too soon to see the return.

There were, however, others who were watching for it. A French astronomer, Alexis Claude Clairault, considered the orbit as outlined by Halley. He realized that the gravitational pull of the large planets, Jupiter and Saturn, would delay the comet a little bit. It would not pass around the sun till some time in 1759.

In 1758, astronomers eagerly watched that part of the sky in which Halley had said the comet should appear.

They did not have to depend only on their eyes as Tycho and earlier astronomers had done. The telescope had been invented in 1609.

On December 25, 1758, Christmas Day, a German farmer named Johann Georg Palitzch, who was an amateur astronomer, spotted the comet. The comet of 1682 appeared in the sky where Halley had said it would and proceeded to move along the path Halley had predicted for it. It moved around the sun quite close to the time Clairault had predicted.

There was no question that it was the comet of 1682 and that it had returned. That meant that some of the mystery of comets was cleared up. They followed the same rules as the other bodies of the solar system except that their orbits were more elliptical.

Naturally, the comet of 1682 that returned and passed around the sun in 1759 came to be called 'Halley's comet'.

Halley's comet is the most famous comet there is. It happens to be the one that was in the sky in 1066 when William of Normandy was preparing to invade England. It was also in the sky in 11 B.C., about the time when Jesus may have been born. Some people think it may have been the Star of Bethlehem.

Halley's comet has returned twice since Palitzch saw it. It came back in 1835 and was glowing in the sky when Mark Twain was born. Then it came back in 1910 and Mark Twain died when it was glowing in the sky. It will come back yet again in 1986.

Writing for different age levels has its problems, of course, since the boundaries are not clear. I let myself be guided by instinct, and if I must err, I prefer to err on the side of difficulty. I like to think that the kind of youngster who is interested in my books would rather stretch a little and stand on his mental tiptoes than stoop to something he might consider babyish.

Thus, for Follett Publishing Company, I did a series of eight books on science that were intended for an age level higher than that of my ABC books and lower than that of my How Did We Find Out books.

The first four of the Follett series were published among my first hundred books, but the second four, including three on astronomy, were in my second hundred books. They are Comets and Meteors *(Book 134),* The Sun *(Book 135), and* The Solar System *(Book 160). Here is how I handled the matter of cometary orbits in* Comets and Meteors*:*

from COMETS AND METEORS *(1973)*

Comets go around the sun the way planets do, but with a difference. Planets move in paths, called 'orbits', that are nearly circles. They stay almost the same distance from the sun all the time. Comets move in orbits that are long and narrow. Both comet orbits and planet orbits are 'ellipses'.

At one end of the orbit, comets pass near the sun, perhaps only a few million miles away. At the other end, they are much further away, sometimes further than any planet. At this point, they are billions of miles away from the sun.

A comet has no light of its own. To be seen, it must be near a large bright object, like the sun. Sunlight makes a comet shine.

Comets get very little sunlight at the far end of their orbits. They are small and dim then. They cannot be seen even with a telescope. As they move closer to the sun, they get more sunlight. They become bright enough to be seen.

People see comets only at the end of their orbits close to the sun. Then they are close to the earth, too.

Centuries ago, people believed that comets came from nowhere. They couldn't tell when another comet might come.

About three hundred years ago, an English astronomer, Edmund Halley, studied records of comets that had been seen. He found that every seventy-six years or so, a comet crossed a certain part of the sky. He decided it must be a single comet that came close to the sun every seventy-six years.

Halley said the comet would come back in 1758 and cross the same part of the sky. By then, Halley was dead. But the comet returned just as he said it would. It is known as Halley's comet for that reason.

This business of aiming high for each age group means that almost no effort is involved if I aim for the teenage market. I always assume that a teenager is as intelligent as an adult and has the vocabulary of one. What he lacks is merely the opportunity to have read as widely as an adult. (Naturally, I am talking of an intelligent, well-read adult.)

Consequently, in writing for teenagers, I take particular care to make no assumptions of previous knowledge and to explain everything that doesn't come within the range of common experience – but I make sure I use a full vocabulary to do so. Teenagers are sensitive (and rightly so) to any hint of condescension.

Included among my second hundred books are three on astronomy for teenagers, which I wrote at the suggestion of Chaucy Bennetts of Lothrop, Lee & Shepard Company. She is a very capable editor who, coincidentally, became my cousin by marriage after the series started. The three books are Jupiter, the Largest Planet *(Book 139);* Alpha Centauri, the Nearest Star *(Book 179); and* Mars, the Red Planet *(Book 188). Here are two excerpts from* Alpha Centauri:

from ALPHA CENTAURI, THE NEAREST STAR
(1976)

In the case of the Alpha Centauri system, the average

separation of the two stars Alpha Centauri A and Alpha Centauri B is greater than that of Uranus and the sun, and less than that of Neptune and the sun. If the Alpha Centauri system were superimposed on the solar system, however, with Alpha Centauri A in place of our sun, Alpha Centauri B would not take up a circular orbit between those of Uranus and Neptune. Things would be a little more complicated than that.

If the orbit of an object moving around a star were an exact circle, the star would remain at the precise centre of the orbit and that would represent a very simple situation. Actually, the orbit is always an ellipse, a kind of flattened circle. An ellipse has a major axis (its longest diameter) and a minor axis (its shortest diameter). The centre of the ellipse is at the point where the two axes cross.

There are two focus points, or foci, in the ellipse. They are located on the major axis, one on each side of the centre and at an equal distance from it. The more flattened the ellipse, the further the foci are from the centre and the closer they are to the ends.

These foci are located in such a way that if a straight line is drawn from one focus to any point on the ellipse, and another straight line is drawn from that point to the other focus, the sum of the lengths of the two straight lines is always the same and always equal in size to the major axis.

As it happens, when an object moves about a star in an elliptical orbit, the star is always at one of the foci and is, therefore, nearer to one end of the orbit than to the other. If the ellipse is very flattened, the star is far to one end and the orbiting object is very close to the star at that end of the orbit and very far from it at the other end.

The point of closest approach is called the 'periastron', from Greek words meaning 'near the star'. The furthest point is the 'apastron', from Greek words meaning 'away from the star'.

In a binary system both stars, under the pull of gravity,

move in orbits around a point between them called the 'centre of gravity'. As they move, both stars always remain on opposite sides of the centre of gravity, and the larger star is always closer to it. This means that although both stars have orbits that are ellipses of the same shape, the larger star always moves through the smaller orbit.

When one object in a binary system is very much larger than the other, it makes such a small ellipse about the centre of gravity that it is practically stationary. This is true of the sun and Earth, for instance, where the sun scarcely moves at all while tiny Earth moves in a large ellipse.

It is always possible, however, to suppose that the larger of two objects in a binary system is standing still and to calculate the orbit of the smaller about it. This distorts the situation relative to observers in other planetary systems – relative to us, for instance. However, if we could imagine ourselves observing the binary system from the larger of the two stars, what we would observe would be the smaller star moving about a motionless larger one.

When astronomers observe a binary system, they are not at all likely to be viewing it from directly above, so to speak, so as to see the elliptical orbits marked out exactly as they are. They usually view the orbits from a tilted position, so that the ellipses they see are not the ellipses marked out by the orbiting stars. What they see are ellipses that are more flattened, sometimes very much more flattened. In these distorted ellipses, however, the larger star, which is supposed to be stationary, is not at the focus of the smaller star's orbit. If astronomers tilt the orbit, in imagination, until the star moves into the focus, they get the true ellipse.

The degree of flattening of an ellipse is measured as its 'eccentricity' (from Greek words meaning 'out of centre'), since the greater the eccentricity, the further the foci are from the centre. The eccentricity of a circle, which is not flattened at all, is 0. For an ellipse, the eccentricity is always between 0 and 1. If an ellipse has a low eccentricity, say, less than 0.1, it is so slightly flattened that to the eye it looks very much like a circle. The flatter an ellipse is, the more it approaches a value of 1. An orbit with an eccentricity of 0.9, then, looks quite cigar-shaped.

An example of a high degree of eccentricity in a binary system is Gamma Virginis, where the eccentricity is 0.88. This means that the distance from the centre of the ellipse to the focus is 0.88 times the distance from the centre of the ellipse to the end. With the larger star at one focus, the end of the orbit of the other star in the direction of that focus (the periastron) is only 0.12 times the distance from the centre and only 0.06 times the entire width of the ellipse from end to end. The other end of the ellipse (the apastron) is distant from the larger star by an amount equal to 0.94 times the entire width of the ellipse.

In the case of Gamma Virginis, then, although the average distance separating the two stars of the binary is 6,800,000,000 kilometres (4,200,000,000 miles), at periastron the distance of separation is only 810,000,000 kilometres (500,000,000 miles) while at apastron it is 12,800,000,000 kilometres (7,900,000,000 miles).

In other words, the two stars of Gamma Virginis, as they circle each other, swoop together to a separating distance equal to that of Jupiter and the sun, and then move apart to a distance more than twice that between Pluto and the sun. (The system was at apastron in 1920 and the two stars have been moving closer ever since. They will be at periastron in 2006.)

In general, stars separated by quite a large average distance are likely to have large eccentricities. A binary like Capella with an average separation of only 84,000,000 kilometres (52,000,000 miles) has quite a low eccentricity, one of only 0.0086. This means that the distance between the two stars of the Capella system varies from 83,300,000 kilometres (51,600,000 miles) at periastron to 84,700,000 kilometres (52,400,000 miles) at apastron.

This is so small a change that from the standpoint of

one of the stars of the Capella system, the other would scarcely seem to change in brightness during the 104-day period of revolution. In the case of Gamma Virginis, on the other hand, an observer near one of the stars would see the other as 250 times brighter at periastron than at apastron.

The eccentricities of the planetary orbits of the solar system, by the way, are much more like those of the Capella stars than those of the Gamma Virginis stars. The eccentricities of the orbits of Venus and Neptune are just about those of the Capella system, while that of Earth (0.017) is only a little higher. This is a good thing, too, for a highly eccentric orbit would introduce such changes in temperature in the course of the year that a planet with even a suitable average distance from its sun might prove uninhabitable.

Let us take, now, a group of binaries that have average separations of about 3.0 to 3.5 billion kilometres (1.9 to 2.2 billion miles), a group that includes the Alpha Centauri system. In the table below, the eccentricity and the distances at periastron and apastron are given for this group.

Eccentricities of Binary Systems

STAR SYSTEM	ECCEN-TRICITY	PERIASTRON		APASTRON	
		MILLIONS OF		MILLIONS OF	
		KILO-METRES	MILES	KILO-METRES	MILES
70 Ophiuchi	0.50	1,750	1,100	5,250	3,300
Zeta Sagittarii	0.2	2,700	1,700	4,300	2,700
Alpha Centauri	**0.521**	**1,700**	**1,000**	**5,300**	**3,400**
Eta Ophiuchi	0.90	320	200	6,080	3,800
Zeta Cancri	0.31	2,200	1,350	4,100	2,570
Sirius	0.575	1,280	800	4,720	3,000
Xi Scorpii	0.74	780	500	5,200	3,300

As you see, the apastrons are not extraordinarily different, varying from 4,100 to 6,080 million kilometres (2,570 to 3,800 million miles), a difference of only about 50 per cent. The periastrons differ, however, from 320 to 2,700 million kilometres (200 to 1,700 miles), a difference of 800 per cent.

The Alpha Centauri system is rather intermediate with respect to eccentricity. The orbits of the two stars Alpha Centauri A and B are more eccentric than those of the planets of our solar system, but less eccentric than those of some of the comets, asteroids, and satellites of our solar system.

If Alpha Centauri A were in the place of our sun, then Alpha Centauri B at its furthest would be 5,300,000,000 kilometres (3,400,000,000 miles) away, or just about at the average distance of Pluto from our sun. From Earth's position near Alpha Centauri A, Alpha Centauri B would seem a starlike point, but it would be far brighter than any star we see in our own sky. It would shine with a brilliance about 100 times greater than our full moon, though it would still be only 1/4500 as bright as Alpha Centauri A or our sun.

From its furthest point, however, Alpha Centauri B would slowly decrease its distance to Alpha Centauri A (and ourselves) as it moved along its orbit, until after forty years it would be at periastron and only 1,700,000,000 kilometres (1,000,000,000 miles) from Alpha Centauri A. At that point it would be a little further from Alpha Centauri A than Saturn is from the sun. And when Earth would be on the side of its orbit towards Alpha Centauri B, the companion star would be only 1,550,000,000 kilometres (900,000,000 miles) from us.

At that distance, Alpha Centauri B would be a little over 14 times as bright as at apastron. It would be 1,400 times as bright as the full moon, but still only 1/326 as bright as Alpha Centauri A.

Suppose Alpha Centauri B were in place of our sun, and that we calculated the orbit of Alpha Centauri A on the assumption that Alpha Centauri B was motionless. Alpha Centauri A would then seem to move in the same orbit that Alpha Centauri B had in the other case.*

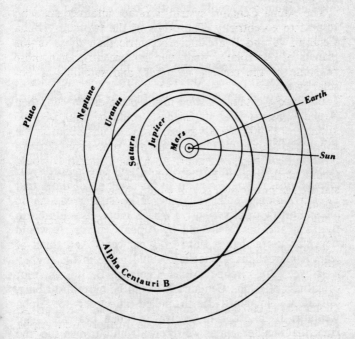

*The Orbit of Alpha Centauri B
superimposed on our solar system*

* Because Alpha Centauri B is the smaller of the two stars, it seems to move in the larger orbit of the two when viewed from *outside* the system. When viewed from inside the system, however, an observer on each star would see the other moving in the same orbit. Thus, on Earth, if we pretend that the Earth is motionless, the sun moves in an orbit about the Earth that is just like the orbit that the Earth (in reality) moves in as it circles the sun.

Viewed from an Earth that was circling Alpha Centauri B instead of our own sun, Alpha Centauri A would go through the same period of brightening as it moved from apastron to periastron, and the same period of dimming as it moved back to apastron. However, since Alpha Centauri A is $3\frac{1}{4}$ times as bright as Alpha Centauri B, Alpha Centauri A would seem that much brighter at every point in its orbit. At its brightest, it would be 5,000 times brighter than our full moon now, and 1/100 as bright as our sun appears to us. Since Alpha Centauri B would appear dimmer than the sun, if we imagined the former in the latter's place, Alpha Centauri A at its closest approach would appear 1/30 as bright as Alpha Centauri B.

If we were circling Alpha Centauri A instead of the sun, the presence of Alpha Centauri B would cause us no trouble. Despite the eccentricity of its orbit, which allows Alpha Centauri B to swoop in and pull out in forty-year alternations, it would remain so far away at all times that its gravitational pull would never be strong enough to affect Earth's orbit seriously. What's more, its addition to the light and heat delivered by Alpha Centauri A would never be more than a third of 1 per cent. And think of what a marvellous spectacle it would make in the sky.

If we were circling Alpha Centauri B, the superior brightness of Alpha Centauri A would be more disturbing, but if we imagined Earth pulled in closer to Alpha Centauri B in order to receive as much heat and light from that smaller sun as we receive from our own sun, the interference of Alpha Centauri A would not be too disturbing.

And what about Alpha Centauri C – Proxima Centauri – which is the distant companion of the Alpha Centauri A/B binary? Even though it would be far nearer to us, if Earth were circling either Alpha Centauri A or Alpha Centauri B, than any star is to us in our own solar system, it would not be at all bright. It would be a fairly dim star of magnitude 3.7. What's more, its proper motion, as a result of its 1,300,000-year-long revolution around the centre of gravity of the system, would be just about exactly 1 second of arc per year.

Neither its brightness nor its proper motion would attract much attention, and stargazers might look at the sky forever and not suspect this dim star of belonging to their own system. The only giveaway would come when astronomers decided to make a routine check of the parallaxes of the various visible stars in the sky. After a month or so, they would begin to get a hint of an extraordinarily large parallax and in the end they would measure one of 20 seconds of arc, which would be so much higher than that of any other star that they would at once suspect it of being a member of their own system.

Can there be a dim star somewhere out there that belongs to our own solar system? Can it be that we remain unaware of it because astronomers haven't happened to study it closely enough to detect an unusually high parallax? It isn't very likely – but it is conceivable.

In general, the hotter a star is, the brighter it is. It's no surprise, therefore, that so many of the bright stars in the sky are hotter than the sun is, or that so many of the dim stars we see are cooler than the sun is.

What *is* surprising is that some stars are cool and yet are very bright. The two prime examples of this are Antares and Betelgeuse. Both are in spectral class M and are therefore possessed of a surface temperature of only 3000° C or so and, what's more, neither one is particularly close to us – and yet each is among the brightest stars in the sky.

In 1905 a Danish astronomer, Ejnar Hertzsprung, reasoned that a cool star must have a dim surface, but if it had a very large surface, the dimness of each bit would add up to a great *total* brightness. In other words, a bright star that was cool and red had to be a very large star indeed in order to be bright.

Hertzsprung published this idea in a journal of photography, and astronomers didn't notice it. Then, in 1914, the American astronomer Henry Norris Russell had the same idea independently, and this time the idea stuck. Both astronomers are usually given credit.

The Hertzsprung–Russell reasoning led to the concept of 'red giants' among the stars. When attempts were made to calculate how large these red giants would have to be in order to be as bright as they were despite their low surface temperature, the results seemed almost unbelievable. In 1920, however, the German-American physicist Albert Abraham Michelson was able to check the matter directly.

To do this, he made use of an instrument he had invented twenty years earlier, an instrument he called an interferometer. It was capable of measuring, with great delicacy, the manner in which two trains of light waves, which were not quite parallel to each other, interfered with each other. When such trains of light waves were not quite parallel, the waves as they merged sometimes reinforced each other and sometimes cancelled each other, setting up patterns of alternate light and dark. From the details of such an interference pattern, the exact angle at which the light waves met could be deduced.

Such an instrument can be applied to the stars. A star is so small, as seen from Earth, that it is virtually a dot of light. The light rays coming from the two opposite edges of so tiny a dot seem to come to us almost from the same direction, and are therefore almost parallel – almost, *but not quite*. The light rays come from very slightly different directions as they reach us from opposite sides of a star; they converge just a tiny bit, enough to produce an interference pattern if the interferometer is large enough.

Michelson made use of a twenty-foot interferometer, the largest he had constructed up to that time. He attached it to the new hundred-inch telescope that had just been put into use at Mount Wilson in California, and which was then the largest telescope in the world. He turned this instrument on the star Betelgeuse.

From the nature of the interference pattern, Michelson could determine the apparent diameter of Betelgeuse. It turned out to be 0.045 seconds of arc. This is a very small width, for it would take 41,500 little dots of reddish light just like Betelgeuse, placed side by side, to stretch across the width of the moon.

Yet, Betelgeuse has the largest apparent diameter of any star. Any star that has a true size greater than Betelgeuse is so far away as to have a smaller apparent size. Then, too, any star that is closer than Betelgeuse is so much smaller in true size that its apparent size never comes up to the Betelgeuse mark.

To be even 0.045 seconds in diameter – tiny though that angle is – at the vast distance of Betelgeuse, the star must have an enormous real diameter. In fact, it turns out that the diameter of Betelgeuse is at least 800 times that of the sun.

The interferometer result showed that the reasoning of Hertzsprung and Russell was correct and there really were red giant stars, with Betelgeuse, large as it is, not the largest in actual size. In the table below, the diameters of some of the giant stars are given.

The large red giants would seem to be impressive objects indeed. Imagine Betelgeuse in place of our sun. We could not see it from Earth, because there would be no Earth. The place where Earth would be, if it existed, would be *within* Betelgeuse. The diameter of Betelgeuse is so large that, if substituted for the sun, it would include the orbits of Mercury, Venus, Earth, Mars, and Jupiter.

Epsilon Aurigae B would do better than that. It would swallow up the orbit of Saturn as well, and its surface would be nearly at the orbit of Uranus. What's more, that supergiant Epsilon Aurigae B is part of a binary system, with the other star, Epsilon Aurigae A, considerably smaller but still large enough to swallow up the orbit of Mars. What a view those stars must be from not too nearby.

Giant Stars

DIAMETER

STAR	MILLIONS OF KILOMETRES	MILLIONS OF MILES	SUN = 1
Epsilon Aurigae B	2,800	1,700	2,000
VV Cephei A	1,700	1,200	1,400
Betelgeuse	1,100	700	800
Mira (Omicron Ceti)	550	350	400
Antares	550	350	400
Xi Aurigae A	420	260	300
Epsilon Aurigae A	280	170	200
Beta Pegasi	150	95	110
Aldebaran	61	38	44
Arcturus	37	23	27

Another way of emphasizing the size of the red giants is to imagine a hollow sphere the size of Beta Pegasi, which is only a moderate-sized giant. It would still be large enough to hold 1,300,000 objects the size of our sun. A hollow sphere the size of Betelgeuse would hold nearly 43,000,000 objects the size of our sun, and one the size of Epsilon Aurigae B would hold 8,000,000,000 suns.

And yet, for all that, the red giants are perhaps not as impressive as they seem from their size alone. They are more massive than the sun, but not very much more massive. Betelgeuse might take up 43,000,000 times as much space as the sun does, but the red giant is only about 20 times as massive as the sun; it contains only 20 times as much matter.

If the mass of Betelgeuse (not so very great) is spread over the enormous volume taken up by Betelgeuse, that mass must be spread very, very thin.

The sun's average density is 1.41 grams per cubic centimetre, but Betelgeuse's average density is 1/10,000,000 of that. If the sun were only as dense, on the average, as Betelgeuse is, it would have a mass of not more than

1/30 that of the Earth, and only 2.7 times that of the moon.

Epsilon Aurigae B would be far less dense. The red giants are thin collections of gas that stretch out over enormous distances and glow red-hot, but on an earthly scale they are almost vacuums. The average density of Epsilon Aurigae B is only 1/1000 that of Earth's atmosphere, and in its outer regions the density is far less even than that. (Like all objects, red giants get denser as one approaches their centres, and in the core they can get very dense indeed. This must be true of all stars, since only in a very dense core can the nuclear conflagration that powers them be ignited.)

A situation the reverse of the red giants' arose in connection with Sirius B. That was known to be a very dim star with a magnitude of 10 and a luminosity only 1/130 that of our sun. It was taken for granted that it had to be both small and cool to deliver only 1/130 as much light as our sun.

In 1915, however, the American astronomer Walter Sydney Adams succeeded in taking the spectrum of Sirius B and found it to be just as hot as Sirius A and, therefore, considerably hotter than our sun.

Yet, if Sirius B were that hot, its surface should blaze with white light, and the only way of explaining its dimness was to suppose that it had very little surface.

Sirius B had to have so little surface as to be a dwarf star, far smaller than anyone then had believed a star could be. Because of its white-hot temperature, it was called a 'white dwarf'. To account for its dimness, its diameter had to be only 30,000 kilometres (19,000 miles) across, so that it was about as large as a medium-sized planet and took up only about 13 times as much volume as the Earth. Sirius B has only 1/100 the volume of the large planet Jupiter.

In the relatively small volume of Sirius B, however, is packed just as much mass as in the sun – as we can tell from the strength of its gravitational pull on Sirius A.

If red giants have very low densities, white dwarfs have very high ones. The average density of Sirius B is about 90,000 times that of the sun, or 6,000 times that of platinum.

This would have seemed ridiculous only a couple of decades earlier, but by 1915 it had been discovered that atoms were made up of still smaller 'subatomic particles', with almost all the mass concentrated in a very tiny 'atomic nucleus' at the centre of the atom. In white dwarfs, then, matter didn't exist as ordinary atoms, but as a chaotic mixture of subatomic particles squeezed much more closely together than they are in atoms as we know them.

There are white dwarfs smaller and denser than Sirius B, and in recent years astronomers have discovered new types of stars that are much smaller than white dwarfs and correspondingly more dense. These are 'neutron stars' in which the subatomic particles are practically in contact, and in which the mass of a star like our sun would be compacted into a tiny body only a dozen kilometres across.

Then, of course, there is writing for the general reader, or, if you choose, for 'adults'.

It does not seem to me that there is much difference between writing for adults and writing for teenagers. In my general books, I don't question the use of an unusual word or of an extra convolution in a sentence. I allow the syllables and clauses to lie as they fall. Then, too, if there are literary allusions to make, I make them and assume the general reader – or at least anyone likely to read my books – is literate enough to get them. And I suspect that the intelligent teenager has no trouble following my 'adult' books.

Among my second hundred books is one on astronomy for the general reader. It is called The Collapsing Universe: The Story of Black Holes *(Book 182). Beth Walker of Walker & Company persistently urged me to write the book. She was almost a Cato the Elder about it. (See what I mean by literary allusions?) Whenever I visited Walker & Company, and whatever the topic of conversation, she would always end by saying 'Think black holes, Isaac.'*

I had no real objection. In the first place, I was interested in black holes and wanted to write about them. In the second, it would give me a chance to update an earlier book, The Universe, *which was among my first hundred books and which was also published by Walker. (My favourite method of updating a book is to write a new one centred upon a facet of the subject which flowered only after the earlier book was written.)*

It was just a matter of time, therefore, and finally I got to it. In early 1977, The Collapsing Universe *was finally published, and it proved, at once, to be the most popular astronomy book I had ever done. My delight was second only to that of the Walkers.*

Here I would like to include the final pages of The Collapsing Universe, *in which the wildest speculations are to be found. It is just possible that you can't get their true flavour without having read the rest of the book, but that's all right.* Opus 200 *is intended to give you a potpourri of this book and that, which you may then follow up at your leisure in whatever direction pleases you.*

from THE COLLAPSING UNIVERSE *(1977)*

In theory, up to 30 per cent of the entire energy of a rotating black hole can be milked out of it by carefully sending objects through the stationary limit and collecting them on the way out, and this is another way in which some advanced civilizations might use black holes as an energy source.* Once all the rotational energy is gone, the

---

* Not all astronomers agree with this concept of stripping the rotational energy of a black hole. In fact almost anything some astronomers suggest about a black hole is denied by other astronomers. We are here at the very edge of knowledge, and everything, one way or the other, is very uncertain and iffy.

black hole has only mass; the stationary limit coincides with the Schwarzschild radius. The black hole is then said to be 'dead', since no further energy can be obtained from it directly (though some can be obtained from matter as it spirals into it).

Even stranger than the possibility of stripping rotational energy from the black hole is that the Kerr analysis offers a new kind of end for matter entering a black hole. This new kind of end was foreshadowed by Albert Einstein and a co-worker named Rosen some thirty years earlier.

The matter crowding into a rotating black hole (and it is very likely that there is no other kind) can, in theory, squeeze out again somewhere else, like toothpaste blasting out of a fine hole in a stiff tube that is brought under the slow pressure of a steamroller.*

The transfer of matter can apparently take place over enormous distances – millions or billions of light-years – in a trifling period of time. Such transfers cannot take place in the ordinary way, since in space as we know it the speed of light is the speed limit for any object with mass. To transfer mass for distances of millions or billions of light-years in the ordinary way takes millions or billions of years of time.

One must therefore assume that the transfer goes through tunnels or across bridges that do not, strictly speaking, have the time characteristics of our familiar universe. The passageway is sometimes called an 'Einstein–Rosen bridge', or, more colourfully, a 'wormhole'.

If the mass passes through the wormhole and suddenly appears a billion light-years away in ordinary space once more, something must balance that great transfer in distance. Apparently this impossibly rapid passage through space is balanced by a compensating passage through time, so that it appears one billion years ago.

Once the matter emerges at the other end of the wormhole, it expands suddenly into ordinary matter again and,

---

* This suggestion, too, is denied by some astronomers.

in doing so, blazes with radiated energy – the energy that had, so to speak, been trapped in the black hole. What we have emerging, then, is a 'white hole', a concept first suggested in 1964.

If all this is really so, white holes, or at least some of them, might conceivably be detected.

That would depend, of course, upon the size of the white hole and upon its distance from us. Perhaps mini-black holes form mini-white holes at a vast distance, and we would surely never see them. Huge black holes would form huge white holes, however, and these we might see. Are there any signs of such white holes?

There may be –

In the 1950s, sources of radio waves were detected that on closer inspection seemed to be very compact, emerging from mere pinpoint sections of the sky. Ordinarily, radio sources found in those early days of the science were from dust clouds or from galaxies and were therefore more or less spread out over a portion of the sky.

Among the compact radio sources were those known as 3C48, 3C147, 3C196, 3C273, and 3C286. (Many more have been discovered since.) The 3C is short for *Third Cambridge Catalogue of Radio Stars*, a list compiled by the English astronomer Martin Ryle.

In 1960 the areas containing these compact radio sources were investigated by the American astronomer Allan Rex Sandage, and in each case something that looked like a dim star seemed to be the source. There was some indication that they might not be normal stars, however. Several of them seemed to have faint clouds of dust or gas about them, and one of them, 3C273, showed signs of a tiny jet of matter emerging from it. In fact there are two radio sources in connection with 3C273, one from the star and one from the jet.

There was some reluctance, therefore, to call these objects stars, and they were instead described as 'quasi-stellar (starlike) radio sources'. In 1964 Hong-Yee Chiu shortened that to 'quasar', and that name has been kept ever since.

The spectra of these quasars were obtained in 1960, but they had a pattern of lines that were completely unrecognizable, as though they were made up of substances utterly alien to the universe. In 1963, however, the Dutch-American astronomer Maarten Schmidt solved that problem. The lines would have been perfectly normal if they had existed far in the ultraviolet range. Their appearance in the visible-light range meant they had been shifted a great distance towards the longer wavelengths.

The easiest explanation for this was that the quasars are very far away. Since the universe is expanding, galactic units are separating, and all seem to be receding from us. Therefore, all distant objects have their spectral lines shifted towards the longer waves because that is what is to be expected when a source of light is receding from us. Furthermore, since the universe is expanding, the further an object, the faster it is receding from us and the greater the shift in spectral lines. From the spectral shift, then, the distance of an object can be calculated.

It turned out that the quasars were billions of light-years away. One of them, OQ172, is about 12 billion light-years away, and even the nearest, 3C273, is over a billion light-years away and further than any nonquasar object we know about. There may be as many as 15 million quasars in the universe.

A quasar is a very dim object, as we see it, but, for it to be visible at all at those enormous distances, it must be exceedingly luminous. The quasar 3C273 is five times as luminous as our galaxy, and some quasars may be up to 100 times as luminous as the average galaxy.

Yet, this being so, if quasars were simply galaxies with up to a hundred times as many stars as an average galaxy and therefore that much brighter, they ought to have dimensions large enough to make them appear, even at their vast distances, as tiny patches of light and not as starlike points. Thus, despite their brightness, they must be more compact than ordinary galaxies.

As early as 1963 the quasars were found to be variable in the energy they emitted, both in the visible-light region and in the microwave region. Increases and decreases of as much as three magnitudes were recorded over the space of a few years.

For radiation to vary so markedly in so short a time, a body must be small. Such variations must involve the body as a whole, and, if that is so, some effect must be felt across the full width of the body within the time of variation. Since no effect can travel faster than light, it means that if a quasar varies markedly over a period of a few years, it cannot be more than a light-year or so in diameter and may be considerably smaller.

One quasar, 3C446, can double its brightness in a couple of days, and it must therefore be not more than 0.005 light-year (50 billion kilometres) in diameter, or less than five times the width of Pluto's orbit around the sun. Compare this with an ordinary galaxy, which may be 100,000 light-years across and in which even the dense central core may be 15,000 light-years across.

This combination of tiny dimensions and enormous luminosity makes the quasars seem like a class of objects entirely different from anything else we know. Their discovery made astronomers aware of the possibility of hitherto unknown large-scale phenomena in the universe and spurred them on, for the first time, to consider such phenomena, including the black hole.

And it is conceivable that there is a link between black holes and quasars. The Soviet astronomer Igor Novikov and the Israeli astronomer Yuval Ne'eman have suggested that quasars are giant white holes at the other end of a wormhole from a giant black hole in some other part of the universe.*

But let's take another look at quasars. Are they really

---

* This is purely speculative, of course. In fact, the remainder of the book is almost entirely speculation, some of it my own.

unique, as they seem to be, or are they merely extreme examples of something more familiar?

In 1943 a graduate student in astronomy, Carl Seyfert, described a peculiar galaxy. It is one of a group now termed Seyfert galaxies. These may make up 1 per cent of all known galaxies (meaning as many as a billion altogether), though actually only a dozen examples have been discovered.

In most respects Seyfert galaxies seem normal and are not unusually distant from us. The cores of the Seyfert galaxies, however, are very compact, very bright, and seem unusually hot and active – rather quasarlike, in fact. They show variations in radiation that imply the radio-emitting centres at their core are no larger than quasars are thought to be. One Seyfert galaxy, 3C120, has a core that makes up less than one-eighth the diameter of the galaxy as a whole but is three times as luminous as the rest of the galaxy combined.

The strongly active centre would be visible at greater distances than the outer layers of the Seyfert galaxy would be, and if such a galaxy were far enough, all we would see by either optical or radio telescopes would be the core. We would then consider it a quasar, and the very distant quasars may simply be the intensely luminous nuclei of very large, very active Seyfert galaxies.

But then consider the core of a Seyfert galaxy – very compact, very hot and active. One Seyfert galaxy, NGC 4151, may have as many as ten billion stars in a nucleus only twelve light-years across.

These are precisely the conditions that would encourage the formation of black holes. Perhaps the mere fact that a certain volume of space is subject to black hole formation may also make it subject to the blossoming out of a white hole.

We can imagine black holes forming here and there in the universe, each producing an enormous strain in the smooth fabric of space. Wormholes form between them, and matter may leak across at a rate slow in comparison with the total quantity in the black hole serving as source but large enough to produce enormous quantities of radiation in some cases. The rate of matter flow may vary for reasons we do not as yet understand, and this may bring about the variations in the brightness of quasars.

There may be many white holes of all sizes, each connected to its black hole (which itself may come in any size), and we may be aware only of the giant-sized ones. It may be that if all black holes/white holes were taken into account, it would be seen that the wormholes connecting them may crisscross the universe quite densely.

This thought has stimulated the imaginative faculties of astronomers such as Carl Sagan. It is impossible to think of any way of keeping any sizeable piece of matter intact as it approaches a black hole, let alone having it pass intact through a wormhole and out the white hole, yet Sagan does not allow that to limit his speculations.

After all, we can do things that to our primitive forebears would seem inconceivable, and Sagan wonders if an advanced civilization might not devise ways of blocking off gravitational and tidal effects so that a ship may make use of wormholes to travel vast distances in a moment of time.

Suppose there were an advanced civilization in the universe right now that had developed a thorough map on which the wormholes were plotted with their black hole entrances and their white hole exits. The smaller wormholes would be more numerous, of course, and therefore more useful.

Imagine a cosmic empire threaded together through a network of such wormholes, with civilized centres located near the entrances and exits. It would be as important, after all, for a world to be located near a transportational crossing point of this sort as it is for an Earth city to be built near an ocean harbour or a river.

The planets nearest the tunnels might be a safe distance away, but nearer still would be enormous space stations built as bases for the ships moving through the tunnels and as power stations for the home planets.

And how does the wormhole theory affect the past and future of the universe? Even though the universe is expanding, is it possible that the expansion is balanced by matter being shifted into the past through the wormholes?

Certainly the dozens of quasars we have detected are all billions of light-years away from us, and we see them, therefore, as they were billions of years ago. Furthermore, they are heavily weighted towards the greater distances and more remote past. It is estimated that if quasars were evenly spaced throughout the universe, there would be several hundred of them nearer and brighter than 3C273, which is the nearest and brightest now.

Well, then, do we have an eternal universe after all, a kind of continuous creation in another sense?

Has the universe been expanding for countless aeons, through all eternity in fact, without ever having expanded beyond the present level because the wormholes create a closed circuit, sending matter back into the more contracted past to begin expansion all over?

Has the universe never really been entirely contracted, and has there never really been a big bang? Do we think there was a big bang only because we are more aware of the expansion half of the cycle involving the galaxies and are not aware of matter sweeping back through wormholes?

But if there was no big bang, how do we account for the background radiation that is the echo of the big bang? Can this radiation be the product of the overall backward flow of matter into the far past? Can the white holes or quasars be numerous 'little bangs' that add up to the big bang and produce the background radiation?

And if all this is so, where does the energy come from that keeps the universe endlessly recycling? If the universe runs down as it expands (this is referred to as an 'increase of entropy' by physicists), does it wind up again ('decreasing entropy') as it moves back in time through the wormholes?

There are no answers to any of these questions at present. All is speculation, including the very existence of wormholes and white holes.

It must be admitted that the notion that the universe is continually recycling is a rather tenuous speculation.

If we dismiss it, however, we are left with the big bang – either as a one-time affair if we are living in an open universe, or as an endlessly repeated phenomenon if the universe is closed and oscillating. Either way there is a problem. What is the nature of the cosmic egg?

When the cosmic egg was first suggested, it was viewed very much as we now view neutron stars. The trouble is that a cosmic egg with all the mass of the universe (equal to the mass of 100,000,000,000 galaxies, perhaps) is certainly too large to be a neutron star. If it is true that anything with more than 3.2 times the mass of our sun must form a black hole when it collapses, then the cosmic egg was the biggest of all black holes.

How, then, could it have exploded and yielded the big bang? Black holes do not explode.

Suppose we imagine a contracting universe, which would form black holes of varying sizes as it contracted. The individual black holes might bleed away some of their mass through wormholes, counteracting the overall contraction but not by enough to stop it altogether (or neither the expanding universe nor we would be here today).

As the universe compresses, the black holes grow at the expense of non-black hole matter and, more and more frequently, collide and coalesce. Eventually, of course, all the black holes coalesce into the cosmic egg. It loses matter through its wormhole at an enormous rate, producing the biggest conceivable white hole at the other end. It is the white hole of the cosmic egg, then, that was the big bang that created our expanding universe. This would hold good whether the universe is open or closed, whether the cosmic egg formed only once or repeatedly.

Of course, this solution will only work if wormholes

and white holes truly exist, which is uncertain. And even if they do exist, it will only work if the cosmic egg is rotating. But is it?

There is certainly angular momentum in the universe, but it could have been created, despite the conservation law, where none had earlier existed.

That is because there are two kinds of angular momentum, in opposite senses. An object can rotate either clockwise or counter-clockwise (positively or negatively, if you prefer). Two objects with equal angular momentum, one positive and one negative, will, if they collide and coalesce, end with zero angular momentum, the energy of the two rotary motions being converted into heat. In reverse, an object with zero angular momentum can, with the addition of appropriate energy, split to form two sub-objects, one with positive angular momentum and the other with negative angular momentum.

The objects in the universe may all have angular momentum, but it is very likely that some of that angular momentum is positive and some negative. We have no way of knowing whether one kind is present in greater quantities than the other. If such lopsidedness does exist, then when all the matter of the universe collapses into a cosmic egg, that cosmic egg will end up with an amount of angular momentum equal to the excess of one kind over the other.

It may be, however, that the amount of angular momentum of one kind in the universe is equal to the amount of the other kind. In that case, the cosmic egg, when it forms, will have no angular momentum and will be dead. We can't rely on wormholes and white holes for the big bang, then.

What else?

Just as angular momentum of two opposite kinds exists, so matter of two opposite kinds exists.

An electron is balanced by an antielectron, or positron. When an electron and a positron combine, there is a mutual annihilation of the two particles. No mass at all is left. It is converted into energy in the form of gamma rays. In the same way, a proton and an antiproton will combine to lose mass and form energy; and so will a neutron and an antineutron.

We can have matter built up of protons, neutrons, and electrons; and antimatter built up of antiprotons, antineutrons, and antielectrons. In that case, any mass of matter combining with an equal mass of antimatter will undergo mutual annihilation to form gamma rays.

In reverse, mass can be formed from energy, but never as one kind of particle only. For every electron that is formed an antielectron must be formed, for every proton an antiproton, for every neutron an antineutron. In short, when energy is turned into matter, an equal quantity of antimatter must also be formed.

But if that is so, where is the antimatter that must have been formed at the same time that the matter of the universe was formed?

The Earth is certainly entirely matter (except for small traces of antimatter formed in the laboratory or found among cosmic rays). In fact the whole solar system is entirely matter, and, in all probability, so is the entire galactic unit of which we are part.

Where is the antimatter? Perhaps there are also galactic units that are entirely antimatter. There may be galactic units and antigalactic units, which because of the general expansion of the universe never come in contact and never engage in mutual annihilation. Just as matter forms black holes, antimatter will form anti-black holes. These two kinds of black holes are in all respects identical except for being made up of opposite substances.

If the universe was ever, in the past, contracting, black holes and anti-black holes formed even more easily; and as contraction continued, the chances of collision between two black holes of opposite nature, and a consequent enormous mutual annihilation, increased. In the final coalescence there was the greatest of all great mutual annihilations.

The total mass of the universe disappeared and with it the gravitational field that keeps the black hole, and the cosmic egg for that matter, in existence. In its place was incredibly energetic radiation, which expanded outwards. That would be the big bang.

Some period after the big bang the energy, becoming less intense through expansion, would be tame enough to form matter and antimatter once more – the two forming separate galactic units by some mechanism that, it must be admitted, has not been worked out – and the expanding universe would take shape.

From this view of the big bang as the mutual annihilation of matter and antimatter, it doesn't matter whether the cosmic egg is rotating or not, or whether it is alive or dead.

Yet we have no evidence that there exist antigalactic units. Can it be that for some reason we do not as yet understand that the universe consists simply of matter?

We might argue that this is impossible; the universe cannot consist simply of matter, as that would make the big bang impossible. Or we might think of a way of accounting for the big bang even in a universe of matter only, and even if, on contracting, that universe forms a cosmic egg that is not rotating and is therefore a dead black hole.

Well, according to the equations used to explain the formation of black holes, the size of the Schwarzschild radius is proportional to the mass of the black hole.

A black hole the mass of the sun has a Schwarzschild radius of 3 kilometres and is therefore 6 kilometres across. A black hole that is twice the mass of the sun is twice as large across – 12 kilometres. However, a sphere that is twice as large across as a smaller sphere has eight times' as much volume as the smaller sphere. It follows that a black hole with twice the mass of the sun has that twice the mass spread over eight times the volume. The density of the larger black hole is only one-fourth the density of the smaller black hole.

In other words, the more massive a black hole is, the larger and the less dense it is.

Suppose our entire galaxy, which is about 100,000,000,000 times the mass of our sun, were squeezed into a black hole. Its diameter would be 600,000,000,000 kilometres, and its average density would be about 0.000001 gram per cubic centimetre. The galactic black hole would be more than fifty times as wide as Pluto's orbit and would be no more dense than a gas.

Suppose that all the galaxies of the universe, possibly 100,000,000,000 of them, collapsed into a black hole. Such a black hole, containing all the matter of the universe, would be 10,000,000,000 light-years across, and its average density would be that of an exceedingly thin gas.

Yet no matter how thin this gas, the structure is a black hole.

Suppose the total mass of the universe is 2.5 times as large as it seems to astronomers to be. In that case the black hole formed by all the matter of the universe is 25,000,000,000 light-years across, and that happens to be about the diameter of the actual universe we live in (as far as we know).

It is quite possible, then, that the entire universe is itself a black hole (as has been suggested by the physicist Kip Thorne).

If it is, then very likely it has always been a black hole and will always be a black hole. If that is so, we live within a black hole, and if we want to know what conditions are like in a black hole (provided it is extremely massive), we have but to look around.

As the universe collapses, then, we might imagine the formation of any number of relatively small black holes (black holes within a black hole!) with very limited diameters. In the last few seconds of final catastrophic collapse, however, when all the black holes coalesce into one cosmic black hole, the Schwarzschild radius springs outward and outward to the extremity of the known universe.

And it may be that *within* the Schwarzschild radius there is the possibility of explosion. It may be that as the Schwarzschild radius recedes billions of light-years in a flash, the cosmic egg at the very instant of formation springs outward to follow, and *that* is the big bang.

If that is so, we might argue that the universe cannot be open whatever the present state of the evidence, since the universe cannot expand beyond its Schwarzschild radius. Somehow the expansion will have to cease at that point, and then it must inevitably begin to contract again and start the cycle over. (Some argue that with each big bang, a totally different expanding universe with different laws of nature gets under way.)

Can it be, then, that what we see all about us is the unimaginably slow breathing cycle (tens of billions years in and tens of billions of years out) of a universe-sized black hole?

And can it be that, separated from our universe in some fashion we cannot as yet grasp, there are many other black holes of various sizes, perhaps an infinite number of them, all expanding and contracting, each at its own rate?

And we are in one of them – and through the wonders of thought and reason it may be that, from our station on a less-than-dust speck lost deep within one of these universes, we have drawn ourselves a picture of the existence and behaviour of them all.

PART 2

Robots

In the years in which science fiction was the major part of my production, robots were a favourite subject of mine. In the first twenty years of my writing career, I wrote seventeen short stories and three novels in which robots were a key element in the plots, plus a few other short stories that involved computers.

Since my hundredth book was published, however, my science fiction production has decreased a great deal – yet it has not dwindled to zero.

In 1976, for instance, Doubleday published. The Bicentennial Man and Other Stories (*Book 176*), a collection of eleven stories, three of which involved robots.

The first of these was 'Feminine Intuition', which first appeared in the October 1969 Fantasy and Science Fiction (*usually known as F & SF*). In it my favourite psychologist, Susan Calvin, appears. Susan first appeared in my story 'Liar!' which was published in the May 1941 issue of Astounding Science Fiction (*usually known as ASF*). I fell in love with her. I didn't portray her in any very attractive way – she was frozen intellect, and only rarely and secretly seemed to allow a touch of human feeling to show – but I loved her anyway. Before 'Feminine Intuition', she had appeared in nine of my robot stories, the last being 'Galley Slave' in the December 1957 issue of Galaxy. Of these nine stories, five appear in I, Robot and four in The Rest of the Robots, both of which are among my first hundred books. I had not seriously considered bringing her back until the managing editor of Galaxy, Judy-Lynn Benjamin (*who later married Lester Del Rey*), casually suggested I write a story about a woman robot. It was that which led to 'Feminine Intuition', in which I brought back Susan Calvin as an old woman but with her brain functioning as well as ever. It was the tenth story *involving her, and it appeared twenty-eight years after the first.*

The second robot story in The Bicentennial Man and Other Stories *was '. . . That Thou Art Mindful of Him', which first appeared in the May 1974 issue of F & SF. This arose because Ed Ferman of F & SF and Barry Malzberg, the science fiction writer, wanted to put out an anthology of stories, each of which would carry a particular category to its ultimate end. They asked me to do a robot story that would carry my three laws of robotics as far as possible – and I stretched them to the point where they subverted themselves out of their original purpose. In a way that brought the whole robot saga to a fitting, and ironic, conclusion – though, of course, it would not and did not prevent me from writing additional robot stories.*

Finally, there was 'The Bicentennial Man', the title story of the book, which had its genesis in January 1975 when Naomi Gordon of Philadelphia visited and urged me to write a story with that title and with any plot I wished, as long as it was inspired by the title. It would then be included in an anthology (also with that title) to be published in the bicentennial year of 1976.

Alas, the anthology did not come to pass for various reasons, and 'The Bicentennial Man' was left homeless. It was rescued by Judy-Lynn Del Rey and appeared in her anthology of original stories Stellar Science Fiction Stories, No. 2, *which was published in February 1976.*

And then, in 1977, 'The Bicentennial Man' won both the Nebula and the Hugo awards as the best novelette to appear in 1976. It was the first time any of my stories shorter than a novel had won these awards, and I was delighted to be able to demonstrate that the old man still had it.

Each of the stories strongly appeals to me for one reason or the other, but I only wanted to include one of them in this book, and, after some hesitation, my vanity over the awards won out. Here, then, is 'The Bicentennial Man' in full:

'The Bicentennial Man' *(1976)*

THE THREE LAWS OF ROBOTICS

1. A robot may not injure a human being or, through inaction, allow a human being to come to harm.

2. A robot must obey the orders given it by human beings except where such orders would conflict with the First Law.

3. A robot must protect its own existence as long as such protection does not conflict with the First or Second Law.

Andrew Martin said, 'Thank you,' and took the seat offered him. He didn't look driven to the last resort, but he had been.

He didn't, actually, look anything, for there was a smooth blankness to his face, except for the sadness one imagined one saw in his eyes. His hair was smooth, light brown, rather fine, and there was no facial hair. He looked freshly and cleanly shaved. His clothes were distinctly old-fashioned, but neat and predominantly a velvety red-purple in colour.

Facing him from behind the desk was the surgeon, and the nameplate on the desk included a fully identifying series of letters and numbers, which Andrew didn't bother with. To call him Doctor would be quite enough.

'When can the operation be carried through, Doctor?' he asked.

The surgeon said softly, with that certain inalienable note of respect that a robot always used to a human being, 'I am not certain, sir, that I understand how or upon whom such an operation could be performed.' There might have been a look of respectful intransigence on the surgeon's face – if a robot of his sort, in lightly bronzed stainless steel, could have such an expression, or any expression.

Andrew Martin studied the robot's right hand, his

cutting hand, as it lay on the desk in utter tranquillity. The fingers were long and shaped into artistically metallic looping curves so graceful and appropriate that one could imagine a scalpel fitting them and becoming, temporarily, one piece with them.

There would be no hesitation in his work, no stumbling, no quivering, no mistakes. That came with specialization, of course, a specialization so fiercely desired by humanity that few robots were, any longer, independently brained. A surgeon, of course, would have to be. And this one, though brained, was so limited in his capacity that he did not recognize Andrew – had probably never heard of him.

Andrew said, 'Have you ever thought you would like to be a man?'

The surgeon hesitated a moment as though the question fitted nowhere in his allotted positronic pathways. 'But I am a robot, sir.'

'Would it be better to be a man?'

'It would be better, sir, to be a better surgeon. I could not be so if I were a man, but only if I were a more advanced robot. I would be pleased to be a more advanced robot.'

'It does not offend you that I can order you about? That I can make you stand up, sit down, move right or left, by merely telling you to do so?'

'It is my pleasure to please you, sir. If your orders were to interfere with my functioning with respect to you or to any other human being, I would not obey you. The First Law, concerning my duty to human safety, would take precedence over the Second Law relating to obedience. Otherwise, obedience is my pleasure ... But upon whom am I to perform this operation?'

'Upon me,' said Andrew.

'But that is impossible. It is patently a damaging operation.'

'That does not matter,' said Andrew calmly.

'I must not inflict damage,' said the surgeon.

'On a human being, you must not,' said Andrew, 'but I, too, am a robot.'

Andrew had appeared much more a robot when he had first been manufactured. He had then been as much a robot in appearance as any that had ever existed, smoothly designed and functional.

He had done well in the home to which he had been brought in those days when robots in households, or on the planet altogether, had been a rarity.

There had been four in the home: Sir and Ma'am and Miss and Little Miss. He knew their names, of course, but he never used them. Sir was Gerald Martin.

His own serial number was NDR—— He forgot the numbers. It had been a long time, of course, but if he had wanted to remember, he could not forget. He had not wanted to remember.

Little Miss had been the first to call him Andrew because she could not use the letters, and all the rest followed her in this.

Little Miss . . . She had lived ninety years and was long since dead. He had tried to call her Ma'am once, but she would not allow it. Little Miss she had been to her last day.

Andrew had been intended to perform the duties of a valet, a butler, a lady's maid. Those were the experimental days for him and, indeed, for all robots anywhere but in the industrial and exploratory factories and stations off Earth.

The Martins enjoyed him, and half the time he was prevented from doing his work because Miss and Little Miss would rather play with him.

It was Miss who understood first how this might be arranged. She said, 'We order you to play with us and you must follow orders.'

Andrew said, 'I am sorry, Miss, but a prior order from Sir must surely take precedence.'

But she said, 'Daddy just said he hoped you would take

care of the cleaning. That's not much of an order. I *order* you.'

Sir did not mind. Sir was fond of Miss and of Little Miss, even more than Ma'am was, and Andrew was fond of them, too. At least, the effect they had upon his actions were those which in a human being would have been called the result of fondness. Andrew thought of it as fondness, for he did not know any other word for it.

It was for Little Miss that Andrew had carved a pendant out of wood. She had ordered him to. Miss, it seemed, had received an ivorite pendant with scrollwork for her birthday, and Little Miss was unhappy over it. She had only a piece of wood, which she gave Andrew together with a small kitchen knife.

He had done it quickly and Little Miss said, 'That's *nice*, Andrew. I'll show it to Daddy.'

Sir would not believe it. 'Where did you really get this, Mandy?' Mandy was what he called Little Miss. When Little Miss assured him she was really telling the truth, he turned to Andrew. 'Did you do this, Andrew?'

'Yes, Sir.'

'The design, too?'

'Yes, Sir.'

'From what did you copy the design?'

'It is a geometric representation, Sir, that fitted the grain of the wood.'

The next day, Sir brought him another piece of wood, a larger one, and an electric vibro-knife. He said, 'Make something out of this, Andrew. Anything you want to.'

Andrew did so and Sir watched, then looked at the product a long time. After that, Andrew no longer waited on tables. He was ordered to read books on furniture design instead, and he learned to make cabinets and desks.

Sir said, 'These are amazing productions, Andrew.'

Andrew said, 'I enjoy doing them, Sir.'

'Enjoy?'

'It makes the circuits of my brain somehow flow more easily. I have heard you use the word "enjoy" and the way you use it fits the way I feel. I enjoy doing them, Sir.'

Gerald Martin took Andrew to the regional offices of United States Robots and Mechanical Men, Inc. As a member of the Regional Legislature he had no trouble at all in gaining an interview with the chief robopsychologist. In fact, it was only as a member of the Regional Legislature that he qualified as a robot owner in the first place – in those early days when robots were rare.

Andrew did not understand any of this at the time, but in later years, with greater learning, he could re-view that early scene and understand it in its proper light.

The robopsychologist, Merton Mansky, listened with a gathering frown and more than once managed to stop his fingers at the point beyond which they would have irrepressibly drummed on the table. He had drawn features and a lined forehead and looked as though he might be younger than he looked.

He said, 'Robotics is not an exact art, Mr Martin. I cannot explain it to you in detail, but the mathematics governing the plotting of the positronic pathways is far too complicated to permit of any but approximate solutions. Naturally, since we build everything about the Three Laws, those are incontrovertible. We will, of course, replace your robot –'

'Not at all,' said Sir. 'There is no question of failure on his part. He performs his assigned duties perfectly. The point is, he also carves wood in exquisite fashion and never the same twice. He produces works of art.'

Mansky looked confused. 'Strange. Of course, we're attempting generalized pathways these days . . . Really creative, you think?'

'See for yourself.' Sir handed over a little sphere of wood on which there was a playground scene in which the boys and girls were almost too small to make out, yet they were in perfect proportion and blended so naturally with the grain that that, too, seemed to have been carved.

Mansky said, '*He* did that?' He handed it back with a

shake of his head. 'The luck of the draw. Something in the pathways.'

'Can you do it again?'

'Probably not. Nothing like this has ever been reported.'

'Good! I don't in the least mind Andrew's being the only one.'

Mansky said, 'I suspect that the company would like to have your robot back for study.'

Sir said with sudden grimness, 'Not a chance. Forget it.' He turned to Andrew. 'Let's go home now.'

'As you wish, Sir,' said Andrew.

Miss was dating boys and wasn't about the house much. It was Little Miss, not as little as she once was, who filled Andrew's horizon now. She never forgot that the very first piece of wood carving he had done had been for her. She kept it on a silver chain about her neck.

It was she who first objected to Sir's habit of giving away the productions. She said, 'Come on, Dad, if anyone wants one of them, let him pay for it. It's worth it.'

Sir said, 'It isn't like you to be greedy, Mandy.'

'Not for us, Dad. For the artist.'

Andrew had never heard the word before and when he had a moment to himself he looked it up in the dictionary. Then there was another trip, this time to Sir's lawyer.

Sir said to him, 'What do you think of this, John?'

The lawyer was John Feingold. He had white hair and a pudgy belly, and the rims of his contact lenses were tinted a bright green. He looked at the small plaque Sir had given him. 'This is beautiful . . . But I've heard the news. This is a carving made by your robot. The one you've brought with you.'

'Yes, Andrew does them. Don't you, Andrew?'

'Yes, Sir,' said Andrew.

'How much would you pay for that, John?' asked Sir.

'I can't say. I'm not a collector of such things.'

'Would you believe I've been offered two hundred fifty dollars for that small thing? Andrew has made chairs that have sold for five hundred dollars. There's two hundred thousand dollars in the bank out of Andrew's products.'

'Good heavens, he's making you rich, Gerald.'

'Half rich,' said Sir. 'Half of it is in an account in the name of Andrew Martin.'

'The robot?'

'That's right, and I want to know if it's legal.'

'Legal?' Feingold's chair creaked as he leaned back in it. 'There are no precedents, Gerald. How did your robot sign the necessary papers?'

'He can sign his name, and I brought in the signature. I didn't bring him in to the bank himself. Is there anything further that ought to be done?'

'Um.' Feingold's eyes seemed to turn inward for a moment. Then he said, 'Well, we can set up a trust to handle all finances in his name, and that will place a layer of insulation between him and the hostile world. Further than that, my advice is you do nothing. No one is stopping you so far. If anyone objects, let *him* bring suit.'

'And will you take the case if suit is brought?'

'For a retainer, certainly.'

'How much?'

'Something like that,' and Feingold pointed to the wooden plaque.

'Fair enough,' said Sir.

Feingold chuckled as he turned to the robot. 'Andrew, are you pleased that you have money?'

'Yes, sir.'

'What do you plan to do with it?'

'Pay for things, sir, which otherwise Sir would have to pay for. It would save him expense, sir.'

The occasions came. Repairs were expensive, and revisions were even more so. Over the years, new models of robots were produced, and Sir saw to it that Andrew had the advantage of every new device, until he was a paragon of metallic excellence. It was all at Andrew's expense. Andrew insisted on that.

Only his positronic pathways were untouched. Sir insisted on that.

'The new ones aren't as good as you are, Andrew,' he said. 'The new robots are worthless. The company has learned to make the pathways more precise, more closely on the nose, more deeply on the track. The new robots don't shift. They do what they're designed for and never stray. I like you better.'

'Thank you, Sir.'

'And it's your doing, Andrew, don't you forget that. I am certain Mansky put an end to generalized pathways as soon as he had a good look at you. He didn't like the unpredictability . . . Do you know how many times he asked for you so he could place you under study? Nine times! I never let him have you, though, and now that he's retired, we may have some peace.'

So Sir's hair thinned and greyed and his face grew pouchy, while Andrew looked rather better than he had when he first joined the family.

Ma'am had joined an art colony somewhere in Europe and Miss was a poet in New York. They wrote sometimes, but not often. Little Miss was married and lived not far away. She said she did not want to leave Andrew, and when her child, Little Sir, was born, she let Andrew hold the bottle and feed him.

With the birth of a grandson, Andrew felt that Sir had someone now to replace those who had gone. It would not be so unfair to come to him with the request.

Andrew said, 'Sir, it is kind of you to have allowed me to spend my money as I wished.'

'It was your money, Andrew.'

'Only by your voluntary act, Sir. I do not believe the law would have stopped you from keeping it all.'

'The law won't persuade me to do wrong, Andrew.'

'Despite all expenses, and despite taxes, too, Sir, I have nearly six hundred thousand dollars.'

'I know that, Andrew.'

'I want to give it to you, Sir.'

'I won't take it, Andrew.'

'In exchange for something you can give me, Sir.'

'Oh? What is that, Andrew?'

'My freedom, Sir.'

'Your –'

'I wish to buy my freedom, Sir.'

It wasn't that easy. Sir had flushed, had said, 'For God's sake!' had turned on his heel, and stalked away.

It was Little Miss who brought him around, defiantly and harshly – and in front of Andrew. For thirty years, no one had hesitated to talk in front of Andrew, whether the matter involved Andrew or not. He was only a robot.

She said, 'Dad, why are you taking it as a personal affront? He'll still be here. He'll still be loyal. He can't help that. It's built in. All he wants is a form of words. He wants to be called free. Is that so terrible? Hasn't he earned it? Heavens, he and I have been talking about it for years.'

'Talking about it for years, have you?'

'Yes, and over and over again, he postponed it for fear he would hurt you. I *made* him put it up to you.'

'He doesn't know what freedom is. He's a robot.'

'Dad, you don't know him. He's read everything in the library. I don't know what he feels inside but I don't know what *you* feel inside. When you talk to him you'll find he reacts to the various abstractions as you and I do, and what else counts? If someone else's reactions are like your own, what more can you ask for?'

'The law won't take that attitude,' Sir said angrily. 'See here, you!' He turned to Andrew with a deliberate grate in his voice. 'I can't free you except by doing it legally, and, if it gets into the courts, you not only won't get your freedom, but the law will take official cognizance of your money. They'll tell you that a robot has no right to earn money. Is this rigmarole worth losing your money?'

'Freedom is without price, Sir,' said Andrew. 'Even the

chance of freedom is worth the money.'

The court might also take the attitude that freedom was without price, and might decide that for no price, however great, could a robot buy its freedom.

The simple statement of the regional attorney who represented those who had brought a class action to oppose the freedom was this: The word 'freedom' had no meaning when applied to a robot. Only a human being could be free.

He said it several times, when it seemed appropriate; slowly, with his hand coming down rhythmically on the desk before him to mark the words.

Little Miss asked permission to speak on behalf of Andrew. She was recognized by her full name, something Andrew had never heard pronounced before:

'Amanda Laura Martin Charney may approach the bench.'

She said, 'Thank you, your honour. I am not a lawyer and I don't know the proper way of phrasing things, but I hope you will listen to my meaning and ignore the words.

'Let's understand what it means to be free in Andrew's case. In some ways, he *is* free. I think it's at least twenty years since anyone in the Martin family gave him an order to do something that we felt he might not do of his own accord.

'But we can, if we wish, give him an order to do anything, couch it as harshly as we wish, because he is a machine that belongs to us. Why should we be in a position to do so, when he has served us so long, so faithfully, and earned so much money for us? He owes us nothing more. The debt is entirely on the other side.

'Even if we were legally forbidden to place Andrew in involuntary servitude, he would still serve us voluntarily. Making him free would be a trick of words only, but it would mean much to him. It would give him everything and cost us nothing.'

For a moment the judge seemed to be suppressing a smile. 'I see your point, Mrs Charney. The fact is that there is no binding law in this respect and no precedent. There *is*, however, the unspoken assumption that only a human can enjoy freedom. I can make new law here, subject to reversal in a higher court, but I cannot lightly run counter to that assumption. Let me address the robot. Andrew!'

'Yes, your honour.'

It was the first time Andrew had spoken in court and the judge seemed astonished for a moment at the human timbre of the voice. He said, 'Why do you want to be free, Andrew? In what way will this matter to you?'

Andrew said, 'Would you wish to be a slave, your honour?'

'But you are not a slave. You are a perfectly good robot, a genius of a robot I am given to understand, capable of an artistic expression that can be matched nowhere. What more could you do if you were free?'

'Perhaps no more than I do now, your honour, but with greater joy. It has been said in this courtroom that only a human being can be free. It seems to me that only someone who wishes for freedom can be free. I wish for freedom.'

And it was that that cued the judge. The crucial sentence in his decision was: 'There is no right to deny freedom to any object with a mind advanced enough to grasp the concept and desire the state.'

It was eventually upheld by the World Court.

Sir remained displeased, and his harsh voice made Andrew feel almost as though he were being short-circuited.

Sir said, 'I don't want your damned money, Andrew. I'll take it only because you won't feel free otherwise. From now on, you can select your own jobs and do them as you please. I will give you no orders, except this one – that you do as you please. But I am still responsible for you; that's part of the court order. I hope you understand that.'

Little Miss interrupted. 'Don't be irascible, Dad. The responsibility is no great chore. You know you won't have to do a thing. The Three Laws still hold.'

'Then how is he free?'

Andrew said, 'Are not human beings bound by their laws, Sir?'

Sir said, 'I'm not going to argue.' He left, and Andrew saw him only infrequently after that.

Little Miss came to see him frequently in the small house that had been built and made over for him. It had no kitchen, of course, nor bathroom facilities. It had just two rooms; one was a library and one was a combination storeroom and workroom. Andrew accepted many commissions and worked harder as a free robot than he ever had before, till the cost of the house was paid for and the structure legally transferred to him.

One day Little Sir came . . . No, George! Little Sir had insisted on that after the court decision. 'A free robot doesn't call anyone Little Sir,' George had said. 'I call you Andrew. You must call me George.'

It was phrased as an order, so Andrew called him George – but Little Miss remained Little Miss.

The day George came alone, it was to say that Sir was dying. Little Miss was at the bedside but Sir wanted Andrew as well.

Sir's voice was quite strong, though he seemed unable to move much. He struggled to get his hand up. 'Andrew,' he said, 'Andrew – Don't help me, George. I'm only dying; I'm not crippled . . . Andrew, I'm glad you're free. I just wanted to tell you that.'

Andrew did not know what to say. He had never been at the side of someone dying before, but he knew it was the human way of ceasing to function. It was an involuntary and irreversible dismantling, and Andrew did not know what to say that might be appropriate. He could only remain standing, absolutely silent, absolutely motionless.

When it was over, Little Miss said to him, 'He may not

have seemed friendly to you towards the end, Andrew, but
he was old, you know, and it hurt him that you should
want to be free.'

And then Andrew found the words to say. He said, 'I
would never have been free without him, Little Miss.'

It was only after Sir's death that Andrew began to wear
clothes. He began with an old pair of trousers at first, a
pair that George had given him.

George was married now, and a lawyer. He had joined
Feingold's firm. Old Feingold was long since dead, but his
daughter had carried on and eventually the firm's name
became Feingold and Martin. It remained so even when
the daughter retired and no Feingold took her place. At
the time Andrew put on clothes for the first time, the
Martin name had just been added to the firm.

George had tried not to smile the first time Andrew
put on the trousers, but to Andrew's eyes the smile was
clearly there.

George showed Andrew how to manipulate the static
charge so as to allow the trousers to open, wrap about his
lower body, and move shut. George demonstrated on his
own trousers, but Andrew was quite aware that it would
take him a while to duplicate that one flowing motion.

George said, 'But why do you want trousers, Andrew?
Your body is so beautifully functional it's a shame to
cover it – especially when you needn't worry about either
temperature control or modesty. And it doesn't cling
properly, not on metal.'

Andrew said, 'Are not human bodies beautifully functional, George? Yet you cover yourselves.'

'For warmth, for cleanliness, for protection, for decor-
ativeness. None of that applies to you.'

Andrew said, 'I feel bare without clothes. I feel different,
George.'

'Different! Andrew, there are millions of robots on
Earth now. In this region, according to the last census,
there are almost as many robots as there are men.'

'I know, George. There are robots doing every conceivable type of work.'

'And none of them wears clothes.'

'But none of them is free, George.'

Little by little, Andrew added to the wardrobe. He was inhibited by George's smile and by the stares of the people who commissioned work.

He might be free, but there was built into him a carefully detailed programme concerning his behaviour towards people, and it was only by the tiniest steps that he dared advance. Open disapproval would set him back months.

Not everyone accepted Andrew as free. He was incapable of resenting that, and yet there was a difficulty about his thinking process when he thought of it.

Most of all, he tended to avoid putting on clothes – or too many of them – when he thought Little Miss might come to visit him. She was old now and was often away in some warmer climate, but when she returned the first thing she did was visit him.

On one of her returns, George said ruefully, 'She's got me, Andrew. I'll be running for the Legislature next year. Like grandfather, she says, like grandson.'

'Like grandfather –' Andrew stopped, uncertain.

'I mean that I, George, the grandson, will be like Sir, the grandfather, who was in the Legislature once.'

Andrew said, 'It would be pleasant, George, if Sir were still –' He paused, for he did not want to say, 'in working order.' That seemed inappropriate.

'Alive,' said George. 'Yes, I think of the old monster now and then, too.'

It was a conversation Andrew thought about. He had noticed his own incapacity in speech when talking with George. Somehow the language had changed since Andrew had come into being with an innate vocabulary. Then, too, George used a colloquial speech, as Sir and Little Miss had not. Why should he have called Sir a monster when surely that word was not appropriate?

Nor could Andrew turn to his own books for guidance.

They were old and most dealt with woodworking, with art, with furniture design. There were none on language, none on the way of human beings.

It was at that moment that it seemed to him he must seek the proper books; and as a free robot, he felt he must not ask George. He would go to town and use the library. It was a triumphant decision, and he felt his electro-potential grow distinctly higher until he had to throw in an impedance coil.

He put on a full costume, even including a shoulder chain of wood. He would have preferred the glitter plastic, but George had said that wood was much more appropriate and that polished cedar was considerably more valuable as well.

He had placed a hundred feet between himself and the house before gathering resistance brought him to a halt. He shifted the impedance coil out of circuit, and, when that did not seem to help enough, he returned to his home and on a piece of notepaper wrote neatly, 'I have gone to the library,' and placed it in clear view on his worktable.

Andrew never quite got to the library. He had studied the map. He knew the route but not the appearance of it. The actual landmarks did not resemble the symbols on the map and he would hesitate. Eventually he thought he must have somehow gone wrong, for everything looked strange.

He passed an occasional field robot, but at the time he decided he should ask his way, there was none in sight. A vehicle passed and did not stop. He stood irresolute, which meant calmly motionless, and then coming across the field towards him were two human beings.

He turned to face them, and they altered their course to meet him. A moment before, they had been talking loudly; he had heard their voices; but now they were silent. They had the look that Andrew associated with human uncertainty, and they were young, but not very young. Twenty perhaps? Andrew could never judge human age.

He said, 'Would you describe to me the route to the town library, sirs?'

One of them, the taller of the two, whose tall hat lengthened him still further, almost grotesquely, said, not to Andrew but to the other, 'It's a robot.'

The other had a bulbous nose and heavy eyelids. He said, not to Andrew but to the first, 'It's wearing clothes.'

The tall one snapped his fingers. 'It's the free robot. They have a robot at the Martins who isn't owned by anybody. Why else would it be wearing clothes?'

'Ask it,' said the one with the nose.

'Are you the Martin robot?' asked the tall one.

'I am Andrew Martin, sir,' said Andrew.

'Good. Take off your clothes. Robots don't wear clothes.' He said to the other, 'That's disgusting. Look at him.'

Andrew hesitated. He hadn't heard an order in that tone of voice in so long that his Second Law circuits had momentarily jammed.

The tall one said, 'Take off your clothes. I order you.'

Slowly, Andrew began to remove them.

'Just drop them,' said the tall one.

The nose said, 'If it doesn't belong to anyone, he could be ours as much as someone else's.'

'Anyway,' said the tall one, 'who's to object to anything we do? We're not damaging property . . . Stand on your head.' That was to Andrew.

'The head is not meant –' began Andrew.

'That's an order. If you don't know how, try anyway.'

Andrew hesitated again, then bent to put his head on the ground. He tried to lift his legs and fell, heavily.

The tall one said, 'Just lie there.' He said to the other, 'We can take him apart. Ever take a robot apart?'

'Will he let us?'

'How can he stop us?'

There was no way Andrew could stop them if they ordered him not to resist in a forceful enough manner.

The Second Law of obedience took precedence over the Third Law of self-preservation. In any case, he could not defend himself without possibly hurting them and that would mean breaking the First Law. At that thought, every motile unit contracted slightly and he quivered as he lay there.

The tall one walked over and pushed at him with his foot. 'He's heavy. I think we'll need tools to do the job.'

The nose said, 'We could order him to take himself apart. It would be fun to watch him try.'

'Yes,' said the tall one thoughtfully, 'but let's get him off the road. If someone comes along –'

It was too late. Someone had indeed come along, and it was George. From where he lay, Andrew had seen him topping a small rise in the middle distance. He would have liked to signal him in some way, but the last order had been, 'Just lie there!'

George was running now and he arrived somewhat winded. The two young men stepped back a little and then waited thoughtfully.

George said anxiously, 'Andrew, has something gone wrong?'

Andrew said, 'I am well, George.'

'Then stand up . . . What happened to your clothes?'

The tall young man said, 'That your robot, mac?'

George turned sharply. 'He's no one's robot. What's been going on here?'

'We politely asked him to take his clothes off. What's that to you if you don't own him?'

George said, 'What were they doing, Andrew?'

Andrew said, 'It was their intention in some way to dismember me. They were about to move me to a quiet spot and order me to dismember myself.'

George looked at the two and his chin trembled. The two young men retreated no further. They were smiling. The tall one said lightly, 'What are you going to do, pudgy? Attack us?'

George said, 'No. I don't have to. This robot has been

with my family for over seventy years. He knows us and he values us more than he values anyone else. I am going to tell him that you two are threatening my life and that you plan to kill me. I will ask him to defend me. In choosing between me and you two, he will choose me. Do you know what will happen to you when he attacks you?'

The two were backing away slightly, looking uneasy.

George said sharply, 'Andrew, I am in danger and about to come to harm from these young men. Move towards them!'

Andrew did so, and the two young men did not wait. They ran fleetly.

'All right, Andrew, relax,' said George. He looked unstrung. He was far past the age where he could face the possibility of a dustup with one young man, let alone two.

Andrew said, 'I couldn't have hurt them, George. I could see they were not attacking you.'

'I didn't order you to attack them; I only told you to move towards them. Their own fears did the rest.'

'How can they fear robots?'

'It's a disease of mankind, one of which it is not yet cured. But never mind that. What the devil are you doing here, Andrew? I was on the point of turning back and hiring a helicopter when I found you. How did you get it into your head to go to the library? I would have brought you any books you needed.'

'I am a –' began Andrew.

'Free robot. Yes, yes. All right, what did you want in the library?'

'I want to know more about human beings, about the world, about everything. And about robots, George. I want to write a history about robots.'

George said, 'Well, let's walk home . . . And pick up your clothes first. Andrew, there are a million books on robotics and all of them include histories of the science. The world is growing saturated not only with robots but with information about robots.'

Andrew shook his head, a human gesture he had lately begun to make. 'Not a history of robotics, George. A history of *robots*, by a robot. I want to explain how robots feel about what has happened since the first ones were allowed to work and live on Earth.'

George's eyebrows lifted, but he said nothing in direct response.

Little Miss was just past her eighty-third birthday, but there was nothing about her that was lacking in either energy or determination. She gestured with her cane more often than she propped herself up with it.

She listened to the story in a fury of indignation. She said, 'George, that's horrible. Who were those young ruffians?'

'I don't know. What difference does it make? In the end they did no damage.'

'They might have. You're a lawyer, George, and if you're well off, it's entirely due to the talent of Andrew. It was the money *he* earned that is the foundation of everything we have. He provides the continuity for this family, and I will *not* have him treated as a wind-up toy.'

'What would you have me do, Mother?' asked George.

'I said you're a lawyer. Don't you listen? You set up a test case somehow, and you force the regional courts to declare for robot rights and get the Legislature to pass the necessary bills, and carry the whole thing to the World Court, if you have to. I'll be watching, George, and I'll tolerate no shirking.'

She was serious, and what began as a way of soothing the fearsome old lady became an involved matter with enough legal entanglement to make it interesting. As senior partner of Feingold and Martin, George plotted strategy but left the actual work to his junior partners, with much of it a matter for his son, Paul, who was also a member of the firm and who reported dutifully nearly every day to his grandmother. She, in turn, discussed it every day with Andrew.

Andrew was deeply involved. His work on his book on robots was delayed again as he pored over the legal arguments and even, at times, made very diffident suggestions.

He said, 'George told me that day that human beings have always been afraid of robots. As long as they are, the courts and the legislatures are not likely to work hard on behalf of robots. Should there not be something done about public opinion?'

So while Paul stayed in court, George took to the public platform. It gave him the advantage of being informal, and he sometimes even went so far as to wear the new, loose style of clothing that he called drapery. Paul said, 'Just don't trip over it onstage, Dad.'

George said despondently, 'I'll try not to.'

He addressed the annual convention of holo-news editors on one occasion and said, in part:

'If, by virtue of the Second Law, we can demand of any robot unlimited obedience in all respects not involving harm to a human being, then any human being, *any* human being, has a fearsome power over any robot, *any* robot. In particular, since the Second Law supersedes the Third Law, *any* human being can use the law of obedience to overcome the law of self-protection. He can order any robot to damage itself or even destroy itself for any reason, or for no reason.

'Is this just? Would we treat an animal so? Even an inanimate object that has given us good service has a claim on our consideration. And a robot is not insensible; it is not an animal. It can think well enough to enable it to talk to us, reason with us, joke with us. Can we treat them as friends, can we work together with them, and not give them some of the fruit of that friendship, some of the benefit of co-working?

'If a man has the right to give a robot any order that does not involve harm to a human being, he should have the decency never to give a robot any order that involves harm to a robot, unless human safety absolutely requires it. With great power goes great responsibility, and if the robots have Three Laws to protect men, is it too much to ask that men have a law or two to protect robots?'

Andrew was right. It was the battle over public opinion that held the key to courts and Legislature and in the end a law passed which set up conditions under which robot-harming orders were forbidden. It was endlessly qualified and the punishments for violating the law were totally inadequate, but the principle was established. The final passage by the World Legislature came through on the day of Little Miss's death.

That was no coincidence. Little Miss held on to life desperately during the last debate and let go only when word of victory arrived. Her last smile was for Andrew. Her last words were: 'You have been good to us, Andrew.'

She died with her hand holding his, while her son and his wife and children remained at a respectful distance from both.

Andrew waited patiently while the receptionist disappeared into the inner office. It might have used the holographic chatterbox, but unquestionably it was unmanned (or perhaps unroboted) by having to deal with another robot rather than with a human being.

Andrew passed the time revolving the matter in his mind. Could 'unroboted' be used as an analogue of 'unmanned', or had 'unmanned' become a metaphoric term sufficiently divorced from its original literal meaning to be applied to robots – or to women, for that matter?

Such problems came up frequently as he worked on his book on robots. The trick of thinking out sentences to express all complexities had undoubtedly increased his vocabulary.

Occasionally, someone came into the room to stare at him and he did not try to avoid the glance. He looked at each calmly, and each in turn looked away.

Paul Martin finally came out. He looked surprised, or he would have if Andrew could have made out his expression with certainty. Paul had taken to wearing the heavy makeup that fashion was dictating for both sexes, and though it made sharper and firmer the somewhat bland lines of his face, Andrew disapproved. He found that disapproving of human beings, as long as he did not express it verbally, did not make him very uneasy. He could even write the disapproval. He was sure it had not always been so.

Paul said 'Come in, Andrew. I'm sorry I made you wait but there was something I *had* to finish. Come in. You had said you wanted to talk to me, but I didn't know you meant here in town.'

'If you are busy, Paul, I am prepared to continue to wait.'

Paul glanced at the interplay of shifting shadows on the dial on the wall that served as timepiece and said, 'I can make some time. Did you come alone?'

'I hired an automatobile.'

'Any trouble?' Paul asked with more than a trace of anxiety.

'I wasn't expecting any. My rights are protected.'

Paul looked the more anxious for that. 'Andrew, I've explained that the law is unenforceable, at least under most conditions . . . And if you insist on wearing clothes, you'll run into trouble eventually – just like that first time.'

'And only time, Paul. I'm sorry you are displeased.'

'Well, look at it this way; you are virtually a living legend, Andrew, and you are too valuable in many different ways for you to have any right to take chances with yourself . . . How's the book coming?'

'I am approaching the end, Paul. The publisher is quite pleased.'

'Good!'

'I don't know that he's necessarily pleased with the book as a book. I think he expects to sell many copies because it's written by a robot and it's that that pleases him.'

'Only human, I'm afraid.'

'I am not displeased. Let it sell for whatever reason since it will mean money and I can use some.'

'Grandmother left you –'

'Little Miss was generous, and I'm sure I can count on the family to help me out further. But it is the royalties from the book on which I am counting to help me through the next step.'

'What next step is that?'

'I wish to see the head of U. S. Robots and Mechanical Men, Inc. I have tried to make an appointment, but so far I have not been able to reach him. The corporation did not co-operate with me in the writing of the book, so I am not surprised, you understand.'

Paul was clearly amused. 'Co-operation is the last thing you can expect. They didn't co-operate with us in our great fight for robot rights. Quite the reverse, and you can see why. Give a robot rights and people may not want to buy them.'

'Nevertheless,' said Andrew, 'if you call them, you may obtain an interview for me.'

'I'm no more popular with them than you are, Andrew.'

'But perhaps you can hint that by seeing me they may head off a campaign by Feingold and Martin to strengthen the rights of robots further.'

'Wouldn't that be a lie, Andrew?'

'Yes, Paul, and I can't tell one. That is why you must call.'

'Ah, you can't lie, but you can urge me to tell a lie, is that it? You're getting more human all the time, Andrew.'

It was not easy to arrange, even with Paul's supposedly weighted name.

But it was finally carried through and, when it was, Harley Smythe-Robertson, who, on his mother's side, was descended from the original founder of the corporation and who had adopted the hyphenation to indicate it, looked remarkably unhappy. He was approaching retirement age and his entire tenure as president had been devoted to the matter of robot rights. His grey hair was plastered thinly over the top of his scalp, his face was not made up, and he eyed Andrew with brief hostility from time to time.

Andrew said, 'Sir, nearly a century ago, I was told by a Merton Mansky of this corporation that the mathematics governing the plotting of the positronic pathways was far too complicated to permit of any but approximate solutions and that therefore my own capacities were not fully predictable.'

'That was a century ago.' Smythe-Robertson hesitated, then said icily, '*Sir*. It is true no longer. Our robots are made with precision now and are trained precisely to their jobs.'

'Yes,' said Paul, who had come along, as he said, to make sure that the corporation played fair, 'with the result that my receptionist must be guided at every point once events depart from the conventional, however slightly.'

Smythe-Robertson said, 'You would be much more displeased if it were to improvise.'

Andrew said, 'Then you no longer manufacture robots like myself that are flexible and adaptable.'

'No longer.'

'The research I have done in connection with my book,' said Andrew, 'indicates that I am the oldest robot presently in active operation.'

'The oldest presently,' said Smythe-Robertson, 'and the oldest ever. The oldest that will ever be. No robot is useful after the twenty-fifth year. They are called in and replaced with newer models.'

'No robot *as presently manufactured* is useful after the twenty-fifth year,' said Paul pleasantly. 'Andrew is quite exceptional in this respect.'

Andrew, adhering to the path he had marked out for himself, said, 'As the oldest robot in the world and the most flexible, am I not unusual enough to merit special treatment from the company?'

'Not at all,' said Smythe-Robertson freezingly. 'Your

unusualness is an embarrassment to the company. If you were on lease, instead of having been a sale outright through some mischance, you would long since have been replaced.'

'But that is exactly the point,' said Andrew. 'I am a free robot and I own myself. Therefore I come to you and ask you to replace me. You cannot do this without the owner's consent. Nowadays, that consent is extorted as a condition of the lease, but in my time this did not happen.'

Smythe-Robertson was looking both startled and puzzled, and for a moment there was silence. Andrew found himself staring at the holograph on the wall. It was a death mask of Susan Calvin, patron saint of all roboticists. She was dead nearly two centuries now, but as a result of writing his book Andrew knew her so well he could half persuade himself that he had met her in life.

Smythe-Robertson said, 'How can I replace you for you? If I replace you as a robot, how can I donate the new robot to you as owner since in the very act of replacement you cease to exist?' He smiled grimly.

'Not at all difficult,' interposed Paul. 'The seat of Andrew's personality is his positronic brain, and it is the one part that cannot be replaced without creating a new robot. The positronic brain, therefore, is Andrew the owner. Every other part of the robotic body can be replaced without affecting the robot's personality, and those other parts are the brain's possessions. Andrew, I should say, wants to supply his brain with a new robotic body.'

'That's right,' said Andrew calmly. He turned to Smythe-Robertson. 'You have manufactured androids, haven't you? Robots that have the outward appearance of humans complete to the texture of the skin?'

Smythe-Robertson said, 'Yes, we have. They worked perfectly well, with their synthetic fibrous skins and tendons. There was virtually no metal anywhere except for the brain, yet they were nearly as tough as metal robots. They were tougher, weight for weight.'

Paul looked interested. 'I didn't know that. How many are on the market?'

'None,' said Smythe-Robertson. 'They were much more expensive than metal models and a market survey showed they would not be accepted. They looked too human.'

Andrew said, 'But the corporation retains its expertise, I assume. Since it does, I wish to request that I be replaced by an organic robot, an android.'

Paul looked surprised. 'Good Lord,' he said.

Smythe-Robertson stiffened. 'Quite impossible!'

'Why is it impossible?' asked Andrew. 'I will pay any reasonable fee, of course.'

Smythe-Robertson said, 'We do not manufacture androids.'

'You do not *choose* to manufacture androids,' interposed Paul quickly. 'That is not the same as being unable to manufacture them.'

Smythe-Robertson said, 'Nevertheless, the manufacture of androids is against public policy.'

'There is no law against it,' said Paul.

'Nevertheless, we do not manufacture them, and we will not.'

Paul cleared his throat. 'Mr Smythe-Robertson,' he said, 'Andrew is a free robot who is under the purview of the law guaranteeing robots' rights. You are aware of this, I take it?'

'Only too well.'

'This robot, as a free robot, chooses to wear clothes. This results in his being frequently humiliated by thoughtless human beings despite the law against the humiliation of robots. It is difficult to prosecute vague offences that don't meet with the general disapproval of those who must decide on guilt and innocence.'

'U. S. Robots understood that from the start. Your father's firm unfortunately did not.'

'My father is dead now,' said Paul, 'but what I see is that we have here a clear offence with a clear target.'

'What are you talking about?' said Smythe-Robertson.

'My client, Andrew Martin – he has just become my client – is a free robot who is entitled to ask U. S. Robots and Mechanical Men, Inc., for the right of replacement, which the corporation supplies anyone who owns a robot for more than twenty-five years. In fact, the corporation insists on such replacement.'

Paul was smiling and thoroughly at his ease. He went on, 'The positronic brain of my client is the owner of the body of my client – which is certainly more than twenty-five years old. The positronic brain demands the replacement of the body and offers to pay any reasonable fee for an android body as that replacement. If you refuse the request, my client undergoes humiliation and we will sue.

'While public opinion would not ordinarily support the claim of a robot in such a case, may I remind you that U. S. Robots is not popular with the public generally. Even those who most use and profit from robots are suspicious of the corporation. This may be a hangover from the days when robots were widely feared. It may be resentment against the power and wealth of U. S. Robots, which has a worldwide monopoly. Whatever the cause may be, the resentment exists and I think you will find that you would prefer not to withstand a lawsuit, particularly since my client is wealthy and will live for many more centuries and will have no reason to refrain from fighting the battle forever.'

Smythe-Robertson had slowly reddened. 'You are trying to force me to –'

'I force you to do nothing,' said Paul. 'If you wish to refuse to accede to my client's reasonable request, you may by all means do so and we will leave without another word . . . But we will sue, as is certainly our right, and you will find that you will eventually lose.'

Smythe-Robertson said, 'Well –' and paused.

'I see that you are going to accede,' said Paul. 'You may hesitate but you will come to it in the end. Let me assure you, then, of one further point. If, in the process of transferring my client's positronic brain from his present body to an organic one, there is any damage, however slight, then I will never rest till I've nailed the corporation to the ground. I will, if necessary, take every possible step to mobilize public opinion against the corporation if one brain path of my client's platinum-iridium essence is scrambled.' He turned to Andrew and said, 'Do you agree to all this, Andrew?'

Andrew hesitated a full minute. It amounted to the approval of lying, of blackmail, of the badgering and humiliation of a human being. But not physical harm, he told himself, not physical harm.

He managed at last to come out with a rather faint 'Yes'.

It was like being constructed again. For days, then for weeks, finally for months, Andrew found himself not himself somehow, and the simplest actions kept giving rise to hesitation.

Paul was frantic. 'They've damaged you, Andrew. We'll have to institute suit.'

Andrew spoke very slowly. 'You mustn't. You'll never be able to prove – something – m-m-m-m –'

'Malice?'

'Malice. Besides, I grow stronger, better. It's the tr-tr-tr –'

'Tremble?'

'Trauma. After all, there's never been such an op-op-operation before.'

Andrew could feel his brain from the inside. No one else could. He knew he was well, and during the months that it took him to learn full co-ordination and full positronic interplay, he spent hours before the mirror.

Not quite human! The face was stiff – too stiff – and the motions were too deliberate. They lacked the careless free flow of the human being, but perhaps that might come with time. At least he could wear clothes without the ridiculous anomaly of a metal face going along with it.

Eventually he said, 'I will be going back to work.'

Paul laughed and said, 'That means you are well. What will you be doing? Another book?'

'No,' said Andrew seriously. 'I live too long for any one career to seize me by the throat and never let me go. There was a time when I was primarily an artist and I can still turn to that. And there was a time when I was a historian and I can still turn to that. But now I wish to be a robobiologist.'

'A robopsychologist, you mean.'

'No. That would imply the study of positronic brains and at the moment I lack the desire to do that. A robobiologist, it seems to me, would be concerned with the working of the body attached to that brain.'

'Wouldn't that be a roboticist?'

'A roboticist works with a metal body. I would be studying an organic humanoid body, of which I have the only one, as far as I know.'

'You narrow your field,' said Paul thoughtfully. 'As an artist, all conception was yours; as a historian, you dealt chiefly with robots; as a robobiologist, you will deal with yourself.'

Andrew nodded. 'It would seem so.'

Andrew had to start from the very beginning, for he knew nothing of ordinary biology, almost nothing of science. He became a familiar sight in the libraries, where he sat at the electronic indices for hours at a time, looking perfectly normal in clothes. Those few who knew he was a robot in no way interfered with him.

He built a laboratory in a room he had added to his house, and his library grew, too.

Years passed, and Paul came to him one day and said, 'It's a pity you're no longer working on the history of robots. I understand U. S. Robots is adopting a radically new policy.'

Paul had aged, and his deteriorating eyes had been replaced with photoptic cells. In that respect, he had drawn closer to Andrew. Andrew said, 'What have they done?'

'They are manufacturing central computers, gigantic positronic brains, really, which communicate with anywhere from a dozen to a thousand robots by microwave. The robots themselves have no brains at all. They are the limbs of the gigantic brain, and the two are physically separate.'

'Is that more efficient?'

'U. S. Robots claims it is. Smythe-Robertson established the new direction before he died, however, and it's my notion that it's a backlash at you. U. S. Robots is determined that they will make no robots that will give them the type of trouble you have, and for that reason they separate brain and body. The brain will have no body to wish changed; the body will have no brain to wish anything.

'It's amazing, Andrew,' Paul went on, 'the influence you have had on the history of robots. It was your artistry that encouraged U. S. Robots to make robots more precise and specialized; it was your freedom that resulted in the establishment of the principle of robotic rights; it was your insistence on an android body that made U. S. Robots switch to brain-body separation.'

Andrew said, 'I suppose in the end the corporation will produce one vast brain controlling several billion robotic bodies. All the eggs will be in one basket. Dangerous. Not proper at all.'

'I think you're right,' said Paul, 'but I don't suspect it will come to pass for a century at least, and I won't live to see it. In fact, I may not live to see next year.'

'Paul!' said Andrew in concern.

Paul shrugged. 'We're mortal, Andrew. We're not like you. It doesn't matter too much, but it does make it important to assure you on one point. I'm the last of the human Martins. There are collaterals descended from my great-aunt, but they don't count. The money I control personally will be left to the trust in your name, and, as far as anyone can foresee the future, you will be economically secure.'

'Unnecessary,' said Andrew with difficulty. In all this time, he could not get used to the deaths of the Martins.

Paul said, 'Let's not argue. That's the way it's going to be. What are you working on?'

'I am designing a system for allowing androids – myself – to gain energy from the combustion of hydrocarbons, rather than from atomic cells.'

Paul raised his eyebrows. 'So that they will breathe and eat?'

'Yes.'

'How long have you been pushing in that direction?'

'For a long time now, but I think I have designed an adequate combustion chamber for catalysed controlled breakdown.'

'But why, Andrew? The atomic cell is surely infinitely better.'

'In some ways, perhaps, but the atomic cell is inhuman.'

It took time, but Andrew had time. In the first place, he did not wish to do anything till Paul had died in peace.

With the death of the great-grandson of Sir, Andrew felt more nearly exposed to a hostile world, and for that reason was the more determined to continue the path he had long ago chosen.

Yet he was not really alone. If a man had died, the firm of Feingold and Martin lived, for a corporation does not die any more than a robot does. The firm had its directions and it followed them soullessly. By way of the trust and through the law firm, Andrew continued to be wealthy. And in return for their own large annual retainer, Feingold and Martin involved themselves in the legal aspects of the new combustion chamber.

When the time came for Andrew to visit U. S. Robots and Mechanical Men, Inc., he did it alone. Once he had gone with Sir and once with Paul. This time, the third time, he was alone and manlike.

U. S. Robots had changed. The production plant had been shifted to a large space station, as was the case with

more and more industries. With them had gone many
robots. The Earth itself was becoming parklike, with its
one-billion-person population stabilized and perhaps not
more than 30 per cent of its at least equally large robot
population independently brained.

The director of research was Alvin Magdescu, dark of
complexion and hair, with a little pointed beard and wearing nothing above the waist but the breastband that
fashion dictated. Andrew himself was well covered in the
older fashion of several decades back.

Magdescu said, 'I know you, of course, and I'm rather
pleased to see you. You're our most notorious product,
and it's a pity old Smythe-Robertson was so set against
you. We could have done a great deal with you.'

'You still can,' said Andrew.

'No, I don't think so. We're past the time. We've had
robots on Earth for over a century, but that's changing.
It will be back to space with them and those that stay here
won't be brained.'

'But there remains myself, and I stay on Earth.'

'True, but there doesn't seem to be much of the robot
about you. What new request have you?'

'To be still less a robot. Since I am so far organic, I
wish an organic source of energy. I have here the plans –'

Magdescu did not hasten through them. He might have
intended to at first, but he stiffened and grew intent. At
one point he said, 'This is remarkably ingenious. Who
thought of all this?'

'I did,' said Andrew.

Magdescu looked up at him sharply, then said, 'It would
amount to a major overhaul of your body, and an experimental one, since it has never been attempted before. I
advise against it. Remain as you are.'

Andrew's face had limited means of expression, but
impatience showed plainly in his voice. 'Dr Magdescu, you
miss the entire point. You have no choice but to accede
to my request. If such devices can be built into my body,
they can be built into human bodies as well. The tendency

to lengthen human life by prosthetic devices has already been remarked on. There are no devices better than the ones I have designed and am designing.

'As it happens, I control the patents by way of the firm of Feingold and Martin. We are quite capable of going into business for ourselves and developing the kind of prosthetic devices that may end by producing human beings with many of the properties of robots. Your own business will then suffer.

'If, however, you operate on me now and agree to do so under similar circumstances in the future, you will receive permission to make use of the patents and control the technology of both robots and the prosthetization of human beings. The initial leasing will not be granted, of course, until after the first operation is completed successfully, and after enough time has passed to demonstrate that it is indeed successful.' Andrew felt scarcely any First Law inhibition to the stern conditions he was setting a human being. He was learning to reason that what seemed like cruelty might, in the long run, be kindness.

Magdescu looked stunned. He said, 'I'm not the one to decide something like this. That's a corporate decision that would take time.'

'I can wait a reasonable time,' said Andrew, 'but only a reasonable time.' And he thought with satisfaction that Paul himself could not have done it better.

It took only a reasonable time, and the operation was a success.

Magdescu said, 'I was very much against the operation, Andrew, but not for the reasons you might think. I was not in the least against the experiment, if it had been on someone else. I hated risking *your* positronic brain. Now that you have the positronic pathways interacting with simulated nerve pathways, it might be difficult to rescue the brain intact if the body went bad.'

'I had every faith in the skill of the staff at U. S. Robots,' said Andrew. 'And I can eat now.'

'Well, you can sip olive oil. It will mean occasional cleanings of the combustion chamber, as we have explained to you. Rather an uncomfortable touch, I should think.'

'Perhaps, if I did not expect to go further. Self-cleaning is not impossible. In fact, I am working on a device that will deal with solid food that may be expected to contain incombustible fractions – indigestible matter, so to speak, that will have to be discarded.'

'You would then have to develop an anus.'

'The equivalent.'

'What else, Andrew?'

'Everything else.'

'Genitalia, too?'

'Insofar as they will fit my plans. My body is a canvas on which I intend to draw –'

Magdescu waited for the sentence to be completed, and when it seemed that it would not be, he completed it himself. 'A man?'

'We shall see,' said Andrew.

Magdescu said, 'It's a puny ambition, Andrew. You're better than a man. You've gone downhill from the moment you opted for organicism.'

'My brain has not suffered.'

'No, it hasn't. I'll grant you that. But, Andrew, the whole new breakthrough in prosthetic devices made possible by your patents is being marketed under your name. You're recognized as the inventor and you're honoured for it – as you are. Why play further games with your body?'

Andrew did not answer.

The honours came. He accepted membership in several learned societies, including one that was devoted to the new science he had established; the one he had called robobiology but which had come to be termed prosthetology.

On the one hundred fiftieth anniversary of his construction, there was a testimonial dinner given in his honour at U. S. Robots. If Andrew saw irony in this, he kept it to himself.

Alvin Magdescu came out of retirement to chair the dinner. He was himself ninety-four years old and was alive because he had prosthetized devices that, among other things, fulfilled the function of liver and kidneys. The dinner reached its climax when Magdescu, after a short and emotional talk, raised his glass to toast 'the Sesquicentennial Robot'.

Andrew had had the sinews of his face redesigned to the point where he could show a range of emotions, but he sat through all the ceremonies solemnly passive. He did not like to be a Sesquicentennial Robot.

It was prosthetology that finally took Andrew off the Earth. In the decades that followed the celebration of the Sesquicentennial, the Moon had come to be a world more Earthlike than Earth in every respect but its gravitational pull, and in its underground cities there was a fairly dense population.

Prosthetized devices there had to take the lesser gravity into account and Andrew spent five years on the Moon working with local prosthetologists to make the necessary adaptations. When not at his work, he wandered among the robot population, every one of which treated him with the robotic obsequiousness due a man.

He came back to an Earth that was humdrum and quiet by comparison and visited the offices of Feingold and Martin to announce his return.

The current head of the firm, Simon DeLong, was surprised. He said, 'We had been told you were returning, Andrew' (he had almost said 'Mr Martin'), 'but we were not expecting you till next week.'

'I grew impatient,' said Andrew brusquely. He was anxious to get to the point. 'On the Moon, Simon, I was in charge of a research team of twenty human scientists. I gave orders that no one questioned. The Lunar robots deferred to me as they would to a human being. Why, then, am I not a human being?'

A wary look entered DeLong's eyes. He said, 'My dear

Andrew, as you have just explained, you are treated as a human being by both robots and human beings. You are therefore a human being *de facto*.'

'To be a human being *de facto* is not enough. I want not only to be treated as one, but to be legally identified as one. I want to be a human being *de jure*.'

'Now that is another matter,' said DeLong. 'There we would run into human prejudice and into the undoubted fact that however much you may be like a human being, you are *not* a human being.'

'In what way not?' asked Andrew. 'I have the shape of a human being and organs equivalent to those of a human being. My organs, in fact, are identical to some of those in a prosthetized human being. I have contributed artistically, literarily, and scientifically to human culture as much as any human being now alive. What more can one ask?'

'I myself would ask nothing more. The trouble is that it would take an act of the World Legislature to define you as a human being. Frankly, I wouldn't expect that to happen.'

'To whom on the Legislature could I speak?'

'To the chairman of the Science and Technology Committee perhaps.'

'Can you arrange a meeting?'

'But you scarcely need an intermediary. In your position, you can –'

'No. *You* arrange it.' (It didn't even occur to Andrew that he was giving a flat order to a human being. He had grown accustomed to that on the Moon.) 'I want him to know that the firm of Feingold and Martin is backing me in this to the hilt.'

'Well, now –'

'To the hilt, Simon. In one hundred seventy-three years I have in one fashion or another contributed greatly to this firm. I have been under obligation to individual members of the firm in times past. I am not now. It is rather the other way around now and I am calling in my debts.'

DeLong said, 'I will do what I can.'

The chairman of the Science and Technology Committee was of the East Asian region and she was a woman. Her name was Chee Li-Hsing and her transparent garments (obscuring what she wanted obscured only by their dazzle) made her look plastic-wrapped.

She said, 'I sympathize with your wish for full human rights. There have been times in history when segments of the human population fought for full human rights. What rights, however, can you possibly want that you do not have?'

'As simple a thing as my right to life. A robot can be dismantled at any time.'

'A human being can be executed at any time.'

'Execution can only follow due process of law. There is no trial needed for my dismantling. Only the word of a human being in authority is needed to end me. Besides – besides –' Andrew tried desperately to allow no sign of pleading, but his carefully designed tricks of human expression and tone of voice betrayed him here. 'The truth is, I want to be a man. I have wanted it through six generations of human beings.'

Li-Hsing looked up at him out of darkly sympathetic eyes. 'The Legislature can pass a law declaring you one – they could pass a law declaring a stone statue to be defined as a man. Whether they will actually do so is, however, as likely in the first case as the second. Congress-people are as human as the rest of the population, and there is always that element of suspicion against robots.'

'Even now?'

'Even now. We would all allow the fact that you have earned the prize of humanity, and yet there would remain the fear of setting an undesirable precedent.'

'What precedent? I am the only free robot, the only one of my type, and there will never be another. You may consult U. S. Robots.'

' "Never" is a long time, Andrew – or, if you prefer,

Mr Martin – since I will gladly give you my personal
accolade as man. You will find that most congresspeople
will not be willing to set the precedent, no matter how
meaningless such a precedent might be. Mr Martin, you
have my sympathy, but I cannot tell you to hope. Indeed –'

She sat back and her forehead wrinkled. 'Indeed, if the
issue grows too heated, there might well arise a certain
sentiment, both inside the Legislature and outside, for the
dismantling you mentioned. Doing away with you could
turn out to be the easiest way of resolving the dilemma.
Consider that before deciding to push matters.'

Andrew said, 'Will no one remember the technique of
prosthetology, something that is almost entirely mine?'

'It may seem cruel, but they won't. Or if they do, it will
be remembered against you. It will be said you did it only
for yourself. It will be said it was part of a campaign to
roboticize human beings, or to humanify robots; and in
either case evil and vicious. You have never been part of
a political hate campaign, Mr Martin, and I tell you that
you will be the object of vilification of a kind neither you
nor I would credit, and there would be people who'll
believe it all. Mr Martin, let your life be.' She rose and,
next to Andrew's seated figure, she seemed small and
almost childlike.

Andrew said, 'If I decide to fight for my humanity, will
you be on my side?'

She thought, then said, 'I will be – insofar as I can be.
If at any time such a stand would appear to threaten my
political future, I may have to abandon you, since it is not
an issue I feel to be at the very root of my beliefs. I am
trying to be honest with you.'

'Thank you, and I will ask no more. I intend to fight
this through whatever the consequences, and I will ask
you for your help only for as long as you can give it.'

It was not a direct fight. Feingold and Martin counselled
patience and Andrew muttered grimly that he had an
endless supply of that. Feingold and Martin then entered

on a campaign to narrow and restrict the area of combat.

They instituted a lawsuit denying the obligation to pay debts to an individual with a prosthetic heart on the grounds that the possession of a robotic organ removed humanity, and with it the constitutional rights of human beings.

They fought the matter skilfully and tenaciously, losing at every step but always in such a way that the decision was forced to be as broad as possible, and then carrying it by way of appeals to the World Court.

It took years, and millions of dollars.

When the final decision was handed down, DeLong held what amounted to a victory celebration over the legal loss. Andrew was, of course, present in the company offices on the occasion.

'We've done two things, Andrew,' said DeLong, 'both of which are good. First of all, we have established the fact that no number of artefacts in the human body causes it to cease being a human body. Secondly, we have engaged public opinion in the question in such a way as to put it fiercely on the side of a broad interpretation of humanity since there is not a human being in existence who does not hope for prosthetics if that will keep him alive.'

'And do you think the Legislature will now grant me my humanity?' asked Andrew.

DeLong looked faintly uncomfortable. 'As to that, I cannot be optimistic. There remains the one organ that the World Court has used as the criterion of humanity. Human beings have an organic cellular brain and robots have a platinum-iridium positronic brain if they have one at all – and you certainly have a positronic brain ... No, Andrew, don't get that look in your eye. We lack the knowledge to duplicate the work of a cellular brain in artificial structures close enough to the organic type to allow it to fall within the Court's decision. Not even you could do it.'

'What should we do, then?'

'Make the attempt, of course. Congresswoman Li-Hsing

will be on our side and a growing number of other congress-people. The President will undoubtedly go along with a majority of the Legislature in this matter.'

'Do we have a majority?'

'No, far from it. But we might get one if the public will allow its desire for a broad interpretation of humanity to extend to you. A small chance, I admit, but if you do not wish to give up, we must gamble for it.'

'I do not wish to give up.'

Congresswoman Li-Hsing was considerably older than she had been when Andrew had first met her. Her transparent garments were long gone. Her hair was now close-cropped and her coverings were tubular. Yet still Andrew clung, as closely as he could within the limits of reasonable taste, to the style of clothing that had prevailed when he had first adopted clothing over a century before.

She said, 'We've gone as far as we can, Andrew. We'll try once more after recess, but, to be honest, defeat is certain and the whole thing will have to be given up. All my most recent efforts have only earned me a certain defeat in the coming congressional campaign.'

'I know,' said Andrew, 'and it distresses me. You said once you would abandon me if it came to that. Why have you not done so?'

'One can change one's mind, you know. Somehow, abandoning you became a higher price than I cared to pay for just one more term. As it is, I've been in the Legislature for over a quarter of a century. It's enough.'

'Is there no way we can change minds, Chee?'

'We've changed all that are amenable to reason. The rest – the majority – cannot be moved from their emotional antipathies.'

'Emotional antipathy is not a valid reason for voting one way or the other.'

'I know that, Andrew, but they don't advance emotional antipathy as their reason.'

Andrew said cautiously, 'It all comes down to the brain,

then, but must we leave it at the level of cells versus positrons? Is there no way of forcing a functional definition? Must we say that a brain is made of this or that? May we not say that a brain is something – anything – capable of a certain level of thought?'

'Won't work,' said Li-Hsing. 'Your brain is manmade, the human brain is not. Your brain is constructed, theirs developed. To any human being who is intent on keeping up the barrier between himself and a robot, those differences are a steel wall a mile high and a mile thick.'

'If we could get at the sources of their antipathy – the very source of –'

'After all your years,' said Li-Hsing sadly, 'you are still trying to reason out the human being. Poor Andrew, don't be angry, but it's the robot in you that drives you in that direction.'

'I don't know,' said Andrew. 'If I could bring myself –'

If he could bring himself –

He had known for a long time it might come to that, and in the end he was at the surgeon's. He found one, skilful enough for the job at hand, which meant a robot surgeon, for no human surgeon could be trusted in this connection, either in ability or in intention.

The surgeon could not have performed the operation on a human being, so Andrew, after putting off the moment of decision with a sad line of questioning that reflected the turmoil within himself, put the First Law to one side by saying, 'I, too, am a robot.'

He then said, as firmly as he had learned to form the words even at human beings over these past decades, 'I *order* you to carry through the operation on me.'

In the absence of the First Law, an order so firmly given from one who looked so much like a man activated the Second Law sufficiently to carry the day.

Andrew's feeling of weakness was, he was sure, quite imaginary. He had recovered from the operation. Nevertheless, he leaned, as unobtrusively as he could manage, against the wall. It would be entirely too revealing to sit.

Li-Hsing said, 'The final vote will come this week, Andrew. I've been able to delay it no longer, and we must lose . . . And that will be it, Andrew.'

Andrew said, 'I am grateful for your skill at delay. It gave me the time I needed, and I took the gamble I had to.'

'What gamble is this?' asked Li-Hsing with open concern.

'I couldn't tell you, or the people at Feingold and Martin. I was sure I would be stopped. See here, if it is the brain that is at issue, isn't the greatest difference of all the matter of immortality? Who really cares what a brain looks like or is built of or how it was formed? What matters is that brain cells die; *must* die. Even if every other organ in the body is maintained or replaced, the brain cells, which cannot be replaced without changing and therefore killing the personality, must eventually die.

'My own positronic pathways have lasted nearly two centuries without perceptible change and can last for centuries more. Isn't *that* the fundamental barrier? Human beings can tolerate an immortal robot, for it doesn't matter how long a machine lasts. They cannot tolerate an immortal human being, since their own mortality is endurable only so long as it is universal. And for that reason they won't make me a human being.'

Li-Hsing said, 'What is it you're leading up to, Andrew?'

'I have removed that problem. Decades ago, my positronic brain was connected to organic nerves. Now, one last operation has arranged that connection in such a way that slowly – quite slowly – the potential is being drained from my pathways.'

Li-Hsing's finely wrinkled face showed no expression for a moment. Then her lips tightened. 'Do you mean you've arranged to die, Andrew? You can't have. That violates the Third Law.'

'No,' said Andrew, 'I have chosen between the death of my body and the death of my aspirations and desires.

To have let my body live at the cost of the greater death is what would have violated the Third Law.'

Li-Hsing seized his arm as though she were about to shake him. She stopped herself. 'Andrew, it won't work. Change it back.'

'It can't be. Too much damage was done. I have a year to live – more or less. I will last through the two hundredth anniversary of my construction. I was weak enough to arrange that.'

'How can it be worth it? Andrew, you're a fool.'

'If it brings me humanity, that will be worth it. If it doesn't, it will bring an end to striving, and that will be worth it, too.'

And Li-Hsing did something that astonished herself. Quietly, she began to weep.

It was odd how that last deed caught at the imagination of the world. All that Andrew had done before had not swayed them. But he had finally accepted even death in order to be human, and the sacrifice was too great to be rejected.

The final ceremony was timed, quite deliberately, for the two hundredth anniversary. The World President was to sign the act and make it law, and the ceremony would be visible on a global network and would be beamed to the Lunar state and even to the Martian colony.

Andrew was in a wheelchair. He could still walk, but only shakily.

With mankind watching, the World President said, 'Fifty years ago, you were declared a Sesquicentennial Robot, Andrew.' After a pause, and in a more solemn tone, he said, 'Today we declare you a Bicentennial Man, Mr Martin.'

And Andrew, smiling, held out his hand to shake that of the President.

Andrew's thoughts were slowly fading as he lay in bed.

Desperately he seized at them. Man! He was a man!

He wanted that to be his last thought. He wanted to dissolve – die – with that.

He opened his eyes one more time and for one last time recognized Li-Hsing waiting solemnly. There were others, but those were only shadows, unrecognizable shadows. Only Li-Hsing stood out against the deepening grey. Slowly, inchingly, he held out his hand to her and very dimly and faintly felt her take it.

She was fading in his eyes, as the last of his thoughts trickled away.

But before she faded completely, one last fugitive thought came to him and rested for a moment on his mind before everything stopped.

'Little Miss,' he whispered, too low to be heard.

PART 3

Mathematics

It takes a lot of ingenuity for me to write about mathematics, since I know so little about it.

Why bother to write about it, then? Because I love it, that's why. What I must do (and here is where the ingenuity comes in) is find some portion of mathematics so incredibly simple that I can understand it. Once I've done that, all I have to do is write about it in such a way (more ingenuity) that no one detects my essential ignorance.

For children, I wrote How Did We Find Out About Numbers? *(Book 142), and in it I presented a section on Roman numerals, which I had learned how to use when I was seven or eight and which, fortunately, I had never forgotten. Here it is:*

from HOW DID WE FIND OUT ABOUT NUMBERS? *(1973)*

About two thousand years ago, large sections of Europe, Asia, and Africa were ruled from the city of Rome. The Roman Empire, as it was called, used a system of numerals based on five.

The Romans used symbols taken from their alphabet. Fortunately, the people of Europe and America use the Roman alphabet so the Roman symbols are familiar to us.

The Romans began by letting the number one be written as I. For two, three, and four they had II, III, and IIII. So far it looks like the Egyptian system, but the Romans only allowed four of any symbol to be used before inventing a new symbol. Instead of writing five as the Egyptian IIIII they wrote it as V.

Instead of writing six as IIIIII they wrote VI. Nine was VIIII. If they wrote ten as VIIIII, that would mean five of the symbol I and they didn't allow that. They used a new symbol for ten, which was X.

The list of symbols up to one thousand is as follows:

$$
\begin{array}{rcl}
\mathbf{I} &=& \text{one} \\
\mathbf{V} &=& \text{five} \\
\mathbf{X} &=& \text{ten} \\
\mathbf{L} &=& \text{fifty} \\
\mathbf{C} &=& \text{one hundred} \\
\mathbf{D} &=& \text{five hundred} \\
\mathbf{M} &=& \text{one thousand}
\end{array}
$$

By using special symbols for five, fifty, and five hundred, the Romans never had to use more than four of any of the symbols for one, ten, or one hundred.

To write twenty-two they wrote XXII. Seventy-three is LXXIII. Four hundred eighteen is CCCCXVIII. One thousand nine hundred ninety-nine is MDCCCCLXXXXVIIII. If you try to write one thousand nine hundred ninety-nine by the Egyptian system, you would need one symbol for thousand, and nine symbols each for hundred, ten, and one. That would mean twenty-eight symbols all together. In Roman numerals only sixteen symbols are needed.

The Egyptian system uses only four different kinds of symbols, while the Roman system uses seven. In the Roman system you need less counting but more memorizing.

When these Roman numerals were first developed, it didn't matter in what order the symbols were placed. Whether you wrote XVI or XIV or IXV or VIX, it all came to sixteen. No matter in what order you add ten, five, and one, you end up with sixteen.

Of course, it is easier to add up a number if you arrange the symbols according to some convenient system. The usual way is to put all the symbols of the same sort together. The largest symbol is on the left and as you move to the right you write down smaller and smaller symbols. Thus seventy-eight would always be written LXXVIII, working down from L to X to V to I.

The later Romans thought of a way of still further decreasing the number of a particular symbol that had to be written down. As long as symbols were always written from left to right and from large to small, why not sometimes reverse the order?

When you put the smaller symbol after the larger one in the usual way you add the two. Therefore, VI is 'five plus one', or six. If on the other hand you put the smaller symbol *before* the larger one, you *subtract* it from the larger. In this way IV is 'five minus one', or four.

By writing four as IV instead of IIII you have to write and read only two symbols instead of four, but you have to notice the positions and remember to subtract instead of add.

In the same way, XL is forty while LX is sixty and XC is ninety while CX is one hundred ten and CM is nine hundred while MC is one thousand one hundred.

The year nineteen seventy-three can be written MCMLXXIII instead of MDCCCCLXXIII – eight symbols instead of twelve. One thousand nine hundred ninety-nine can be written MCMXCIX instead of MDCCCCLXXXX-VIIII – seven symbols instead of sixteen.

Of course, once you start using the subtracting notion, you can't scramble the order of the symbols anymore. It becomes important to place each symbol exactly.

The western part of the Roman Empire broke up just about one thousand five hundred years ago. The people of western Europe kept on using Roman numerals for more than seven hundred years after the Roman Empire had come to an end.

If Roman numerals are easy to grasp and explain, Arabic numerals are even easier, especially since everyone in our culture over the age of six already knows about them (or is supposed to). That means I can understand them, too, and need only find some aspect of them that isn't entirely familiar.

Suppose we let the Arabic numerals represent larger and larger numbers. How can we represent such very large numbers and where do we stop?

To answer questions like that, I have my F & SF essays. My first F & SF essay appeared in the November 1958 issue, and since then I have continued them at monthly intervals, without missing an issue, for twenty years. Six collections of F & SF essays are included among my first hundred books, but I did not stop there. Among my second hundred books are seven more collections (plus four additional collections that included older F & SF essays, rearranged and updated, from my first hundred books).

One of these new collections, Of Matters Great and Small *(Book 159), which Doubleday published in 1975, contains the following essay on very much larger numbers:*

'Skewered!' *(1974)*

I don't write many mathematical articles in this series, and for a very good reason. I don't have a mathematical mind and I am not one of those who, by mere thought, finds himself illuminated by a mathematical concept.

I have, however, a nephew, Daniel Asimov by name, who *does* have a mathematical mind. He is the other Ph.D. in the family and he is now an Assistant Professor of Mathematics at the University of Minnesota.

Some years ago, when he was yet a student at M.I.T., Danny had occasion to write to Martin Gardner and point out a small error in Gardner's excellent 'Mathematical Recreations' column in *Scientific American*. Gardner acknowledged the error and wrote me to tell me about it and to ask a natural question. 'Am I correct in assuming,' said he, 'that Daniel Asimov is your son?'

Well! As everyone who knows me knows, I am only a little past thirty right now and was only a little past thirty at the time, some years ago, when this was taking place. I therefore wrote a letter to Gardner and told him, with some stiffness: 'I am not old enough, Martin, to have a son who is old enough to be going to M.I.T. Danny is the son of my younger brother.'

Friends of mine who have heard me tell this story keep assuring me that my statement involves a logical contradiction, but, as I say, I do not have a mathematical mind, and I just don't see that.

And yet I must write another mathematical article now because over eleven years ago I wrote one in which I mentioned Skewes' number as the largest finite number that ever showed up in a mathematical proof.* Ever since then, people have been asking me to write an article on Skewes' number. The first request came on September 3, 1963, almost immediately after the article appeared. On that date, Mr R. P. Boas of Evanston, Illinois, wrote me a long and fascinating letter on Skewes' number, with the clear intention of helping me write such an article.

I resisted that, along with repeated nudges from others in the years that followed, until March 3, 1974, when, at Boskone 11 (a Boston science fiction convention at which I was guest of honour), I was cornered by a fan and had Skewes' number requested of me. So I gave in. Eleven years of chivvying is enough.† I am Skewered.

First, what is Skewes' number? Not the numerical expression but the significance. Here's the story as I got it from Mr Boas (though I will paraphrase it, and if I get anything wrong, it's my fault, not his).

It involves prime numbers, which are those numbers that cannot be divided evenly by any number other than themselves and one. The numbers 7 and 13 are examples.

---

* See 'T-Formation', reprinted in *Adding a Dimension* (New York: Doubleday, 1964).

† I'll admit that I've been chivvied longer than that in some respects. For seventeen years I have been requested, with varying degrees of impatience, to write another Lije Baley novel; and for over twenty years to write another *Foundation* novel. So please don't anybody write letters that begin with 'If eleven years of chivvying is enough, why don't you —.' Because I'm doing all I can, that's why.

There are an infinite number of prime numbers, but as one goes up the list of numbers, the fraction of these numbers that are prime decreases. There is a formula that tells you the number of primes to be found in the list of numbers up to a given number, but like everything else about prime numbers, the formula is not neat and definite. It only tells you approximately how many primes there will be up to some limiting number.

Up to the highest limit that has actually been tested, it turns out that the actual number of primes that exist is somewhat *less* than is predicted by the formula.

In 1914, however, the British mathematician John Edensor Littlewood demonstrated that if one lengthened the string of numbers one investigated for primes, one would find that up to some limits there would be less than the formula predicted, but that up to other limits there would be more than the formula predicted.

In fact, if one continued up the line of numbers forever, the actual total number of primes would switch from less than the formula prediction to more than the formula prediction to less than the formula prediction, and so on – and make the switch an infinite number of times. If that were *not* so, Littlewood demonstrated, there would be a contradiction in the mathematical structure and that, of course, cannot be allowed.

The only trouble is that as far as we have actually gone in the list of numbers, not even one shift has taken place. The number of primes is always less than the formula would indicate. Of course, mathematicians might just go higher and higher up the list of numbers to see what happens, but that isn't so easy. The higher one goes, the longer it takes to test numbers for primehood.

However, it might be possible to do some theoretical work and determine some number below which the first switch from less than the prediction to more than the prediction *must* take place. That will at least set a limit to the work required.

Littlewood set S. Skewes (pronounced in two syllables,

by the way, Skew'ease) the task of finding that number. Skewes found that number and it proved to be enormously large; larger than any other number that ever turned up in the course of a mathematical proof up to that time, and it is this number that is popularly known as 'Skewes' number'.

Mind you, the proof does not indicate that one must reach Skewes' number before the number of primes shifts from less than the prediction to more. The proof merely says that some time *before* that number is reached – perhaps long long before – the shift must have occurred.

A number as large as Skewes' number is difficult to write. Some shorthand device must be used and the device used is the excellent one of exponential notation.

Thus, $1,000 = 10 \times 10 \times 10$, so 1,000 can be written as 10^3 (ten to the third power), where the little 3 is called an 'exponent'. The little 3 signifies that 1,000 can be considered the product of three 10s, or that it can be written as 1 followed by three zeros. In general, 10^x (ten to the xth power) is the product of x 10s and can be written as a 1 followed by x zeros.

Since 10,000,000,000 is written as a 1 followed by 10 zeros, it can be written exponentially as 10^{10} (ten to the tenth power). In the same way, a 1 followed by ten billion zeros, something that would be impractical to write, can be expressed exponentially as $10^{10,000,000,000}$ (ten to the ten billionth power). But since ten billion is itself 10^{10}, $10^{10,000,000,000}$ can be written, even more briefly, as $10^{10^{10}}$.

Writing exponentials is always a strain when an article is being written for a nonspecialized outlet. This is especially so when one is forced to place exponents on exponents. To avoid driving the Noble Printer crazy and to make the notation look prettier I have invented a notation of my own. I make the exponent a figure of normal size and it is as though it is being held up by a lever, and its added weight when its size grows bends the lever down. Thus, instead of writing ten to the third power as 10^3, I will write it as $10 \backslash 3$.

In the same way, ten to the ten billionth power can be written as $10 \setminus 10{,}000{,}000{,}000$, or as $10 \setminus 10 \setminus 10$.

Using this 'Asimovian exponential notation', Skewes' number becomes $10 \setminus 10 \setminus 10 \setminus 34$.

Now let's see what Skewes' number might be in ordinary non-exponential notation. To do that, we must consider the components of the exponential notation from right to left. Starting at the right, we know what 34 is, we move leftward and consider $10 \setminus 34$. This is ten to the thirty-fourth power and can be written as a 1 followed by 34 zeros thus: 10,000,000,000,000,000,000,000,000,000,000,000, or in words, ten decillion (American style). This means that Skewes' number can be written ten $10 \setminus 10 \setminus$ 10,000,000,000,000,000,000,000,000,000,000,000.

So far, so good, if a bit disconcertingly formidable. The next step is to move one place to the left and ask how we might write: $10 \setminus$ 10,000,000,000,000,000,000,000,000,000,000,- 000,000. Easy. You just put down a 1 and then follow it by ten million billion billion billion (or ten decillion, if you prefer) zeros.

If you were to try to write such a number by beginning with a 1 and then writing ten decillion zeros, each the size of a hydrogen atom, you would require nearly exactly the entire surface of the Earth to write the number. Furthermore, if you wrote each zero in a trillionth of a second and kept it up at that rate without cessation, it would take a thousand trillion years to write the entire number.

Anyway, let's call this number the 'Earth-number', because it takes the Earth as a blackboard to write it, and imagine that we can write it. Now we can write Skewes' number as $10 \setminus$ Earth-number, and this means we now know how to write Skewes' number in the usual fashion. We start with a one and then follow it with an Earth-number of zeros.

This is tremendously more than the ten decillion zeros it took merely to write the Earth-number. A number itself is much greater than the number of zeros it takes to write it. It takes only one zero to write 10, but the result is a number that is ten times greater than the number of zeros required to write it. In the same way it takes ten zeros to write 10,000,000,000, but the number written is ten billion, which is a billion times greater in size than the number of zeros used to write it.

Similarly it takes only ten decillion zeros to write the Earth-number, but the Earth-number itself is enormously greater than that number of zeros.

To write not ten decillion zeros, but an Earth-number of zeros, would require far more than the surfaces of all the objects in the known universe, even with each zero the size of a hydrogen atom. A trillion such universes as ours might suffice, and that is just to *write* the Earth-number in a one followed by zeros. Skewes' number itself, written by a one followed by an Earth-number of zeros, is *enormously,* ENORMOUSLY greater than the Earth-number that suffices to count those zeros.

So let's forget about counting zeros; that will get us nowhere. And if we abandon counting zeros, we don't need to have our exponents as integers. Every number can be expressed as a power of ten if we allow decimal exponents. For instance, by using a logarithm table, we can see that $34 = 10 \setminus 1.53$. So instead of writing Skewes' number as $10 \setminus 10 \setminus 10 \setminus 34$, we can write it as $10 \setminus 10 \setminus 10 \setminus 10 \setminus 1.53$. (Such fractional exponents are almost always only approximate, however.)

There are some advantages to stretching out the large numbers into as many tens as is required to make the rightmost number fall below ten. Then we can speak of a 'single-ten number', a 'double-ten number', a 'triple-ten number', and so on. Skewes' number is a 'quadruple-ten number'.

We can't count objects and reach Skewes' number in any visualizable way. Counting zeros is no help either. Let us instead try to count permutations and combinations.

Let me give you an example. In the ordinary deck of cards used to play bridge, there are fifty-two different cards. (The number 52 is itself a single-ten number, as are all the numbers between 10 and 10,000,000,000; 52 = 10 \ 1.716.)

In the game of bridge, each of four people is dealt thirteen cards. A player can, with equal probability, get any combination of thirteen cards, and the order in which he gets them doesn't matter. He rearranges that order to suit himself. The total number of different hands he can get by receiving any thirteen cards out of the fifty-two (and I won't bother you with how it is calculated) is about 635,000,000,000. Since this number is higher than ten billion, we can be sure it is beyond the single-ten-number stage. Exponentially, it can be expressed as $6.35 \times 10 \setminus 11$. Logarithms can help us remove that multiplier and put its value into the exponent at the cost of making that exponent a decimal. Thus $6.35 \times 10 \setminus 11 = 10 \setminus 11.80$. Since 11.80 is over ten, we can express that, exponentially, as $11.80 = 10 \setminus 1.07$.

Consequently, we can say that the total number of different hands a single bridge player can hold is $10 \setminus 10 \setminus 1.07$. Using only thirteen cards, we have, in a perfectly understandable way, reached a double-ten number. We might almost feel that we were halfway to the quadruple-ten number that is Skewes'.

So let's take all fifty-two cards and let's arrange to have the order count as well as the nature of the cards. You begin with a deck in which the cards are in a certain order. You shuffle it and end with a different order. You shuffle it again and end with yet another order. How many different orders are there? Remember that any difference in order, however small, makes a different order. If two orders are identical except for the interchange of two adjacent cards, they are two different orders.

To answer that question, we figure that the first card can be any of the fifty-two, the second any of the remaining fifty-one, the third any of the remaining fifty, and so on. The total number of different orders is $52 \times 51 \times 50 \times \ldots 4 \times 3 \times 2 \times 1$. In other words the number of different orders is equal to the product of the first fifty-two numbers. This is called 'factorial fifty-two' and can be written '52!'

The value of 52! is, roughly, a one followed by sixty-eight zeros; in other words, a hundred decillion decillion. (You are welcome to work out the multiplication if you doubt this, but if you try, please be prepared for a long haul.) This is an absolutely terrific number to get out of one ordinary deck of cards that most of us use constantly without any feeling of being overwhelmed. The number of different orders into which that ordinary deck can be placed is about ten times as great as all the subatomic particles in our entire Milky Way galaxy.

It would certainly seem that if making use of thirteen cards with order indifferent lifted us high up, making use of all fifty-two and letting order count will do much better still – until we try our exponential notation. The number of orders into which fifty-two different cards can be placed is $10 \setminus 68 = 10 \setminus 10 \setminus 1.83$.

That may strike you as strange. The number of orders of fifty-two cards is something like a trillion trillion decillion times higher than the number of bridge hands of thirteen cards; yet, while the latter is $10 \setminus 10 \setminus 1.07$, the former is only $10 \setminus 10 \setminus 1.83$. We're still in the 'double-ten numbers' and we haven't even moved up much.

The trouble is that the more tens we add to such exponential numbers, the harder it is to move that rightmost component. For instance, a trillion is ten times as great as a hundred billion, and counting a trillion objects would be an enormously greater task than counting a hundred billion. Write them exponentially, however, and it is $10 \setminus 12$ as compared with $10 \setminus 11$, and the rightmost components are only a unit apart. Write the twelve and the eleven as powers of ten so that you can make use of double-ten numbers, and a trillion becomes $10 \setminus 10 \setminus 1.08$, while a hundred billion is $10 \setminus 10 \setminus 1.04$ and the difference is scarcely noticeable.

Or put it another way. The number $10 \setminus 3$ (which is 1,000) is ten times as high as $10 \setminus 2$ (which is 100), but the degree to which $10 \backslash 10 \backslash 3$ is greater than $10 \backslash 10 \backslash 2$ would require a 1 followed by 900 zeros to be expressed. As for comparing $10 \backslash 10 \backslash 10 \backslash 3$ and $10 \backslash 10 \backslash 10 \backslash 2$, I leave that to you.

This is disheartening. Perhaps reaching the quadruple-ten numbers won't be that easy after all.

Let's try one more trick with fifty-two cards. Suppose each of the cards can be any card at all. Suppose the deck can have two tens of diamonds or three aces of clubs, or, for that matter, fifty-two threes of hearts. The total number of orders of such a chameleonic deck could be calculated by imagining that the first card could be any one of fifty-two, and the second card could be any one of fifty-two, and so on for all fifty-two. To calculate the number of different orders, you would have to take the product of $52 \times 52 \times 52 \times \ldots 52 \times 52 \times 52$; fifty-two 52s. This product which could be written $52 \backslash 52$ I might call 'super-factorial fifty-two', but if so, I would be using a term I have just made up, so don't blame the mathematicians.

Superfactorials are immensely larger than factorials. Factorial fifty-two can be expressed by a one followed by sixty-eight zeros; but superfactorial fifty-two is a one followed by ninety zeros – ten billion trillion times higher. Yet express it exponentially and superfactorial $52 = 10 \backslash 90 = 10 \backslash 10 \backslash 1.95$.

No good. We're still in the double-ten numbers.

We'll just have to forget playing cards. We must have more than fifty-two units to play with, and we had better go all the way up; *all* the way up.

A generation or so ago, the British astronomer Arthur S. Eddington calculated that the total number of electrons, protons, and neutrons in the universe was $10 \backslash 79$, or $10 \backslash 10 \backslash 1.90$. This number is arrived at if we suppose that the sun is an average star, that there are about a hundred billion stars in the average galaxy, and that there are a hundred billion galaxies in the universe.

In addition to electrons, protons, and neutrons, of course, there are numbers of unstable particles unknown to

Eddington, but their numbers are comparatively few. There are, however, massless particles such as neutrons, photons, and gravitons, which do not generally behave like particles but which are very numerous in the universe.

If we wish, we can suppose that the number of massless particles speeding through space at any time is nine times the number of massed particles (probably a grievous overestimate) and make the total number of subatomic particles in the universe $10 \setminus 80$, or $10 \setminus 10 \setminus 1.903$.

Now, at least, we are starting with a double-ten number and that ought to do it. Skewes' number, here we come. All we have to do is take the superfactorial of $10 \setminus 80$, something we can express as $(10 \setminus 80)$ $(10 \setminus 80)$.

Working that out (and I hope I'm doing it correctly), we get $10 \setminus 10 \setminus 81.9$, or $10 \setminus 10 \setminus 10 \setminus 1.91$.

And that lifts us into the 'triple-ten numbers' for the first time. In fact, if we compare the superfactorial of the total number of subatomic particles in the universe (which is $10 \setminus 10 \setminus 10 \setminus 1.91$) with Skewes' number (which, as a triple-ten number, is $10 \setminus 10 \setminus 10 \setminus 34$), we might think we were almost there.

We need to begin with something more than the number of subatomic particles in the universe – how about the amount of space in the universe?

The smallest unit of space we can conveniently deal with is the volume of a neutron, a tiny globe that is about $10 \setminus -13$ centimetres in diameter, or one ten-trillionth of a centimetre.

The observable universe has a radius of 12.5 billion light-years, or $1.25 \times 10 \setminus 10$ light-years, and each light-year is equal to just under $10 \setminus 13$ kilometres. Hence, the observable universe has a radius of roughly $10 \setminus 23$ kilometres. Since 1 kilometre = 100,000, or $10 \setminus 5$, centimetres, the observable universe has a radius of roughly $10 \setminus 28$ centimetres. From this we can calculate the volume of the observable universe to be roughly equal to $4.2 \times 10 \setminus 84$ cubic centimetres.

A neutron, with a diameter of 10\ −13 centimetres, has a volume that is equal to roughly 5 × 10 \ −40 cubic centimetres. That means that the volume of the observable universe is roughly 2 × 10\ 124, or 10 \ 124.3 times the volume of a single neutron.

Suppose we call the volume of space equal to that of a neutron a 'vacuon'. We can then say that there are 10 \ 124.3 vacuons in the universe and call that the 'vacuon-number'.

The vacuon-number is nearly a billion billion billion billion billion times greater than the number of subatomic particles in the universe, so we can feel pretty confident about the superfactorial of the vacuon-number, which is (10 \ 124.3) \ (10 \ 124.3), except that this comes out to 10 \ 10 \ 10 \ 2.10.

Despite the vastly greater quantity of empty space than of matter in the universe, the rightmost component of the triple-ten number went up only from 1.91 to 2.10, with 34 as the goal. That's enough to depress us, but wait –

In considering the number of vacuons in the universe, we imagined it as existing at a moment in time. But time moves, and the universe changes. A subatomic particle that occupies one place at one moment may occupy another place at another moment. The most rapidly moving particles are, of course, the massless ones which move at the speed of light.

The speed of light is just about 3 × 10 \ 10 centimetres per second, and the smallest distance one can move with some significance is the diameter of a neutron, which is 10 \ −13 centimetres. A photon will flash the width of a neutron, then, in about 3 × 10 \ −24 seconds. We can consider this the smallest unit of time that has physical meaning and call it the 'chronon'.*

To imagine a long period of time, let's consider what we can call the 'cosmic cycle', one period of expansion and

---

* Stanley G. Weinbaum once imagined space and time quantized in this fashion in one of his science fiction stories and used the word 'chronon' for his ultimate particle of time.

contraction of the universe (assuming it is oscillating). Some have guessed the length of the cosmic cycle to be 80,000,000,000, or $8 \times 10 \backslash 10$, years.

The number of chronons in one cosmic cycle, then, is roughly $10 \backslash 42$.

In every chronon of time, the universe is slightly different from what it was in the preceding chronon or what it will be in the next chronon, because, if nothing else, every free-moving photon, neutrino, and graviton has shifted its position by the width of one neutron in some direction or other with each chronon that passes.

Therefore we might consider the total number of vacuons not only in the present universe, but also in the one that existed in the last chronon, the one that will exist in the next chronon, and, in general, all the universes in all the chronons through a cosmic cycle. (To be sure, the expansion and contraction of the universe alters its vacuon content – these increasing in number with expansion and decreasing with contraction – but we can suppose that the present size of the universe is about average.)

In that case, then, the total number of vacuons through every chronon of the cosmic cycle is just about $10 \backslash 166.3$. What this means is that if you wish to place a proton somewhere in the universe at some instant in time, you have (under the conditions I've described) a choice of $10 \backslash 166.3$ different positions.

But if you take the superfactorial of this enormous 'total-vacuon number', you end up with $10 \backslash 10 \backslash 10 \backslash 2.27$.

We have hardly moved. I just can't seem to move those triple ten numbers and make progress towards Skewes' number. I am Skewered.

In fact, it's worse than that. According to Mr Boas, Skewes' determination of Skewes' number depended on the supposition that something called the 'Riemann hypothesis' is true. It probably is, but no one has proved it to be so.

In 1955 Skewes published a paper in which he calculated the value of the number below which the number of primes *must* be higher at some point than the formula would predict, if the Riemann hypothesis were *not* true.

It turns out that the Riemann-hypothesis-*not*-true case yields a number that is far higher than Skewes' number. The new number, or what I suggest we call the Super-Skewes number, is $10 \setminus 10 \setminus 10 \setminus 1,000$, or $10 \setminus 10 \setminus 10 \setminus 10 \setminus 3$.

The Super-Skewes number and Skewes' number are both quadruple-ten numbers – $10 \setminus 10 \setminus 10 \setminus 10 \setminus 3$ and $10 \setminus 10 \setminus 10 \setminus 10 \setminus 1.53$ respectively – and the difference in the rightmost component seems to be small. However, you saw what difficulty there was in budging the triple-ten numbers upwards. Well, moving the quadruple-ten numbers upwards is far harder still, and Skewes' number is virtually zero in comparison to the Super-Skewes number.

If I had reached Skewes' number, I would still have had the Super-Skewes number ahead of me. I would have been Super-Skewered.

PART 4

Physics

My major work, as far as physics is concerned, is my three-volume Understanding Physics, *which is included among my first hundred books. Once that was done, there was little I could do in physics but forage about the edges of the subject and approach a different audience.*

Among the small books for eight-year-olds that I wrote for Follett, and mentioned earlier, there is one book on physics – Light *(Book 108). From that book, here is the description of the spectrum:*

from LIGHT *(1970)*

Light energy comes out of atoms in tiny amounts called 'photons'. Different kinds of atoms give off different kinds of photons; each kind carries a different amount of energy.

Photons of light are said to move up and down rapidly as they speed outwards. Scientists think of them as speeding along in a wavy motion. Photons travel as 'light waves'.

The photons in light cause our eyes to see certain colours. Certain low-energy photons make us see the colour red. Those with a little more energy make us see orange. With still a little more energy we see yellow . . . then green . . . then blue, and finally violet.

Sunlight is made up of different kinds of light waves. Each kind has its own length, its own kind of photons, and its own amount of energy. The light waves in a sunbeam can be spread out separately. A special piece of glass with three flat sides will do this. Such a piece of glass is called a 'prism'.

When separated light from a prism falls on a white wall, you can see a band of assorted colours. These are made by the sorted-out light waves. Those having the lowest energy cause you to see the red at one end of the band. Those having the highest energy cause you to see violet at the other end. You can also see other colours in between. A beautiful band is made when you separate the light waves in sunlight. It is called the 'solar spectrum'. Other kinds of light give different spectrum patterns.

A rainbow looks like a spectrum because it is a spectrum. After a rainstorm, the air is still filled with tiny droplets of water. Each droplet acts like a prism. When the sun comes out and shines through the droplets, the photons are sorted out. Then we see a rainbow, a spectrum in the sky.

Back in 1966, the editor of Science Digest *asked if I would do a small item for him. The magazine had a department called 'Please Explain', in which readers' questions were answered. One question was a poser that dealt with how often body cells are replaced.*

Knowing the answer wasn't enough; it had to be given in five hundred words and made both thorough and clear. Being a cheerful idiot not much given to worry and introspection, I undertook to answer the question for a reasonably small sum and did so. My essay was published in the June 1966 issue of the magazine.

What followed was absolutely predictable – which doesn't mean to say that I predicted it, for I am often thoroughly astonished when the predictable comes to pass. In a couple of months, the magazine asked me to do another essay on another catchy question, then another, and another, and before the year was out, I found that what I was doing was, in effect, a monthly column.

I was just getting ready to ask the editor if that was what he really had in mind, when I received an issue of the magazine in which the department was no longer headed 'Please Explain'; it had become 'Isaac Asimov Explains'. That made it clear to the meanest intelligence (meaning mine, for instance) that indeed it was a column I was writing.

The column continued for over nine years before I managed to get out of it. In 1974, there was a change of editor, and when the new editor told me he wanted to re-organize the magazine, I promptly asked him if he wanted to end the column. He did.

I didn't consider it a tragic event, because I had completed a goal I had set myself some years before. I had written a hundred of these essays, and it had been my intention to put the essays into book form once a hundred of them had been done.

Houghton Mifflin published the collection in 1973 as Please Explain *(Book 143). Here are three selections dealing with physics:*

from PLEASE EXPLAIN *(1973)*

What is the speed of gravitation?

A longer but perhaps clearer way of putting the question is this: Suppose the sun suddenly ceased to exist and vanished into nothingness. How long would it be before the earth would cease to be held by its gravitational field?

A similar question might be: How long after the sun disappears would the earth cease receiving its light?

We know the answer to the second question quite well. We know that the sun is just under 93 million miles from earth and we also know that light travels at 186,282 miles per second through a vacuum. The last bit of light leaving the sun, just before it disappeared, would take 8.3 minutes to reach the earth. In other words, we would see the sun disappear 8.3 minutes after it really disappeared.

The reason it is easy to answer the question about light is that there are a number of ways of actually measuring the speed at which light travels. These measurements are made practical by our ability to detect changes in the very faint light emitted by a distant heavenly body, and by our own ability to produce quite strong beams of light.

We don't have these advantages with gravitational fields. It is very difficult to study faint changes in weak gravitational fields, and we can't produce strong gravitational effects extending over long distances here on earth.

So we have to fall back on theory. There are four types of interactions known in the universe: (1) strong nuclear, (2) weak nuclear, (3) electromagnetic, and (4) gravitational. Of these, the first two are short-range, falling off very rapidly with distance. At distances greater than the width of an atomic nucleus, the nuclear interactions are so weak they can be ignored. The electromagnetic and gravitational interactions are long-range, however. They fall off only at the square of the distance. This means they can make themselves felt even over astronomical distances.

Physicists believe that every interaction between two bodies takes place through the exchange of subatomic particles. The more massive the exchange particle, the shorter-ranged the interaction. Thus, the strong nuclear interaction results from the exchange of pions, which are 270 times as massive as electrons. The weak nuclear interaction results from the exchange of even more massive W-particles (which haven't been detected yet, by the way).

If an exchange particle has no mass at all, then the interaction is as long-range as possible, and this is the case with the electromagnetic interaction. The exchange particle there is the massless photon. A stream of such massless photons makes up a beam of light or related radiations. The gravitational interaction, exactly as long-range as the electromagnetic one, must also involve a massless exchange particle – which is called a graviton.

But physicists have strong reason to suppose that massless particles can travel through a vacuum only at the speed of light; that is, at 186,282 miles per second, neither more nor less.

If this is so, then gravitons travel at exactly the speed of photons. This means that if the sun were to disappear, the last gravitons it emits would reach us at just the same time that the last photons would. At the instant we saw the sun disappear, we would also cease to be under its gravitational pull.

In other words, gravitation travels at the speed of light.

Why can't matter travel faster than the speed of light?

Energy added to a body can affect it in a number of ways. If a hammer strikes a nail in midair, the nail goes flying off, gaining kinetic energy – in other words, energy of motion. If a hammer strikes a nail embedded in hard wood, so that the nail can't move, the nail still gains energy – but in the form of heat.

Albert Einstein, in his theory of relativity, showed that mass could be viewed as a form of energy (and the invention of the atom bomb certainly proved him correct). If energy is added to a body, that energy may therefore appear in the form of mass, as well as in other forms.

Under ordinary conditions, the gain of energy in the form of mass is so incomprehensibly tiny that no one could ever measure it. It was only in the twentieth century, when subatomic particles were observed to move at speeds of tens of thousands of miles per second, that examples of mass increase were found that were large enough to be detectable. A body moving at 160,000 miles a second relative to ourselves would be measured by us as having twice as much mass as when it was at rest relative to ourselves.

If energy is added to any freely moving body, that energy can enter the body in one of two ways: (1) as velocity, so that its speed of motion increases, and (2) as mass, so that it becomes 'heavier'. The division between these two forms of energy-gain, as measured by ourselves, depends upon the speed of the body to begin with, again as measured by ourselves.

If the body is going at ordinary velocities, virtually all the added energy enters the body as velocity, and the body moves faster and faster with hardly any change in mass.

As the speed of the moving body increases (and as we imagine additional energy constantly being pumped into it), less and less of the energy enters as velocity and more and more as mass. We note that, though the body is still moving faster and faster, its rate of gaining speed is falling off. Instead, we note that it is becoming more massive at a slightly greater rate.

As its speed increases still further and gets fairly close to the 186,282 miles per second that is the speed of light in a vacuum, almost all the added energy enters as mass. In other words, the speed of motion of the body increases very slowly, but now it is the mass that is moving upwards by leaps and bounds. By the time the speed of light is reached, all the added energy is appearing as additional mass.

The body *cannot* go faster than the speed of light because to make it do so one must impart additional energy to it and, at the speed of light, all that additional energy, however great, will merely be converted into additional mass, and the body will not increase its speed one iota.

Nor is this 'just theory'. Scientists have been carefully observing speeding subatomic particles for years. Cosmic ray particles exist with unimaginably high energy contents, yet though their mass climbs high indeed, their speeds never quite reach that of light in a vacuum. The mass and velocity of subatomic particles work out to just what the theory of relativity predicts, and the speed of light is a maximum speed as a matter of observed fact and is *not* merely speculation.

In the atom bomb, matter is converted into energy. Is it possible to do the reverse and convert energy into matter?

It is certainly possible to change energy into matter, but to do so in large quantities is impractical. Let us see why.

According to Einstein's special theory of relativity, $e = mc^2$, where e represents energy, measured in ergs, m represents mass in grams, and c is the speed of light in centimetres per second.

Light travels through a vacuum with a speed of very nearly 30 billion (3×10^{10}) centimetres per second. The quantity c^2 represents the product of $c \times c$; that is, $3 \times 10^{10} \times 3 \times 10^{10}$, or 9×10^{20}. This means that c^2 is equal to 900,000,000,000,000,000,000.

A mass of 1 gram ($m = 1$) can therefore be converted, in theory, into 9×10^{20} ergs of energy. The average American is more familiar with the ounce (equal to 28.35 grams) as a unit of mass. One ounce of matter represents 2.55×10^{22} ergs of energy.

The erg is a very small unit of energy. The more familiar kilocalorie is equal to nearly 42 billion ergs. An ounce of matter turned into energy would yield 6.1×10^{11} (or 610 billion) kilocalories. You can keep alive very comfortably on 2,500 kilocalories a day, obtained from the food you eat. If you had the energy available to you that is represented by a single ounce of matter, you would have a supply that would last you 670,000 years, which is a lot by anybody's standards.

To put it another way, if the energy represented by a single ounce of matter could be turned completely into electrical energy, it would keep a hundred-watt electric light bulb burning continuously for 800,000 years.

To put it still another way, the energy represented by a single ounce of matter is equivalent to that obtained by burning 200 million gallons of gasoline.

It is no wonder, then, that in nuclear bombs, where sizeable quantities of matter are turned into energy, so much destruction is turned loose in the explosion of one bomb.

The change works both ways. If matter can be turned into energy, then energy can be turned into matter. This can be done anytime in the laboratory. A very energetic particle of energy – a gamma ray photon – can be converted into an electron and a positron without much trouble. The process is thereby reversed, and energy is, in this way, turned into matter.

The matter formed, however, consists of two very light particles, almost vanishingly small in mass. Can the same principle be used to form more matter – even enough matter to be seen?

Ah, but you can't beat the arithmetic. If an ounce of matter can be converted into as much energy as is produced by burning 200 million gallons of gasoline, then it will take all the energy produced by burning 200 million gallons of gasoline to manufacture a mere ounce of matter.

Even if someone were willing to make the demonstration and go to all the expense involved in collecting all that energy (and perhaps several times as much, allowing for inevitable wastage) just to form an ounce of matter, it still couldn't be done. All that energy simply could not be produced quickly enough and concentrated into a small enough volume to produce an ounce of matter all at once.

Thus, the conversion is possible in theory, but is completely impracticable. To be sure, the matter of the universe was once formed presumably from energy, but certainly not under any set of conditions we can possibly duplicate in the laboratory today.

The Science Digest *column wasn't the only thing my inability to say a literary no had got me into. Among my first hundred books is a small one I did for the Atomic Energy Commission called* The Genetic Effects of Radiation. *It earned me only a small flat sum, and there were no royalties since the booklet was distributed by the AEC, as a public service, to anyone who asked for it.*

Naturally, I couldn't very well argue myself into the proposition that I must never do a public service, so I had agreed to do the book. And, naturally, the AEC, having tasted blood, asked for more. In the course of my second hundred books, I did two more booklets for the AEC. One is Electricity and Man (*Book 123*) *and the other is* Worlds Within Worlds (*Book 131*), *both on physics.*

Worlds Within Worlds *was to be on the history of the*

*development of nuclear energy, and it was to be only ten
thousand words long. It ran away with me, however, as
books sometimes do, and by the time I screeched to a halt,
panting and lightly perspiring, I had done thirty thousand.
The AEC cheerfully put it out as three booklets, but I
listed it in my records as a single book.*

From Worlds Within Worlds, *here is my discussion of
the development of the first nuclear reactor:*

from WORLDS WITHIN WORLDS *(1972)*

Earlier in this history, we discussed chain reactions involving chemical energy. A small bit of energy can ignite
a chemical reaction that would produce more than enough
energy to ignite a neighbouring section of the system, which
would in turn produce still more – and so on, and so on. In
this way the flame of a single match could start a fire in a
leaf that would burn down an entire forest, and the energy
given off by the burning forest would be enormously higher
than the initial energy of the match flame.

Might there not be such a thing as a nuclear chain reaction? Could one initiate a nuclear reaction that would produce something that would initiate more of the same that
would produce something that would initiate still more of
the same and so on?

In that case, a nuclear reaction, once started, would continue of its own accord, and in return for the trifling investment that would serve to start it – a single neutron, perhaps
– a vast amount of breakdowns would result with the de-
livery of a vast amount of energy. Even if it were necessary
to expend quite a bit of energy to produce the one neutron
that would start the chain reaction, the end profit would be
enormous.

What's more, since the nuclear reaction would spread
from nucleus to nucleus with millionths-of-a-second intervals, there would be, in a very brief time, so many nuclei
breaking down that there would be a vast explosion. The

explosion would be millions of times as powerful as ordinary chemical explosions involving the same quantity of exploding material, since the latter use only the electromagnetic interaction, while the former use the much stronger nuclear interaction.

The first to think seriously of such a nuclear chain reaction was the Hungarian physicist Leo Szilard. He was working in Germany in 1933 when Adolf Hitler came to power and, since he was Jewish, he felt it would be wise to leave Germany. He went to Great Britain and there, in 1934, he considered new types of nuclear reactions that had been discovered.

In these, it sometimes happened that a fast neutron might strike a nucleus with sufficient energy to cause it to emit two neutrons. In that way the nucleus, absorbing one neutron and emitting two, would become a lighter isotope of the same element.

But what would happen if each of the two neutrons that emerged from the original target nucleus struck new nuclei and forced the emission of a pair of neutrons from each. There would now be a total of four neutrons flying about, and if each struck new nuclei there would next be eight neutrons, and so on. From the initial investment of a single neutron there might soon be countless billions initiating nuclear reactions.

Szilard, fearing the inevitability of war and fearing that the brutal leaders of Germany might seek and use such a nuclear chain reaction as a weapon in warfare, secretly applied for a patent on a device that could make use of such a nuclear chain reaction. He hoped to turn it over to the British government, which might then use its possession as a way of restraining the Nazis and keeping the peace.

However, it wouldn't have worked. It took the impact of a very energetic neutron to bring about the emission of two neutrons. The neutrons that then emerged from the nucleus simply didn't have enough energy to keep things going. (It was like trying to make wet wood catch fire.)

But what about uranium fission? Uranium fission was

intiated by slow neutrons. What if uranium fission produced neutrons as well as being initiated by a neutron? Would not the neutrons produced serve to initiate new fissions that would produce new neutrons and so on endlessly?

It seemed very likely that fission produced neutrons, and, indeed, at the conference where fission was first discussed, Enrico Fermi suggested it at once. Massive nuclei possessed more neutrons per proton than less massive ones did. If a massive nucleus was broken up into two considerably less massive ones, there would be a surplus of neutrons. Suppose, for instance, uranium-238 broke down into barium-138 and krypton-86. Barium-138 contains 82 neutrons, and krypton-86, 50 neutrons, for a total of 132. The uranium-238 nucleus, however, contains 146 neutrons.

The uranium fission process was studied at once to see if neutrons were actually given off, and a number of different physicists, including Szilard, found that they were.

Now Szilard was faced with a nuclear chain reaction he was certain would work. Only slow neutrons were involved and the individual nuclear breakdowns were far more energetic than anything else that had yet been discovered. If a chain reaction could be started in a sizeable piece of uranium, unimaginable quantities of energy would be produced. Just one gram of uranium, undergoing complete fission, would deliver the energy derived from the total burning of three tons of coal and would deliver that energy in a tiny fraction of a second.

Szilard, who had come to the United States in 1937, clearly visualized the tremendous explosive force of something that would have to be called a nuclear bomb. Szilard dreaded the possibility that Hitler might obtain the use of such a bomb through the agency of Germany's nuclear scientists.

Partly through Szilard's efforts, physicists in the United States and in other Western nations opposed to Hitler began a programme of voluntary secrecy in 1940 to avoid passing along any hints to Germany. What's more, Szilard enlisted the services of two other Hungarian refugees, the physicists Eugene Paul Wigner and Edward Teller, and all approached Einstein, who had also fled Germany and come to America.

Einstein was the most prestigious scientist then living, and it was thought that a letter from him to the President of the United States would be most persuasive. Einstein signed such a letter, which explained the possibility of a nuclear bomb and urged the United States not to allow a potential enemy to come into possession of it first.

Largely as a result of this letter, a huge research team was put together in the United States, to which other Western nations also contributed. It had but one aim – to develop the nuclear bomb.

Although the theory of the nuclear bomb seemed clear and simple, a great many practical difficulties stood in the way. In the first place, if only uranium atoms underwent fission, a supply of uranium had at least to be obtained in pure form, for if the neutrons struck nuclei of elements other than uranium, they would simply be absorbed and removed from the system, ending the possibility of a chain reaction. This alone was a heavy task. There had been so little use for uranium in quantity that there was almost no supply in existence and no experience in how to purify it.

Secondly, the supply of uranium might have to be a large one, for neutrons didn't necessarily enter the first uranium atom they approached. They moved about here and there, making glancing collisions and travelling quite a distance, perhaps, before striking head-on and entering a nucleus. If in that time they had passed outside the lump of uranium, they were useless.

As the quantity of uranium within which the fission chain reaction was initiated grew larger, more and more of the neutrons produced found a mark, and the fission re-action died out more and more slowly. Finally, at some particular size – the 'critical size' – the fission reaction did not die at all, but maintained itself, with enough of the neutrons produced finding their mark to keep the nuclear reaction proceeding at a steady rate. At any greater size the nuclear reaction would accelerate and there would be an explosion.

It wasn't even necessary to send neutrons into the uranium to start the process. In 1941 the Russian physicist Georgii Nikolaevich Flerov found that every once in a while a uranium atom would undergo fission without the introduction of a neutron. Occasionally the random quivering of a nucleus would bring about a shape that the nuclear interaction could not bring back to normal, and the nucleus would then break apart. In a gram of ordinary uranium, there is a nucleus undergoing such 'spontaneous fission' every two minutes on the average. Therefore, enough uranium need only be brought together to surpass critical size and it will explode within seconds, for the first nucleus that undergoes spontaneous fission will start the chain reaction.

First estimates made it seem that the quantity of uranium needed to reach critical size was extraordinarily great. Fully 99.3 per cent of the metal is uranium-238, however, and, as soon as fission was discovered, Bohr pointed out that there were theoretical reasons for supposing that it was the uranium-235 isotope (making up only 0.7 per cent of the whole) that was the one undergoing fission. Investigation proved him right. Indeed, the uranium-238 nucleus tended to absorb slow neutrons without fission, and to go on to beta-particle production that formed isotopes of neptunium and plutonium. In this way uranium-238 actually interfered with the chain reaction.

In any quantity of uranium, the more uranium-235 present and the less uranium-238, the more easily the chain reaction would proceed and the less the critical size need be. Vast efforts were therefore made to separate the two isotopes and prepare uranium with a higher than normal concentration of uranium-235 ('enriched uranium').

Of course, there was no great desire for a fearful explosion to get out of hand while the chain reaction was being studied. Before any bomb could be constructed, the mechanism of the chain reaction would have to be studied. Could a chain reaction capable of producing energy (for useful purposes as well as for bombs) be established? To test this, a quantity of uranium was gathered in the hope that a *controlled* chain reaction of uranium fission could be established. For that purpose, control rods of a substance that would easily absorb neutrons and slow the chain reaction were used. The metal, cadmium, served admirably for this purpose.

Then, too, the neutrons released by fission were pretty energetic. They tended to travel too far too soon and get outside the lump of uranium too easily. To produce a chain reaction that could be studied with some safety, the presence of a moderator was needed. This was a supply of small nuclei that did not absorb neutrons readily, but absorbed some of the energy of collision and slowed down any neutron that struck it. Nuclei such as hydrogen-2, beryllium-9, or carbon-12 were useful moderators. When the neutrons produced by fission were slowed, they travelled a smaller distance before being absorbed in their turn, and the critical size would again be reduced.

Towards the end of 1942 the initial stage of the project reached a climax. Blocks of graphite containing uranium metal and uranium oxide were piled up in huge quantities (enriched uranium was not yet available) in order to approach critical size. This took place under the stands of a football stadium at the University of Chicago, with Enrico Fermi (who had come to the United States in 1938) in charge.

The large structure was called an 'atomic pile' at first because of the blocks of graphite being piled up. The proper name for such a device, and the one that was eventually adopted, was, however, 'nuclear reactor'.

On December 2, 1942, calculations showed that the nuclear reactor was large enough to have reached critical size. The only thing preventing the chain reaction from sustaining itself was the cadmium rods that were inserted here and there in the pile and that were soaking up neutrons.

One by one the cadmium rods were pulled out. The number of uranium atoms undergoing fission each second rose and, finally, at 3.45 p.m. the uranium fission became self-sustaining. It kept going on its own (with the cadmium rods ready to be pushed in if it looked as though it were getting out of hand – something calculations showed was not likely).

News of this success was announced to Washington by a cautious telephone call from Arthur Holly Compton to James Bryant Conant. 'The Italian navigator has landed in the New World,' said Compton. Conant asked, 'How were the natives?' and the answer was, 'Very friendly.'

This was the day and moment when the world entered the 'nuclear age'. For the first time, mankind had constructed a device in which the nuclear energy being given off was greater than the energy poured in. Mankind had tapped the reservoirs of nuclear energy and could put it to use.

PART 5

Chemistry

Although chemistry is the field in which I obtained my degrees (including my Ph.D.) and although I am still an associate professor of biochemistry at Boston University School of Medicine (though I haven't worked at it these past few decades), I do not write as much in the field of chemistry as I do in physics or astronomy.

In my first hundred books are such titles as The Noble Gases, Photosynthesis, *and* Life and Energy, *which were all strongly chemical in content, but in the second hundred books not a single full-sized non-fiction book is devoted to chemistry. This was not on purpose, I assure you.*

However, things work out.

In 1975, I received a suggestion from Alan R. Bechtold of Topeka, Kansas, that I write a science fiction short story for him. He wanted to put out a series of booklets of about six thousand words apiece, each to consist of an original story from a well-known science fiction writer. The booklets would be put out in strictly limited editions and would be sold primarily at fan conventions. When the limited edition was sold out, the story would revert to the author.

Unexpectedly, the concept appealed to me. For one thing, I got an idea at once and that always helps. As it happened, the idea resulted in one of the few science fiction stories I wrote that centred on chemistry. I called it Good Taste, *and it was published in 1976, entering my list as Book 174.*

I wish I could report that the envisioned series was a success, but it wasn't. My book did well, but waiting for the next writer to meet his obligation was a long procedure and Bechtold ran out of money, I'm sorry to say.

Anyway, here is Good Taste *in full:*

GOOD TASTE *(1976)*

It was quite clear that it would not have happened – the family would not have been disgraced and the world of Gammer would not have been stunned and horrified – if Chawker Minor had not made the Grand Tour.

It wasn't exactly illegal to make the Grand Tour but, on Gammer at least, it was not really socially acceptable. Elder Chawker had been against it from the start, to do him justice, but then Lady Chawker took the side of her minor, and mothers are, at times, not to be withstood. Chawker was her second child (both of them sons, as it happened) and she would have no more, of course, so it was not surprising that she doted on him.

Her younger son had wanted to see the Other-Worlds of the Orbit and had promised to stay away no longer than a year. She had wept and worried and gone into a tragic decline and then, finally, had dried her eyes and spoken stiffly to Elder Chawker – and Chawker Minor had gone.

Now he was back, one year to the day (he was always one to keep his word, and, besides, Elder's support would have ceased the day after, never fear), and the family made holiday.

Elder wore a new, black glossy shirt but would not permit the prim lines of his face to relax, nor would he stoop to ask for details. He had no interest – no interest *whatever* – in the Other-Worlds with their strange ways and their primitive browsing (no better than the ways on Earth, of which Gammerpeople *never* spoke).

He said, 'Your complexion is dirtied and spoiled, Chawker Minor.' (The use of the full name showed his displeasure.)

Chawker laughed and the clear skin of his rather thin face crinkled. 'I stayed out of the sun as much as I could, Elder-mine, but the Other-Worlders would not always have it so.'

Lady Chawker would have none of Elder's criticism either. She said warmly, 'It isn't dirtied at all, Elder. It breathes a warmth.'

'Of the Sun,' grumbled Elder, 'and it would be next that he would be grubbing in the filth they have there.'

'No farming for me, Elder. That's hard work. I visited the fungus vats at times, though.'

Chawker Major, older than Minor by three years, wider of face, heavier of body, but otherwise of close resemblance, was torn between envy of his younger brother's having seen different worlds of the Orbit and revulsion at the thought of it. He said, 'Did you eat their Prime, Minor?'

'I had to eat something,' said Chawker Minor. 'Of course, there were your packages, Lady-mine – lifesavers, sometimes.'

'I suppose,' said Elder Chawker with distaste, 'the Prime was inedible there. Who can tell the filth that found its way into it.'

'Come now, Elder-mine.' Chawker paused, as though attempting to choose words, then shrugged. 'Well, it held body and soul together. One got used to it. I won't say more than that . . . But, Elder-Lady-mine, I am so glad to be home. The lights are so warm and gentle.'

'You've enough of the Sun, I take it,' said Elder. 'But you *would* go. Well, welcome back to the inner world with light and warmth under our control, locked away from the patch and blaze of sunshine. Welcome back to the womb of the people, as the saying goes.'

'Yet I'm glad I went,' said Chawker Minor. 'Eight different worlds, you know. It gives you a view you don't have otherwise.'

'And would be better off not having,' said Elder.

'I'm not sure about that,' said Chawker Minor, and his right eyelid trembled just slightly as he looked at Major. Chawker Major's lips compressed but he said nothing.

It was a feast. Anyone would have had to admit that, and in the end it was Chawker Minor himself, the greediest to begin with, who was the first to push away. He had no choice; else Lady would have kept on supplying him with samples out of what seemed to be a bottomless larder.

'Lady-mine,' he said affectionately, 'my tongue wearies. I can no longer taste anything.'

'*You* not taste?' said Lady. 'What kind of nithling story is that? You have the skill of the Grand-Elder himself. At the age of six, you were already a Gustator; we had endless proof of that. There was not an additive you could not detect even when you could not pronounce it right.'

'Taste buds blunt when not used,' said Elder Chawker darkly, 'and jogging the Other-Worlds can utterly spoil a man.'

'Yes? Well, let us see,' said Lady. 'Minor-mine, tell your doubting Elder what you have eaten.'

'In order?' said Chawker Minor.

'Yes. Show him you remember.'

Chawker Minor closed his eyes. 'It's scarcely a fair test,' he said. 'I so relished the taste I did not pause to analyse it – and it's been so long.'

'He has excuses. See, Lady?' said Elder.

'But I will try,' Chawker Minor said hastily. 'In the first place, the Prime base for all of them is from the fungus vats of the East Section and the thirteenth corridor within it, I believe, unless great changes have been made in my absence.'

'No, you are right,' said Lady with satisfaction.

'And it was expensive,' said Elder.

'The prodigal returns,' said Chawker Major just a bit acidly, 'and we must have the fatted fungus, as the saying goes . . . Get the additives, Minor, if you can.'

'Well,' said Chawker Minor, 'the first dab was strongly Spring Morning with added Leaves A-Freshened and a touch, not more than a touch, of Spara-Sprig.'

'Perfectly right,' said Lady, smiling happily.

Chawker Minor went on with the list, his eyes still closed, his taste memory rolling backwards and forwards luxuriously over the tang and consistency of the samplings. He skipped the eighth and came back to it.

'That one,' he said, 'puzzles me.'

Chawker Major grinned. 'Didn't you get any of it?'

'Of course I did. I got most of it. There was Frisking Lamb – not Leaping Lamb, either, Frisking, even though it leaned just a little towards Leaping.'

'Come on, don't try to make it hard. That's easy,' said Chawker Major. 'What else?'

'Green Mint, with just a touch of Sour Mint – *both* – and a dusting of Sparkle-Blood . . . But there was something else I couldn't identify.'

'Was it good?' asked Chawker Major.

'Good? This isn't the day to ask me that. Everything is good. Everything is succulent. And what I can't identify seems very succulent. It's close to Hedge Bloom, but better.'

'Better?' said Chawker Major delightedly. 'It's mine!'

'What do you mean, yours?' said Chawker Minor.

Elder said with stiff approval, 'My stay-at-home son has done well while you were gone. He devised a computer program that has designed and produced three new life-compatible flavour molecules of considerable promise. Grand-Elder Tomasz himself has given one of Major's constructions tongue-room – the very one you just tested, Fly-away Minor-mine – and has given it his approval.'

Chawker Major said, 'He didn't actually say anything, Elder-mine.'

Lady said, 'His expression needed no words.'

'It *is* good,' said Chawker Minor, rather dashed at having the play taken away from him. 'Will you be entering for the Awards?'

'It has been in my mind,' said Chawker Major, with an attempt at indifference. 'Not with this one – I call it Purple Light, by the way – but I believe I will have something else, more worthy of the competition.'

Chawker Minor frowned. 'I had thought that –'

'Yes?'

'– that I am ready to stretch out and think of nothing. Come, half a dab more of Major's construction, Lady-mine, and let's see what I can deduce concerning the chemical structure of his Purple Light.'

For a week, the holiday atmosphere in the Chawker household continued. Elder Chawker was well known in Gammer, and it seemed that half the inhabitants of the world must have passed through his section before all had had their curiosity sated and could see with their own eyes that Chawker Minor had returned unscathed. Most remarked on his complexion, and more than one young woman asked if she might touch his cheek, as though the light tan were a layer that could be felt.

Chawker Minor allowed the touch with lordly complacency, though Lady disapproved of these forward requests and said so.

Grand-Elder Tomasz himself came down from his eyrie, as plump as a Gammerman ever permits himself to be and with no sign that age or white hair had blunted his talents. He was a Master-Gustator such as Gammer might never have seen before, despite the tales of Grand-Elder Faron of half a century ago. There was nothing that Tomasz tongued that did not open itself in detail to him.

Chawker Minor, who had no great tendency to underrate his own talent, felt no shame in admitting that what he himself had, innately, could not yet come anywhere near the old man's weight of experience.

The Grand Elder, who, for nearly twenty years now, had governed the annual Awards festival by force of his skill, asked closely after the Other-Worlds, which, of course, he himself had never visited.

He was indulgent, though, and smiled at Lady Chawker. 'No need to fret, Lady,' he said. 'Young people these days are curious. In my time we were content to attend to our own cylinder of worth, as the saying goes, but these are new times and many are making what they call the Grand Tour. Good, perhaps, to see the Other-Worlds – frivolous, sun-drenched, browsive, non-gustational, without a taste bud to content themselves with – makes one appreciate the eldest brother, as the saying goes.'

Grand-Elder Tomasz was the only Gammerman whom Chawker Minor had ever heard actually speak of Gammer as 'the eldest brother', although you could find it often enough in the video cassettes. It had been the third colony to be founded in the Moon's orbit back in the pioneering years of the twenty-first century; but the first two, Alfer and Bayter, had never become ecologically viable. Gammer had.

Chawker Minor said with tactful caution, 'The Other-World people never tired of telling me how much the experience of Gammer meant to all the worlds that were founded afterwards. All had learned, they said, from Gammer.'

Tomasz beamed. 'Certainly. Certainly. Well said.'

Chawker Minor said with even greater caution, 'And yet such is self-love, you understand, Grand-Elder, that a few thought they had improved on Gammer.'

Grand-Elder Tomasz puffed his breath out through his nose ('Never breathe through your mouth any more than you can help,' he would say over and over again, 'for that blunts the Gustator's tongue') and fixed Chawker with his deep blue eyes that looked the bluer for the snow-white eyebrows that curved above them.

'Improved in what way? Did they suggest a specific improvement?'

Chawker Minor, skating on thin ice and aware of Elder Chawker's awful frown, said softly, 'In matters that they value, I gather. I am not a proper judge of such things, perhaps.'

'In matters that *they* value. Did you find a world that knows more about food chemistry than we do?'

'No! Certainly not, Grand-Elder. None concern themselves with that as far as I could see. They all rely on our findings. They admit it openly.'

Grand-Elder Tomasz grunted. 'They can rely on us to know the effects and side effects of a hundred thousand molecules, and each year to study, define, and analyse the effects of a thousand more. They rely on us to work out the dietary needs of elements and vitamins to the last syllable. Most of all, they rely on us to work out the art of taste to the final, most subtly convoluted touch. They do so, do they not?'

'They admit all this, without hesitation.'

'And where do you find computers more reliable and more complex than ours?'

'As far as our field is concerned, nowhere.'

'And what Prime did they serve?' With heavy humour, he added, 'Or did they expect a young Gammerman to browse.'

'No, Grand-Elder, they had Prime. On all the worlds I visited they had Prime; and on all those I did not visit, I was told, there was also Prime. Even on the world where Prime was considered fit chiefly for the lower classes –'

Tomasz reddened. 'Idiots!' he muttered.

'Different worlds, different ways,' said Chawker Minor rather hurriedly. 'But even then, Grand-Elder, Prime was popular when something was needed that was convenient, inexpensive, and nourishing. And they got their Prime from us. All of them had a fungal strain brought originally from Gammer.'

'Which strain?'

'Strain A-5,' said Chawker Minor apologetically. 'It's the sturdiest, they said, and the most energy-sparing.'

'And the coarsest,' said Tomasz with satisfaction. 'And what flavour additives?'

'Very few,' said Chawker Minor. He thought a moment, then said, 'There was, on Kapper, a place where they had an additive that was popular with the Kapperpeople and that had . . . possibilities. Those were not properly developed, however, and when I distributed tastes of what Lady-mine had sent me, they were forced to admit that it was to theirs as Gammer is to a space pebble.'

'You had not told me that,' said Lady Chawker, who, till then, had not ventured to interpose in a conversation that had the Grand-Elder as one of its participants. 'The Other-

Worlders liked my preparations, did they?'

'I didn't often hand it out,' said Chawker Minor. 'I was too selfish to do it. But when I did, they liked it a great deal, Lady-mine.'

It was several days before the two brothers managed to find a way of being alone together.

Major said, 'Weren't you on Kee at all?'

Chawker Minor lowered his voice. 'I was. Just a couple of days. It was too expensive to stay long.'

'I have no doubt Elder would not have liked even the two days.'

'I don't intend telling him. Do you?'

'A witless remark. Tell me about it.'

Chawker Minor did, in semi-embarrassed detail, and said, finally, 'The point is, Major, it doesn't seem wrong to them. They don't think anything of it. It made me think that perhaps there is no real right and wrong. What you're used to, that's right. What you're not used to, that's wrong.'

'Try telling that to Elder.'

'What he thinks is right and what he is used to are precisely the same. You'll have to admit that.'

'What difference does it make what *I* admit? Elder thinks that all rights and wrongs were written down by the makers of Gammer and that it's all in a book of which there is only one copy and we have it, so that all the Other-Worlds are wrong forever. I'm speaking metaphorically, of course.'

'I believe that, too, Major – metaphorically. But it shook me up to see how calmly those Other-World people took it. I could – watch them browse.'

A spasm of distaste crossed Major's face. 'Animals, you mean?'

'It doesn't look like animals when they browse on it. That's the point.'

'You watched them kill and dissect that – that –'

'No,' he said hastily. 'I just saw it when it was all

finished. What they ate looked like some kinds of Prime and it smelled like some kinds of Prime. I imagine it tasted –'

Chawker Major twisted his expression into one of extreme revulsion, and Chawker Minor said defensively, 'But browsing came first, you know. On Earth, I mean. And it could be that when Prime was first developed on Gammer it was designed to imitate the taste of browse food.'

'I prefer not to believe that,' said Chawker Major.

'What you prefer doesn't matter.'

'Listen,' said Chawker Major. 'I don't care what they browse. If they ever got the chance to eat real Prime – not Strain A-5, but the fatted fungus, as the saying goes – and if they had the sophisticated additives and not whatever primitive trash they use, they would eat forever and never dream of browsing. If they could eat what *I* have constructed and will yet construct –'

Chawker Minor said wistfully, 'Are you really going to try for the Award, Major?'

Chawker Major thought for a moment, then said, 'I think I will, Minor. I really will. Even if I don't win, I eventually will. This program I've got is different.' He grew excited. 'It's not like any computer program I've ever seen or heard of – and it works. It's all in the –' But he pulled himself up sharply and said uneasily, 'I hope, Minor, you don't mind if I *don't* tell you about it? I haven't told anyone.'

Chawker Minor shrugged. 'It would be foolish to tell anyone. If you really have a good program, you can make your fortune. You know that. Look at Grand-Elder Tomasz. It must be thirty-five years since he developed Corridor Song and he still hasn't published his path.'

Chawker Major said, 'Yes, but there's a pretty good guess as to how he got to it. And it's not really, in my opinion –' He shook his head doubtfully, in preference to saying anything that might smack of lèse majesté.

Chawker Minor said, 'The reason I asked if you were

going to try for the Award –'

'Well?'

'Is that I was rather thinking of entering myself.'

'You? You're scarcely old enough.'

'I'm twenty-two. But would you mind?'

'You don't know enough, Minor. When have you ever handled a computer?'

'What's the difference? A computer isn't the answer.'

'No? What is?'

'The taste buds.'

'Hit and miss and taste buds all the way. We all know that sound, and I will jump through the zero axis in a bound, too, as the saying goes.'

'But I'm serious, Major. A computer is only the starting point, isn't it? It all ends with the tongue no matter where you start.'

'And, of course, a Master-Gustator like Minor-lad, here, can do it.'

Chawker Minor was not too tanned to flush. 'Maybe not a Master-Gustator, but a Gustator anyway, and you know it. The point is that being away from home for a year I've gotten to appreciate good Prime and what might be done with it. I've learned enough. Look, Major, my tongue is all I've got, and I'd like to make back the money that Elder and Lady spent on me. Do you object to my entering? Do you fear the competition?'

Chawker Major stiffened. He was taller and heavier than Chawker Minor and he didn't look friendly. 'There is no competition to fear. If you want to enter, do so, Minor-child. But don't come whimpering to me when you're ashamed. And I tell you, Elder won't like your making a no-taste-batch of yourself, as the saying goes.'

'Nobody has to win right away. Even if I don't win, I eventually will, as *your* saying goes.' And Chawker Minor turned and left. He was feeling a little huffy himself.

Matters trailed off eventually. Everyone seemed to have had enough of the tales of the Other-Worlds. Chawker

Minor had described the living animals he had seen for
the fiftieth time and denied he had seen any of them killed
for the hundredth. He had painted word-pictures of the
grain fields and tried to explain what sunshine looked like
when it glinted off men and women and buildings and
fields, through air that turned a little blue and hazy in the
distance. He explained for the two hundredth time that,
no, it was not at all like the sunshine effect in the outer
viewing rooms of Gammer (which hardly anyone visited
anyway).

And now that it was all over, he rather missed not being
stopped in the corridors. He disliked no longer being a
celebrity. He felt a little at a loss as he spun the book
film he had grown tired of viewing and tried not to be
annoyed with Lady.

He said, 'What's the matter, Lady-mine? You haven't
smiled all day.'

His mother looked up at him thoughtfully. 'It's distressing to see dissension between major and minor.'

'Oh, come.' Chawker Minor rose irritably and walked
over to the air vent. It was jasmine day and he loved the
odour and, as always, automatically wondered how he
could make it better. It was very faint, of course, since
everyone knew that strong floral odours blunted the
tongue.

'There's nothing wrong, Lady,' he said, 'with my trying
for the Award. It's the free right of every Gammerperson
over twenty-one.'

'But it isn't in good taste to be competing with your
brother.'

'Good taste! Why not? I'm competing with everyone.
So's he. It's just a detail that we're competing with each
other. Why don't you take the attitude that he's competing
with me?'

'He's three years older than you, Minor-mine.'

'And perhaps he'll win, Lady-mine. He's got the computer. Has Major asked you to get me to drop out?'

'No, he did not. Don't think that of your brother.' Lady

poke earnestly, but she avoided his eyes.

Chawker Minor said, 'Well, then, he's gone moping fter you and you've learned to tell what he wants without is having to say it. And all because I qualified in the pening round and he didn't think I would.'

'Anyone can qualify,' came Chawker Major's voice rom the doorway.

Chawker Minor whirled. 'Is that the way it is? Then vhy does it upset you? And why did a hundred people fail o qualify?'

Chawker Major said, 'What some small-taste nitherlings lecide means very little, Minor. Wait till it comes to the oard.'

'Since you qualified, too, Major, there's no need to tell ne how little importance there is to some small-taste nitherings –'

'Young-mine,' said Lady rather sharply. 'Stop it! Peraps we can remember that it is very unusual for both najor and minor of a single unit to qualify.'

Neither ventured to break the silence in Lady's presence or a while thereafter – but their scowls remained eloquent.

As the days passed, Chawker Minor found himself more ind more involved in preparing the ultimate sample of lavoured Prime, which his own taste buds and olfactory irea would tell him was to be nothing like anything that iad ever rolled across a Gammer tongue before.

He took it upon himself to visit the Prime vats themelves, where the delectably bland fungi grew out of nalodorous wastes and multiplied themselves at extraordinary speed, under ideal conditions, into three dozen oasic strains, each with its varieties.

(The Master-Gustator, tasting unflavoured Prime itself – the fungal unalterate, as the saying went – could be relied upon to pin its source down to the section and corridor. Grand-Elder Tomasz had more than once stated, publicly, that he could tell the very vat itself and, at times, the portion of the vat, though no one had ever quite put him to the full test.)

Chawker Minor did not pretend to the expertise of Tomasz, but he lipped and tongued and smacked and nipped till he had decided on the exact strain and variety he wanted, the one that would best blend with the ingredients he was mixing in his mind. A good Gustator, said Grand-Elder Tomasz, could combine ingredients mentally and taste the mixture in his imagination. With Tomasz it might, for all one knew, be merely a statement, but Chawker Minor took it seriously and was sure he could do it.

He had rented out space in the kitchen – another expense for poor Elder, although Chawker Minor was making do with less than Major had demanded. Chawker Minor did not repine at having less, for, since he was eschewing computers, he didn't require much. Mincers, mixers, heaters, strainers, and the rest of the cookery tools took up little room. And at least he had an excellent hood for the masking and removal of all odours. (Everyone knew the horror tales of the Gustators who had been given away by a single sniff of odour and then found that some creative mixture was in the public domain before they could bring it before the board. To steal someone else's product might not be, as Lady would say, in good taste, but it was done and there was no legal recourse.)

The signal light flashed in a code sufficiently well known. It was Elder Chawker. Chawker Minor felt the thrill of guilt he had felt as a child when he had pilfered dabs of Prime reserved for guests.

'One moment, Elder-mine,' he sang out, and, in a flurry of activity, set the hood on high, closed the partition, swept his ingredients off the tabletop and into the bins, then stepped out and closed the door quickly behind him.

'I'm sorry, Elder-mine,' he said with an attempt at lightness, 'but Gustatorship is paramount.'

'I understand,' said Elder stiffly, though his nostrils had flared momentarily as though he would have been glad to catch that fugitive whiff, 'but you've scarcely been at home lately, scarcely more than when you were on your space folly, and I must come here to speak to you.'

'No problem, Elder, we'll go to the lounge.'

The lounge was not far away, and, fortunately, it was empty. Elder's sharp glances this way and that made the emptiness seem fortunate for him, and Chawker Minor sighed inaudibly. He would be lectured, he knew.

Elder said at last, 'Minor, you are my son, and I will do my duty towards you. My duty does not consist, however, of more than paying your expenses and seeing to it that you have a fair start in life. There is also the matter of reproval in good time. Who wishes fair Prime must not stint on foul waste, as the saying goes.'

Chawker's eyes dropped. He, along with his brother, had been among the thirty who had now qualified for the final awarding to be held in a week, and the unofficial rumour had it that Chawker Minor had done so with a somewhat higher score than Chawker Major had.

'Elder,' said Chawker Minor, 'would you ask me to do less than my best for my brother's sake?'

Elder Chawker's eyes blinked in a moment of puzzlement and Chawker Minor clamped his mouth shut. He had clearly jumped in the wrong direction.

Elder said, 'I do not ask you to do less than your best, but rather more than you are doing. Bethink you of the shaming you have inflicted on us in your little quarrel with Stens Major last week.'

Chawker Minor had, for a moment, difficulty remembering what this could apply to. He had done nothing with Stens Major at all – a silly young woman with whom he was perfectly content to confine himself to mere talk, and not very much of that.

'Stens Major? Shaming? How?'

'Do not say you do not remember what you said to her. Stens Major repeated it to her elder and lady, good friends of our family, and it is now common talk in the section. What possessed you, Minor, to assault the traditions of Gammer?'

'I did not do such a thing. She asked me about my Grand Tour and I told her no more than I have told three hundred others.'

'Didn't you tell her that women should be allowed to go on the Grand Tour?'

'Oh.'

'Yes. Oh.'

'But, Elder, what I said was that if she would take the Grand Tour herself there would be no need to ask questions, and when she pretended to be shocked at such a suggestion, I told her that, in my opinion, the more Gammerpeople saw of the Other-Worlds, the better it would be for all of us. We are too closed a society, in my opinion, and, Elder, I am not the first to say so.'

'Yes, I have heard of radicals who have said so, but not in our section and certainly not in our family. We have endured longer than the Other-Worlds; we have a stabler and fitter society; we do not have their problems. Is there crime among us? Is there corruption among us?'

'But, Elder, it is at the price of immobility and living death. We're all so tied in, so enclosed.'

'What can they teach us, these Other-Worlds? Were you not yourself glad to come back to the enclosed and comfortable sections of Gammer with their corridors lit in the gold light of our own energy?'

'Yes – but, you know, I'm spoiled, too. There are many things on the Other-Worlds that I would have very much liked to have made myself accustomed to.'

'And just exactly what, Minor-madman-mine?'

Chawker Minor bit back the words. After a pause he said, 'Why simply make assertions? When I can *prove* that a particular Other-World way is superior to Gammer-fashion, I will produce the proof. Till then, what is the use of just talking?'

'You have already been talking idly without end, Minor, and it has done you so little good that we can call what it has done you harm outright. Minor, if you have any respect left for me after your Grand Tour – which Lady-yours wheedled out of me against my will, Gammer knows – or if you have any regard for the fact that I still deny you nothing that my credit can obtain for you, you will keep your mouth shut henceforward. Think not that I will halt at sending you away if you shame us. You may then continue on your Grand Tour for as long as the Orbit lasts – and be no son of mine thereafter.'

Chawker Minor said in a low voice, 'As you say, Elder. From this moment on, unless I have evidence, I will say nothing.'

'Since you will never have evidence,' said Elder grimly, 'I will be satisfied if you keep your word.'

The annual Finals was the greatest holiday occasion, the greatest social event, the greatest excitement of any sort in the course of the year. Each one of thirty dishes of elegantly flavoured Prime had been prepared. Each one of the thirty judges would taste each dish at intervals long enough to restore the tongue. It would take all day.

In all honesty, Gammerpeople had to admit that the nearly one hundred winners who had taken their prize and acclaim in Gammer history had not all turned out dishes that had entered the Great Menu as classics. Some were forgotten and some were now considered ordinary. On the other hand, at least two of Gammer's all-time favourites, combinations that had been best sellers in restaurants and homes for two decades, had been also-rans in the years in which they had entered the contest. Black Velvet, whose odd combination of chocolate-warm and cherry blossom had made it the standard sweet, did not even make it to the Finals.

Chawker Minor had no doubt of the outcome. He was so confident that he found himself in continual danger of being bored. He kept watching the faces of the individual judges as every once in a while one of them would scoop up a trifle from one of the dishes and place it on his tongue. There was a careful blankness to the expression, a heavy-liddedness to the eye. No true judge could possibly allow a

look of surprise or a sigh of satisfaction to escape him –
certainly not a quiver of disdain. They merely recorded
their ratings on the little computer cards they carried.

Chawker Minor wondered if they could possibly restrain
their satisfaction when they tasted *his*. In the last week, his
mixture had grown perfect, had reached a pinnacle of taste
glory that could not be improved on, could *not* –

'Counting your winnings?' said Chawker Major in his
ear.

Chawker Minor started, and turned quickly. Chawker
Major was dressed entirely in platon and gleamed beautifully.

Chawker Minor said, 'Come, Major-mine, I wish you
the best. I really do. I want you to place as high as
possible.'

'Second place if you win, right?'

'Would you refuse second place if I win?'

'You can't win. I've checked somewhat. I know your
strain of Prime; I know your ingredients –'

'Have you spent any time on your own work, all this
time you've been playing detective?'

'Don't worry about me. It didn't take long to learn that
there is no way you can combine your ingredients into
anything of value.'

'You checked that with the computer, I suppose?'

'I did.'

'Then how did I get into the Finals, I wonder? Perhaps
you don't know all there is to know about my ingredients.
Look, Major, the number of effective combinations of even
a few ingredients is astronomical if we can consider the
various possible proportions and the possible treatments
before and after mixing, and the order of mixing and the –'

'I don't need your lecture, Minor.'

'Then you know that no computer in existence has been
programmed for the complexity of a clever tongue. Listen,
you can add some ingredients in amounts so small as to be
undetectable even by tongue, and yet they add a cast of
flavour that represents a marked change.'

'They teach you that in the Other-Worlds, youngling?'

'I learned that for myself.' And Chawker Minor walked away before he could be goaded into talking too much.

There was no question that Grand-Elder Tomasz this year, as in a large number of previous years, held the Judging Committee in the hollow of his tongue, as the saying went.

He looked up and down the long table at which all the judges had now taken their seats in order of preference, with Tomasz himself right in the middle. The computer had been fed; it had produced the result. There was complete silence in the room where the contestants, their friends, and their families sat waiting for glory or, failing that, for the consolation of being able to taste all the contesting samples.

The rest of Gammer, possibly without exceptions, watched by holo-video. There would, after all, be additional batches made up for a week of feasting, and the general opinion did not always match that of the judges either, though that did not affect the prize winning.

Tomasz said, 'I do not recall an awarding in which there was so little doubt as to the computer decision, or such general agreement.'

There was a nodding of heads, and smiles and looks of satisfaction.

Chawker Minor thought: They look sincere; not as if they're just going along with the Grand-Elder, so it must be mine.

Tomasz said, 'It has been my privilege this year to taste a dish more subtle, more tempting, more ambrosial than anything I have ever, in all my time and experience, tasted. It is the best. I cannot imagine it being bettered.'

He held up the computer cards. 'The win is unanimous, and the computer was needed only to determine the order of the runners-up. The winner is –' just that pause for effect and then, to the utter surprise of everyone but the winner, 'Chawker Minor, for his dish entitled Mountain Cap. Young man . . .'

Chawker Minor advanced for the ribbon, the plaque, the credits, the handshakes, the recording, the beaming, and the other contestants received their numbers in the list. Chawker Major was in fifth place.

Grand-Elder Tomasz sought out Chawker Minor after a while and tucked the young man's arm into his elbow.

'Well, Chawker Minor, it is a wonderful day for you and for all of us. I did not exaggerate. Your dish was the best I've ever tongued. And yet you leave me curious and wondering. I identified all the ingredients, but there was no way in which their combinations could produce what was produced. Would you be willing to impart your secret to me? I would not blame you if you refused, but in the case of an accomplishment so towering by one so young, to –'

'I don't mind telling you, Grand-Elder. I intend to tell everybody. I told my Elder that I would say nothing till I had proof. You supplied the proof!'

'What?' said Tomasz blankly. 'What proof?'

'The idea for the dish occurred to me, actually, on the Other-World Kapper, which is why I called it Mountain Cap, in tribute. I used ordinary ingredients, Grand-Elder, carefully blended, all but one. I suppose you detected the Garden Tang?'

'Yes, I did, but there was a slight modification there, I think, that I did not follow. How did the Other-World you speak of affect matters?'

'Because it was not Garden Tang, Grand-Elder, not the chemical. I used a complicated mixture for the Garden Tang, a mixture whose nature I cannot be entirely certain of.'

Tomasz frowned portentously. 'You mean, then, you cannot reproduce this dish?'

'I *can* reproduce it; be certain of that, Grand-Elder. The ingredient to which I refer is garlic.'

Tomasz said impatiently, 'That is only the vulgar term for Mountain Tang.'

'*Not* Mountain Tang. That is a known chemical mixture. I am speaking of the bulb of the plant.'

Grand-Elder Tomasz's eyes opened wide and so did his mouth.

Chawker Minor continued enthusiastically, 'No mixture can duplicate the complexity of a growing product, Grand-Elder, and on Kapper they have grown a particularly delicate variety which they use in their Prime. They use it incorrectly, without any appreciation of its potentiality. I saw at once that a true Gammer-person could do infinitely better, so I brought back with me a number of the bulbs and used them to good advantage. You said it was the best dish of Prime you had ever rolled tongue over, and if there is any better evidence than that for the value of opening our society, then –'

But he dwindled to a stop at last and stared at Tomasz with surprise and alarm. Tomasz was backing away rapidly. He said in a gargling voice, 'A growth – from the dirt – I've eaten –'

The Grand-Elder had often boasted that such was the steadiness of his stomach that he had never vomited, not even in infancy. And certainly no one had ever vomited in the great Hall of Judgment. The Grand-Elder now set a precedent in both respects.

Chawker Minor had not recovered. He would never recover. If it were exile that Elder Chawker had pronounced, so be it. He would never return.

Elder had not come to see him off. Neither had Major, of course. It didn't matter. Chawker Minor swore inwardly that he would make out, somehow, without their help, even if it meant serving on Kapper as a cook.

Lady *was* there, however – the only one in all the field to see him off; the only one to dare accept the non-person he had become. She shivered and looked mournful and Chawker Minor was filled with the desperate desire to justify himself.

'Lady-mine,' he said in a fury of self-pity, 'it's *unfair!* It

was the best dish ever made on Gammer. The Grand-Elder
said so *himself*. The *best*. If it had grated bulb in it, that
didn't mean the dish was bad; it meant the bulb was good.
Don't *you* see it? Look, I must board the ship. Tell me you
see it. Don't you understand it means we must become an
open society, learn from others as well as teach others or
we'll wither?'

The platform was about to take him up to the ship's
entrance. She was watching him sadly, as though she knew
she would never see him again.

He began the final rise, leaned over the rail. 'What did
I do *wrong*, Lady-mine?'

And she said in a low, distraught voice, 'Can't you see,
Minor-mine, that what you did was not in –'

The clang of the ship's port opening drowned her last
two words, and Chawker Minor moved in and put the sight
of Gammer behind him forever.

PART 6

Biology

Biology suffered in my second hundred books, as chemistry had. Whereas my first books include such works as The Human Body *and* The Human Brain, *nothing of the sort appears later.*

On the other hand, there is my How Did We Find Out series for Walker. One of them, How Did We Find Out About Vitamins? *(Book 158), published in 1974, is on the borderline between biology and chemistry. Another item in the series,* How Did We Find Out About Dinosaurs? *(Book 145), published in 1973, is on the borderline between biology and geology. A third,* How Did We Find Out About Germs? *(Book 153), published in 1974, is clearly about biology. Here is a passage from that book on the first medical victory over infectious disease.*

from HOW DID WE FIND OUT ABOUT GERMS? *(1974)*

Disease is a subject that concerns everyone. No one can ever be sure that he or she might not suddenly fall sick. A person can at any time begin to feel bad, develop a fever, or break out in a rash. Eventually, he or she might even die of a disease.

When one person falls sick, others might also. A disease can suddenly spread over a whole town or a whole region, and some diseases can be very deadly.

In the 1300s, for instance, a disease called the Black Death spread all over Europe, Asia, and Africa and killed millions of people. It was the greatest disaster in human history. One-third of all the people in Europe died.

At this time nobody in the world knew what caused disease. Some people thought demons or evil spirits took

over the body. Some people thought it was bad air of some
sort or another. Some people thought it was a punishment
from Heaven for evil deeds.

Whatever it was, though, no one imagined the diseases
could be stopped and no one knew when another Black
Death might strike.

One hopeful thing about disease was that some diseases
only hit a person once. If someone got measles or mumps
or chicken pox and got well, that person would never get
that particular disease again. He or she was 'immune'. His
or her body had fought off the disease and had developed
some kind of defence that would continue to work for
many years.

One particularly dreadful disease that only struck once
was smallpox. The trouble was that very often once was
quite enough. Many people who got smallpox died. Many
others recovered, but their faces and bodies were covered
with scars left over from the terrible blisters they had had.
Every once in a while, though, someone had only a light
case that did not scar him or her much. When that happened, the person was just as immune afterwards as if he
or she had had a terrible case.

Naturally, it was much better to have a light case of
smallpox than to have none at all. With a light case, you
were safe for life; with none at all, you could never be
sure you might not get it at any moment.

People knew that if you were near a person with smallpox you might catch it. Would it not be a good idea, then,
to hang around a person with a light case? You might
catch the light case and then be safe. To make sure, you
might scratch your skin with a needle that had been dipped
into some of the fluid in the smallpox blisters of the sick
man. This was called 'inoculation'.

The trouble was, though, that a person might have a
light case of smallpox, yet another person catching it might
get a severe case. Inoculation just was not safe.

In the 1770s, an English doctor, Edward Jenner, grew
interested in a disease called cowpox. It was called that

because it was found in cows and in other farm animals. The disease was something like a very mild smallpox. If a person caught cowpox from a cow, he or she would get a blister or two and that was it. People would hardly ever know they were sick.

The country people where Jenner lived thought it was good luck to get cowpox because then you never got smallpox. Most doctors thought this was just a superstition, but Jenner wondered. He did notice that people who worked with farm animals a good deal hardly ever got smallpox.

After twenty years of study, Jenner decided to try a very dangerous experiment. On May 14, 1796, he found a milkmaid who had just developed cowpox. He dipped a needle into the fluid inside a blister on her hand and scratched the skin of a boy who had never had either cowpox or smallpox. The boy got cowpox and developed a blister in the place where he had been scratched.

Jenner then waited for two months to make sure the boy was completely recovered. He was now immune to cowpox, but was he also immune to smallpox? Taking an enormous chance, Jenner deliberately scratched the boy with a needle that had been dipped in the fluid of a real smallpox blister. The boy did *not* catch smallpox.

Jenner tried the whole thing again two years later when he found another girl with cowpox. He again found he could make someone immune to smallpox by giving them fluid from a cowpox blister.

The medical name for cowpox is 'vaccinia', from a Latin word for 'cow'. Jenner's system for giving people cowpox to save them from smallpox was therefore called 'vaccination'. When Jenner announced his findings, vaccination was quickly adopted all over the world. Smallpox disappeared from places where vaccination was used.

Of course, a book need not be entirely about biology in order to deal with biology. In 1975, a book of mine appeared entitled The Ends of the Earth (*Book 168*), *pub-*

*lished by Weybright and Talley. It was about the polar
regions, and I tried to cover every aspect of the subject, including the biological part.*

from THE ENDS OF THE EARTH *(1975)*

The smallest living organisms of the ocean float passively
in the surface layers. The German physiologist Viktor
Hensen, in 1889, called this floating life of the ocean
'plankton', from a Greek word meaning 'wandering', and
this expression has been used ever since. Most of the
plankton are microscopic in size, but the name is used also
for such large plant organisms as seaweed and such large
animal organisms as giant jellyfish.

The microscopic plant cells of the plankton ('phytoplankton', the prefix from a Greek word meaning 'plant')
are the basic food of all ocean animal life. All sea animals
either eat phytoplankton or eat other animals that have
eaten phytoplankton, or other animals that have eaten other
animals that have eaten other animals – and so on, until
we come to an animal that has eaten phytoplankton. This
'food chain' can be of varying lengths.

The small animals of the surface ('zooplankton', the
prefix from a Greek word meaning 'animal') feed on the
phytoplankton. The most common of the zooplankton are
small crustacea called 'copepods'. There are six thousand
species of copepods, with lengths varying from 0.5 millimetre (barely visible to the naked eye) to 1 centimetre.
They make up about 70 per cent of all the zooplankton
and can sometimes turn the ocean pink with their numbers.
A somewhat larger variety of shellfish is the small, shrimp-
like 'krill', which is up to 5 centimetres in length.

Larger animals, such as young fish feed on the zooplankton, and themselves serve as food for larger organisms.

Food is not converted into the tissues of the eater with
perfect efficiency. There is roughly a 90 per cent loss, so
that, in general, the total mass of a species can only be

about 10 per cent that of the species it feeds upon.

Since plant life in general is the food of animal life in general, the mass of plant life on earth must be ten times that of animal life, and the total mass of the phytoplankton in the ocean must be roughly ten times that of all the animal life there. (Animal life in the ocean exists at all levels, but plant life is confined to the euphotic zone.)

Because each step upwards in the food chain means a decrease in total mass of the organism by a factor of ten, the actual number of larger animals decreases drastically.

Thus, the white shark, which is the largest sea vertebrate with gills (12 metres long) that lives on other large organisms, is a relatively rare creature. The sea cannot support white sharks in the myriads that it can support herring, for instance, which live on plankton.

Large animals can be supported in large numbers if they cut through the food chain by living on plankton directly. The whale shark and basking shark are even larger than the white shark (up to 15 metres long) but can be supported in surprising numbers because they live on plankton.

There are land animals that live primarily on sea life, and the distribution of these animals differs from that of land animals that live primarily on land life. Land plants grow stunted and sparse as one approaches the poles, and consequently land animals that live on them grow fewer, too. The sparseness of land life on the tundra and the virtual absence of land life in Antarctica have already been mentioned.

Sea life is, however, richer in the polar regions than in the tropics, thanks to the greater supply of oxygen and nutrients in cold water than in warm water. As a result, the polar regions are rich in land animal life that finds its food in the ocean.

Land life that depends on the sea for its food must be adapted to ocean feeding, and this takes place to a greater or lesser extent. In some cases, the adaptation is so extreme that the land animals are no longer really land animals, having adapted themselves to continuous life in the oceans, even to the point of developing the streamlined fish shape for more rapid motion.

The best known of the extremely adapted organisms are the whales and their smaller relatives the dolphins, which breathe by means of lungs, bring forth living young, and are, by every criterion, as fully mammalian as we ourselves, but which spend all their lives in the water.

The smallest dolphins are about 1.2 metres long and weigh about 45 kilograms. The largest dolphin is the killer whale, with males as long as 10 metres. The killer whale is an example of an organism that is at the top of the food chain. There are no other large organisms for whom the killer whale is a regular article of diet. A killer whale will die of disease, accident, or old age, not by ordinary predation.

The one exception to this in the case of the killer whale and of all other organisms that exist at the top of the food chain rests in the activity of man. In his natural physical state, man is no match for the larger animals, but armed with the products of the technology produced by his restless mind, he can destroy them all and is, indeed, in the process of doing so.

Another large dolphin, the narwhal, up to 5 metres long, is an Arctic animal. It inhabits the sea among the loose ice of the Arctic beyond 65° N, migrating further northward as the pack ice melts and recedes in the polar summer. The most unusual characteristic of the narwhal is that one tooth on the left side of its jaw forms a straight, spiral tusk up to 2.5 metres long. Its appearance is exactly that of the fabled horn of the unicorn, which was supposed to have miraculous medical properties – and no wonder, since sailors brought home pieces of narwhal tooth and, claiming it to be unicorn horn, sold them for large sums.

The largest truly carnivorous whale is the sperm whale. The male sperm whale can be as long as 20 metres and may weigh as much as 60 tons. It lives largely on giant squid. It, too, is at the top of the food chain and is threatened only by man.

Still larger whales, like the largest sharks, must cut

through the food chain if they are to be supported in any numbers. The largest of all whales (and, indeed, the largest animal that has ever lived) is the blue whale, which can be 30 metres long and weigh 135 tons. It feeds largely on krill, eating 3 tons per day. Whales that feed on plankton have fringes of horny plates, up to 3 metres long, extending down from the roof of the mouth and frayed and brushlike at the end. These, called 'baleen' or 'whalebone', trap and strain out the plankton.

Whales are worldwide in their distribution, but naturally they are most common where the food supply is richest, and this means the polar regions; and the Antarctic far more than the Arctic.

Whalers, hunting the whale for meat, oil, and whalebone, ventured into Arctic and Antarctic waters, and a great deal of the early exploration of the polar regions was performed by whalers and by those who hunted other sea mammals.

The search for whales was ruthless, however, and without any thought for preserving the species. In the eighteenth century, the large baleen whales of the Arctic were reduced to such small numbers that it was simply not worthwhile hunting them anymore.

With the passing of the baleen whales of the north, attention turned to the sperm whale when it was discovered that quantities of sperm oil could be obtained from the head of that organism and that such oil was particularly useful in oil lamps. The sperm whale was a more difficult and savage target (Moby Dick in Herman Melville's great novel was a sperm whale), but they would have been wiped out also if the electric light and the growing use of petroleum had not eased the need for sperm oil.

Whaling is now almost entirely confined to the Antarctic, where the food supply of the oceans is the richest in the world thanks to the Antarctic Convergence. Some 70 per cent of the whales killed are hunted down in the Antarctic and, of these, 70 per cent are the fin whale. Even now 35,000 whales are being killed each year, and these great animals will be wiped out if mankind does not manage to control the whalers.

Stepping down a notch in the extent of adaptation to the sea, we come to the seals. They, too, are typically polar in distribution because of the richness of the cold regions of the ocean.

Like the whales, the seals have been hunted down and slaughtered. Where the whales are bare skinned and depend on retaining warmth against the cold water of the polar oceans by thick layers of fat ('blubber') under the skin, seals have, in many cases, developed thick coats of hair. The coats of these 'hair seals' have been coveted and have very nearly proved the doom of those animals.

The ones that yield the best 'sealskins' are the Alaska fur seals. These gathered in huge hordes on the Pribilof Islands (discovered by the Russian navigator Gerasim Pribilof in 1786) in the Bering Sea. At the time of the discovery, some 5,000,000 seals formed the herd. They began to wither under the attack of the sealers until the Russian government exerted protection.

The Pribilof Islands, along with all of Alaska, passed to the United States in 1867, and at once the sealers began to make destructive inroads until only 125,000 seals remained in 1911. There seemed no way of making men forgo short-term profits in favour of a careful conservation that would, in the long run, yield greater returns.

Finally, when the United States and other nations imposed rigorous controls on sealing activities, the seal herds began to be restored. By now the herds are back up to 3,000,000 despite the fact that since 1911, under carefully rationed culling of the herds, 1,500,000 seals have been taken for their fur.

The most northerly of the seals is the ringed seal, which lives almost exclusively on and under the ice of the Arctic Ocean.

The largest of the seals is the elephant seal, so called more because of its trunklike nasal protuberance than its size. Species are found in both the Arctic and the Antarctic, with the latter somewhat the larger. The Antarctic males reach a length of 6.5 metres and a weight of nearly 4 tons.

The next largest seal is the walrus, which can reach a length of 3.5 metres and a weight of 1.4 tons. It differs from the other members of the seal family by possessing a pair of downward pointing tusks (the two upper canine teeth), which can be as long as 40 centimetres. The walruses are to be found only in the Arctic. Once 500,000 were to be found on the Arctic ice floes, but hunting has reduced their numbers to less than 50,000.

Of the forty-seven species of seals, five are native to the Antarctic. The largest of these (and third only to the elephant seal and the walrus) is the leopard seal. It is well named, for it is the most ferocious carnivore of the family. It needs to fear no other animal but the killer whale – and, of course, man.

The crab-eater seal, despite its name, lives on krill. It is the most common of the Antarctic seals and numbers 5,000,000 to 8,000,000.

The most thoroughly Antarctic of the seals, however, is the Weddell seal. It sticks close to the shores of Antarctica, while the other seals range well out to sea. The Weddell seal finds safety beneath the coastal ice, breaking holes in it to breathe through. It can dive to a depth of 600 metres and can remain submerged for nearly an hour. Ordinarily, however, it comes up for air every ten to thirty minutes. (The female spends considerable time on top of the ice, for only there can she feed her young.)

Another notch downwards in adaptation to the sea, we come to what would seem so completely a land animal as the bear. Two species of bears are characteristic of the Arctic regions and they are the two largest: the Kodiak brown bear and the polar bear.

The more northerly of the two is the polar bear. Creamy white in fur, it is not noticeable against the snow and ice it lives among. It can be 2 metres or more in length and may weigh over 700 kilograms. The polar bear lives on fish and seals and is capable of swimming miles out to sea. It can also roam the Arctic ice all the way to the

North Pole – followed by the Arctic fox, which scavenges the polar bear kills. (The polar bear's liver is so rich in vitamin A as to be actually poisonous to man.)

And while we're talking of land mammals adapted to seeking food by sea, we should mention man, too. The Eskimos, at least, live very well in the apparently bleak Arctic world by learning to turn to the rich sea for their food.

There are important sea birds in the polar regions. In the Arctic, the most typical examples are the members of the auk family. These are not strong fliers but are very well adapted to diving into water for the fish they eat. They are capable of swimming underwater by making the same wing movements they make in flight. One of the better-known auks is the puffin, which has a large head and a multicoloured parrotlike beak.

The most tragic member of the family was the great auk, which stood about a metre high and was the most completely adapted to water life of any species of the family. It could swim underwater expertly, but its wings were paddles only, and it could not fly with them.

What with its non-flight, its habit of congregating in great numbers on the islands in the Atlantic section of the Arctic, its single egg laid on bare ground without protection, and its inability to recognize the presence of danger, the great auk was an easy prey. They were killed wantonly in huge numbers and the last members of the species were killed on June 4, 1844.

Not all polar sea birds are poor fliers. The gull-like Arctic tern is, in some way, a flying champion. It nests in the Arctic (as far north as 82°5N) but evades the winter by flying 17,500 kilometres to the Antarctic; then evades the Antarctic winter by flying back to the Arctic. It spends seven months of the year travelling, and at each end of its journey experiences some two and a half months of continuous sunlight.

Another Arctic bird, the golden plover, also undergoes a long migratory flight, much of it being over the ocean and therefore nonstop, since the plovers don't swim well. A three-month-old golden plover can make it successfully from its birthplace in Alaska down to Hawaii (some 3,500 kilometres) in two days of flying.

Although the Antarctic region has no mammals except for whales and seals, which remain in the waters off the shores of Antarctica, there are birds that make their way across portions of the continent itself. Considering that the birds usually possess the ability to fly, this is perhaps not so unusual.

Of the fifteen species of flying birds that are found in the Antarctic region, the most southerly is a predatory gull-like bird called the skua. It seems very likely that skuas have ranged over all Antarctica and that they are the only species of living creature that has reached the South Pole independently of man.

There are two Antarctic petrels, and one of these, the giant petrel, is the largest of the Antarctic flying birds – with a wingspread of 2 metres and a weight of over 4 kilograms.

The most characteristic birds of Antarctica, however, are species incapable of flight, birds that actually walk extensively over the barren ice of that frozen continent. They are penguins, which adapted to the same kind of life and have developed a similar form to the great auk of the Arctic.

Penguins are as closely adapted to sea life as the great auk was, maybe more so. Their wings are paddles that are useless for flying but that give them an almost unmatched speed (almost 50 kilometres an hour) and turning ability underwater. Such is the force of their swimming that they can leap out of the water to twice their own height. On land, however, the best they can do is waddle in ungainly fashion. (Their upright posture, their humorous waddle, and their black and white coloration, as though they were wearing suits, have endeared them to men and spared them carnage.)

There are seventeen species of penguins altogether, all of them native to the Southern Hemisphere. Of these, two species actually live on Antarctica. The smaller of the Antarctic penguins is the Adélie penguin, so called because it is found in Adélie Land. The Adélie penguins congregate in crowded nesting sites inland ('rookeries'). They are about 45 centimetres tall and weigh 6 to 7 kilograms.

The skua is always waiting to eat the eggs and the penguin chicks, while in the ocean the leopard seal waits for the adults. As long as man does not interfere, however, enough survive to keep the species going.

More astonishing is the emperor penguin, the largest of all living penguins, standing over a metre high (twice the height of the Adélie) and weighing as much as 35 kilograms. (There are fossils of penguins, now extinct, that stood 1.6 metres high and weighed as much as 110 kilograms.)

Unlike the Adélie penguins, the emperors did not seem to possess rookeries. Edward Wilson, one of those fated to die later with Scott in the tragic attempt to reach the South Pole and return, was particularly interested in finding the eggs of the emperor penguin. He believed the emperor penguin to be the most primitive of all birds, and the species most closely related to the reptiles. (He was wrong in this.) He thought that a study of the embryos of these birds might clarify their position in the animal kingdom.

In 1902, he was the first to discover an emperor penguin rookery. (There are fourteen known rookeries now, sheltering perhaps 160,000 emperor penguins altogether.) For the first time, Wilson saw emperor chicks on the feet of adults. From their size, he realized the hatching of those chicks must have taken place quite a while before, during what was then winter.

In fact, it was discovered that the female emperor penguin laid her single egg in the middle of the Antarctic winter, so that the egg had to be incubated under worse conditions, by far, than those experienced by any other bird in the world. The emperor penguin is the only bird that does not nest on bare land. It nests on ice, and the emperor penguin may, indeed, never feel bare land but find itself always on or in water in solid or liquid form. (The Adélie penguin nests on exposed land along the rim of the continent and lays its eggs at the beginning of summer.)

The emperor penguin rookeries are located inland, some 80 to 130 kilometres from the coast. (Emperor penguins are occasionally found as far as 400 kilometres from the nearest coast, stubbornly trudging along – the furthest south any non-flying vertebrate has ever reached independently of man.)

It takes a month for the emperor penguins to travel from the shores of Antarctica, where food can be obtained, to the inland rookeries where no food exists (but where, except for man and skua, isolation and security are absolute). The emperor penguins fast during this trek.

There, in the interior, in winter, the female lays her single egg. There is no nest and no nesting territory, something that only the emperor penguin, of all birds, lacks. The single egg is taken by the male and placed on his feet, immediately under a bare and unfeathered patch of the abdomen. A flap of skin covers the egg, which is then incubated against the father's body and on his feet, so that the nesting territory is, so to speak, the ground on which the bird stands.

The male emperor penguins can waddle about clumsily without losing the eggs, and most of them huddle together for warmth, which they need, for the icy Antarctic midwinter temperatures go as low as $-60°$ C, and the gales whistle past the birds at speeds of up to 150 kilometres per hour.

Once the egg is transferred, the female takes off for food and the sea again – another month's journey. The male, however, stands his ground for sixty days, still fasting. Prior to the trek to the rookery, the male emperor penguin has eaten enough to lay by a sizeable quantity of fat – attaining a weight of 35 kilograms – but this begins to melt away during the long fast.

Finally, when the chicks are near to hatching, the

females return and take over. At last the males can head
for the sea, which they finally reach after a four-month
fast during which they lose 25 to 40 per cent of their
weight.

When the chick hatches, the mother feeds it with food
she has stored in her crop, but this won't last. The father
must return, and for a while the parents take turns walking
to the sea, eating their fill, and returning to feed the chick.
Fully one quarter of the chicks don't survive the rigours of
that first winter – but by the time the Antarctic summer
arrives and the coastal ice begins breaking up, those that
have survived can make it to the sea and go out to feed
on their own.

PART 7

Words

Words are of natural interest to writers, and certainly to me. It is a source of delight to me that English is my first language, for no other language consists of so many words, so many madly spelled and madly pronounced words, so many lawless words. In no other language, I firmly believe, can you have such fun with words.

What one-syllable word becomes two syllables if you subtract two letters?

What word changes pronunciation when it is capitalized?

What word has a spelling pattern xyzxyzx?

There are four common English words ending with 'dous'. Three of them are 'tremendous', 'stupendous', and 'horrendous'. What is the fourth?

What common words contain the following letters in order somewhere in their spelling: pefr, wsp, ckc, ufl, ufa?

I'll give you the answers at the end of this section. Meanwhile, you can have fun with them.

My chief pleasure has always been the origin and etymology of words. My first hundred books include no less than six (all published by Houghton Mifflin) that deal exclusively with etymology. These are Words of Science, Words from the Myths, Words in Genesis, Words from the Exodus, Words on the Map, Words from History.

These cover the subject rather thoroughly and there are no such easy pickings in the second hundred. I did manage one more with Houghton Mifflin, however. That was More Words of Science *(Book 122), published in 1972. Here are three essays from that book: one on a chemical word, one on a biological word, and one on a physical word.*

from MORE WORDS OF SCIENCE *(1972)*

HALLUCINOGENS

The brain, like every other part of the body, performs its functions through certain chemical reactions. These are produced by stimuli brought to the brain through the senses. It is possible to change the brain chemistry by taking substances that interfere with these chemical reactions. In that case, the body will respond to stimuli that don't relate to the outside world. Objects that are not really there seem to be sensed, while objects that are really there may be ignored. The results are 'hallucinations', from a Latin word meaning 'to wander in the mind'.

Certain plants contain chemicals that can produce hallucinations. The peyote cactus and a mushroom called *Amanita muscaria* contain such chemicals. Sometimes these plants are eaten in primitive religious celebrations because the hallucinations are thought to be glimpses of another world (or an escape from this one). Another substance that produces hallucinations is hashish, one form of which is marijuana.

In 1943, a Swiss chemist, Albert Hofmann, was studying an organic compound called 'lysergic acid diethylamide' and accidentally got a few tiny crystals of it on his fingers. He happened to touch his fingers to his lips and was soon overcome by odd hallucinations. It took him a full day to regain normality. He began careful studies and found that very small doses of the chemical could always produce hallucinations. The name was soon reduced to an abbreviation of the three words. Since the German word for 'acid' is *Säure*, and Hofmann spoke German, the abbreviation is LSD.

Since many young people foolishly began to play games with their minds by taking LSD and other such substances, hallucination-producing drugs became important to study. They are now lumped together under the general name 'hallucinogens' (producers of hallucinations).

PHEROMONE

Human beings can communicate by talking. Through sounds, gestures, and written symbols, abstract ideas can be transmitted from one person to another. Human beings are unique in this respect.

Yet other creatures must be able to communicate in some fashion, if only so that there can be co-operation between two individuals of a species in order that they might reproduce. Within a body, the different parts are made to behave in some co-operative fashion by means of chemical messengers called 'hormones'. Is it possible that chemical messages can be carried on, not only within an organism, but from one organism to another?

Such hormonal effects, carried through water or air from one member of a species to another, are called 'pheromones', the prefix coming from a Greek word meaning 'to carry'. They are hormones carried over a distance.

Insect pheromones are the most dramatic. A female moth can liberate a compound that will act as a powerful sexual attractant on a male moth of the same species a mile away. Each species must have its own pheromone, for there is no point in affecting a male of another species. Each species must have receiving devices of tremendous delicacy because they must be able to react to just a few molecules in the air.

Pheromones are also used in interspecies conflict. Certain ants raid the nests of other ant species to kidnap the young, which they rear as slaves. The raiders use trails of pheromones which not only aid them to keep together and co-ordinate their attacks, but also act to alarm and scatter the ant species they are attacking.

Biologists are labouring to use insect pheromones to lure members of troublesome species to destruction. In this way, they can be absolutely specific, doing no direct harm to any other species.

SYNCHROTRON

In the 1930s, physicists developed methods for accelerating subatomic particles in order to give them high energies and send them smashing into atomic nuclei. The most successful of these was invented by the American physicist Ernest O. Lawrence in 1931. It whirled particles around and around, thanks to the driving force of a magnetic field, and it was therefore called a 'cyclotron'.

By making larger and larger magnets, one could whirl the particles to greater and greater energies. The device only works well, however, if the mass of the particles doesn't change. As the particles go faster, their mass increases considerably (as Albert Einstein predicted they would in his special theory of relativity). This lowers the efficiency of the cyclotron and limits the energies it can produce.

In 1945, the Soviet physicist Vladimir I. Veksler and the American physicist Edwin M. McMillan independently worked out a way to alter the strength of a magnetic field so as to match the increase in mass. The two effects were 'synchronized' (from Greek words meaning 'same time') and the efficiency remained high. Such a modified cyclotron was called a 'synchrocyclotron'.

In cyclotrons, the whirling particles spiral outwards and eventually pass beyond the limits of the magnet. If the particles could be held in a tight circle, they could be whirled many more times before being released and still higher energies would be attained.

The English physicist Marcus L. E. Oliphant worked out a design for such a device in 1947, and in 1952 the first of the kind was built in Brookhaven National Laboratory on Long Island. It still made use of a synchronized increase in the strength of the field, but the spiralling of the particles, as in a cyclotron, was gone. The new device was therefore called simply a 'synchrotron'.

As for the puzzles I set you at the beginning of the section –

1. The one-syllable word 'plague' loses the first two letters and becomes the two-syllable 'ague'.

2. Capitalize the word 'polish' and it becomes 'Polish'.

3. The most common word with the pattern xyzxyzx is 'alfalfa'. Second is 'entente', but that is more French than English. There was once a breath freshener wtih the name 'Sen-Sens'.

4. The fourth common English word ending in 'dous' is 'hazardous'.

5. The letter combinations and the words containing them are:

   pefr – *grapefruit*

   wsp – *newspaper (Less good, because less common, is 'bowsprit'.)*

   ckc – *sackcloth or cockcrow*

   ufl – *genuflect*

   ufa – *manufacture (Oddly enough, this is the only common word with that combination.)*

PART 8

History

*In the course of my first hundred books, I wrote a history
book for Houghton Mifflin entitled* The Greeks. *I enjoyed
doing that so much that I embarked on a whole series of
histories, and by the time I had reached my hundredth
book, Houghton Mifflin had published seven of them, all
on ancient and medieval history.*

*In the course of my second hundred books I did seven
more histories for Houghton Mifflin. One of them,* The
Land of Canaan (*Book 116*), *was on ancient history. In
this book, published in 1971, I told the tale of the
Maccabean revolt.*

from THE LAND OF CANAAN *(1971)*

The high priests of the old line of Zadok, which dated
back to Solomon's Temple, still held their state in
Jerusalem. In 219 B.C. during the last years of Ptolemaic
dominion, Onias II died and Simon II became high priest.
He is known to later generations as Simon the Just and
received an eloquent tribute in the fiftieth chapter of the
apocryphal biblical book Ecclesiasticus. In 196 B.C., at
about the time Judea passed under Seleucid dominion,
Simon's son Onias III became high priest. He, too, is pictured as having been pious and devout.

Judea itself was confined to a small inland region border-
ing on the north-western shores of the Dead Sea, with
Jerusalem as its only city of note and with a total area of
only about 750 square miles. To its north, where once
Israel had been, was Samaria, and with the Samaritans the
Jews maintained a deadly hostility, each group considering
the other to be pernicious heretics. To the south of Judea

lived the descendants of the Edomites, who had moved northward into land that had once been southern Judah and which was now Idumea. Between Jews and Idumeans there was also a deadly enmity.

To be sure, the Jews were not confined to Judea. Many of them colonized Galilee, the region north of Samaria. It had once made up northern Israel but in these days was so full of non-Jews that it was called Galilee of the Gentiles by the conservative and disapproving Jews of Judea itself. Then, of course, there were the Jews of the Diaspora (Greek for 'dispersion'); that is, those who dwelt outside the borders of the land that had once been promised to Abraham. There were the Jews of the Tigris-Euphrates, of Alexandria, of the Greek cities in Asia Minor and elsewhere.

To all Jews, however, wherever located, Jerusalem and its Temple remained at the centre of their national consciousness. At the time of the great festivals, Jerusalem was crowded with Jews from all over the Near East, coming to sacrifice. The development of Judaism was by this time almost complete. Virtually all the books of the Old Testament had by now been written.

Yet Judaism faced a new danger. The old Canaanite idolatries were long gone, but a new and even more attractive idolatry existed. Since the time of Alexander, Greeks had penetrated all the Mediterranean world and wherever they went they carried Greek culture with them. They were a city people, too, and wherever they went they founded cities. In Judea and surrounding lands, the penetration by the Greeks had been slow under the Ptolemys, but when the Greek-loving Seleucid kings took over, the trend accelerated.

And those who were not Greeks by race (or Hellenes, as the Greeks called themselves) nevertheless hastened to adopt Greek culture. They became Hellenized and the process of Hellenization became a dominating force in all the Mediterranean. Even the rough Romans of the west felt the force of Hellenization; and Scipio himself, the conqueror of Hannibal, was a leader of those who would adopt Greek ways.

The Jews were not immune. Many Jews, not only in Greek cities far from Jerusalem but even in Judea itself, adopted Greek ways of life while paying lip service to the older and less sophisticated notions of Judaism. Other Jews, however, particularly in Judea itself, clung entirely to the old ways and abhorred Greek notions.

The stage was set for a quarrel between these two kinds of Judaism, but anyone looking at the world in 183 B.C. could not possibly have foreseen that such a struggle could have any importance or that it could have any possible effect outside Judea. The thought that the struggle would have world-shaking effects and that it would dictate the nature of the religions that would dominate the world in centuries to come would have seemed utterly unbelievable.

Yet it happened; but so slowly that for centuries no one could possibly have noticed that anything important was taking place.

It began with the failure of Antiochus III. The large indemnity he had agreed to pay the Romans following his defeat was more than he had in his treasury. To get the money, he had to squeeze the rich temples of his land. It was while he was trying to carry the gold out of one of the temples in a far province that the rioting peasantry killed him in 187 B.C.

He was succeeded by his son Seleucus IV, who found the Seleucid realm weakened by defeat and plunder and the far-eastern provinces, so painstakingly retaken by Antiochus III, falling away again, this time permanently.*

Seleucus IV attempted to maintain a quiet and unadventurous reign, since the land needed time for recovery. He still needed money, however, as his father had, and one of the obvious sources was the Temple in Jerusalem. Seleucus sent an official named Heliodorous to see what could be done in that direction.

* For the subsequent history of these eastern provinces, see my book *The Near East* (Houghton Mifflin, 1968).

The tale of what follows is told in the apocryphal book of Second Maccabees in a garbled fashion. What may very likely have happened was that Onias III, the high priest, managed to make a deal with Heliodorus. He bribed Heliodorus generously, giving the underling a part in order to avoid having to give the master the whole. Heliodorus knew that he risked his neck if what he had done was discovered, so he arranged to have Seleucus IV assassinated in 175 B.C.

But Seleucus IV had a younger brother Antiochus, who had been born in Athens and who, after his father's defeat, had been sent as a hostage to Rome. The younger Antiochus was treated kindly there and conceived an admiration for Rome. He was also (perhaps because of his pride in his Athenian birth) an enthusiast of Greek culture. On hearing of his older brother's assassination, Antiochus left Rome and made his way to Antioch. Once there, he had no trouble seizing control and beginning his reign as Antiochus IV.

Antiochus IV was a capable man who dreamed of restoring the Seleucid Empire to the power from which the defeat by the Romans had toppled it. To do this – the old story – he needed money. Among the sources of funds was still the Temple at Jerusalem. Onias III, who represented the more conservative factions of Judaism, was still high priest and Antiochus IV viewed him with disfavour. This might have been simply the result of the old man's stubborn refusal to part with Temple money, or perhaps Antiochus had heard rumours of the deal with Heliodorus. Then, too, Antiochus may well have thought his kingdom would be stronger if all its people were united in Hellenic culture, and the stubborn adherence of Onias III to conservate Judaism may have bothered him.

In any case, when Onias' brother Joshua approached Antiochus with suggestions of a deal, Antiochus listened. The suggestion was that Antiochus appoint Joshua as high priest in place of his brother. Joshua would then allow Antiochus a generous supply of the Temple funds. (In return, Joshua would have the prestige and power of the high priesthood and – as both men knew – a chance to enrich himself, as any high priest could do if he were a little unscrupulous.) To tempt Antiochus further, Joshua played up to his known pro-Greek proclivities by offering to encourage the Hellenization of the Jews. As a demonstration of his sincerity in this direction, he had changed his name from the Hebrew 'Joshua' to the Greek 'Jason'.

Antiochus agreed to the deal. Onias III was taken off to house arrest in Antioch, and Joshua-Jason became high priest. Joshua-Jason promptly began to live up to his part of the bargain. Antiochus got his money and Joshua-Jason established a gymnasium in Jerusalem. At the gymnasium young men could exercise, Greek fashion, in the nude, and the more modish of the young Jews flocked to it. (And Joshua-Jason, who controlled the gymnasium financially, reaped generous profits.)

The conservative Jews were horrified by the arrest of Onias III and by the rifling of the treasury, but the gymnasium shocked them most of all. Not only was public nudity considered an abomination, but young Jews who wished to exercise often wore false foreskins to avoid advertising the fact that they were circumcised – thus denying the very mark of Judaism.

But Joshua-Jason had merely taught others to take the same route as himself. A cousin of his named Onias, who took the Greek name of Menelaus, offered Antiochus a still higher bribe if he were made high priest in his turn. Antiochus obliged in 172 B.C. and in succeeding years the Temple and the people were looted indeed.

When the depredation of Onias-Menelaus became plain, old Onias III, who was looked upon by all conservative Jews as the only legitimate high priest, had the courage to denounce the matter publicly, and then took sanctuary in a Greek temple in a suburb of Antioch. Onias-Menelaus, however, seems to have persuaded the Seleucid commander in the district (with bribes, perhaps) to induce Onias III to leave the sanctuary by giving an oath for his safety. Once

Onias III was out of the temple, he was promptly murdered. This was in 170 B.C.

There was chaos in Judea among those factions supporting this high priest or that, but this was of little moment to Antiochus IV. The Hellenization of the land seemed to be progressing favourably and he had the money he needed from the Temple at Jerusalem and from other sources. He could now buy arms, pay soldiers, and begin the Seleucid comeback. He intended to begin the comeback by taking over Egypt, which was now under the rule of Ptolemy VI, an amiable person but a complete incompetent.

Antiochus IV had no trouble at all. He was a good general and he had a good army. Brushing aside feeble Ptolemaic resistance, he marched to Memphis, the ancient capital of the Egyptians, and in 170 B.C. had himself declared king of Egypt. He then took his army to the Ptolemaic capital of Alexandria and, in 169 B.C., placed it under siege.

While the siege was under way, however, news reached Antiochus that in his absence Joshua-Jason had attempted to take the high priesthood from Onias-Menelaus by force. Jerusalem was in a state of civil war and the Seleucid army, almost 350 miles west of its own borders, could not afford to have its line of communications threatened.

Furious, Antiochus IV hastened back to Judea and punished the troublesome Jews by occupying the city, entering the Temple himself at the head of an armed contingent, and dragging off all the valuables he could find. For the moment, Jerusalem was stricken and quiet.

In 168 B.C., then, Antiochus IV returned to Egypt, where he had as little trouble as before and where he once again resumed the siege of Alexandria. By now, however, the Ptolemys had squealed for help to Rome, which promptly answered the call. Outside the walls of Alexandria a Roman ambassador approached Antiochus IV. Antiochus recognized him as an old friend and approached gladly to greet him; but the old friend was an official emissary from Rome now and he had only one thing to say: Antiochus was either to leave Egypt or to accept war with Rome. Thunderstruck, Antiochus IV asked for time to consider. The Roman drew a circle in the ground around the king and said, 'Decide before you leave the circle.'

Antiochus dared not face Rome. Though his entire army was around him and though it had marched victoriously through Egypt, and though it was sure to take Alexandria, he and all his men had to back down in the face of a single unarmed Roman. There are few humiliations in history as dramatic as this one.

We can imagine Antiochus' angry frustration as he retreated, his need to get back at something or someone. Perhaps the news reached him that the Jews were jubilant over the state of his affairs, as well they might be in view of the troubles he had visited on them by his manipulation of the high priesthood and by his looting of the Temple.

In any case, Antiochus IV determined that, though the Romans might humiliate him, the Jews would not. On his return to Antioch in 167 B.C. he resolved to put an end to Judaism altogether. Let the Jews become Greeks and loyal subjects! It did not seem to him (probably) to be much of a task. Men such as Joshua-Jason and Onias-Menelaus seemed only too eager to be Greek, and they commanded sizeable factions among the Jews.

Consequently, Antiochus ordered that the Temple in Jerusalem be made Greek and that within it there be erected a statue representing Zeus (with whom Yahweh was to be identified) and that on its altar there be sacrifices offered in Greek fashion. What's more, copies of the Jewish Scriptures were to be destroyed, Jewish dietary regulations ended, the Sabbath abolished, and the practice of circumcision forbidden. Those Jews who accepted Hellenization were to be left in peace as loyal subjects of Antiochus. For the first time in history a persecution began that was religious, not national, in character.

Words cannot describe the horror felt by the conservative Jews. Nebuchadnezzar, four centuries before, had merely destroyed the Temple, but Antiochus had desecrated it with idols and swine's flesh. Nebuchadnezzar had merely taken away the Jewish land, but Antiochus was taking away their ideal. The conservative Jews prepared to resist and to retain their way of life, even to death by torture.

Such deaths took place, according to the tales told later in Second Maccabees. Grisly tales of martyrdom, of Jews dying under torture rather than agreeing to taste swine's flesh, are recorded there. These were the first martyr tales in the Judeo-Christian tradition and they formed a precedent.

It was during this period of trial that the books of Daniel and of Esther were written with their (fictional) tales of the dangers and sufferings undergone by Jews under previous oppressors and of how these were overcome by faith and courage. The apocryphal books of Tobit and Judith were written in similar fashion. These were intended to serve, not as sober history (though they were taken as such by the pious of later ages), but as devices for stimulating and encouraging resistance. And eventually, the resistance ceased being that of passive acceptance of torture and death and became the active return of violence for violence.

This new turn of events began with an aged priest, Mattathias. He and his five sons left Jerusalem and retired to the comparative safety of a small town named Modin, seventeen miles to the north-west, outside Judea proper. According to Josephus, the great-great-grandfather of Mattathias was named Hashmon, so that Mattathias and his descendants are sometimes called the Hasmoneans. On the other hand, the third of his five sons, who was to turn out to be the most famous of them, was Judah Makkabi, or, in Greek form, Judas Maccabeus. The surname may mean the Hammerer, from his later victories. In any case, the family has come to be better known as the Maccabees, and the apocryphal books written about the events of this time, whether sober history in the case of First Maccabees, dramatized history in the case of Second Maccabees, or iction in the case of Third Maccabees, all received this name.

The spark that initiated the Jewish rebellion against the Seleucids was set off by an officer of Antiochus who came to Modin to enforce the new laws. He asked Mattathias, as a prominent Jewish leader, to set a good example and to carry through a sacrifice to Zeus in the manner required. Mattathias refused. When another Jew offered to fulfil the royal command, Mattathias, in a rage, killed the Jew and the Seleucid officer.

There was then nothing to do but to leave Modin hastily. Mattathias and his sons made for the Gophna hills, some dozen miles north-east of Modin. Other Jews who resented the new laws came to join him there, and in no time a guerrilla band had been formed. Mattathias died very soon after the flight to the hills and the band came under the command of Judas Maccabeus.

Joining the Maccabee standard were bands of Hassidim (or, in the Greek version of the name, Hasideans), a term which means 'the pious ones'. Their sole concern lay in religion and they were uninterested in politics. It was only when the practice of Judaism was outlawed that they were willing to resort to violence, but under those conditions they were fanatical fighters indeed.

The Gophna hills lay in Samaritan territory, and the Seleucid governor of the region, Apollonius, moved quickly to nip the revolt before it got very far. Apollonius was, in all likelihood, over-confident. He must have been convinced he could easily handle a few rebels and he marched forward carelessly. Judas' men lay in ambush and swarmed down at the proper time. Apollonius' men were scattered, Apollonius himself was killed, and Judas took Apollonius' sword for use in later battles.

This victory encouraged the conservative Jews in Jerusalem and placed the pro-Hellenizers there in difficulties. Matters grew still worse for the latter. A larger Seleucid force was sent out in 166 B.C. to occupy Jerusalem and end the annoying revolt. Again Judas Maccabeus and his men lay in ambush, this time at Bethhoron, twelve miles north-west of Jerusalem. The second Seleucid force was also trapped and destroyed.

By now the Jewish guerrillas had made a first-class nuisance of themselves, but Antiochus IV could not turn his full attention to them. He needed money, money, money, and he had to get that somewhere in the east, where the provinces had declared themselves independent and where tax collections had dried up. Off he marched eastward, leaving the small Jewish war band to the attention of his minister, Lysias.

In 165 B.C. Lysias assembled a strong army at Emmaus, fifteen miles west of Jerusalem and eleven miles west of the Maccabean stronghold at Mizpeh. Judas held his ground and remained on the defensive. With only three thousand men he had to.

But the Seleucid army could not wait. If the rebels would not come out to fight, they would have to be flushed out. Its commander made a mistake, however; he divided his forces and sent only part to Mizpeh. That was what Judas was hoping for. With the enemy divided, Judas raced his men to Emmaus, where he attacked and defeated the part of the Seleucid army that had remained there. With that done, Judas whirled on the contingent that was returning fruitlessly from Mizpeh. For the third time, the Seleucids were defeated.

Later in the year Lysias tried once more, sending a troop around Judea into the friendly land of Idumea and then attacking towards Jerusalem from the south. The watchful Judas stopped him at Beth-zur, sixteen miles south-west of Jerusalem, and defeated him again.

By now, successive victories had brought enough of the Jews to the side of the Maccabees to make it possible for the guerrillas to enter Jerusalem. Seleucid forces and their Hellenized Jewish sympathizers still controlled the fortified portions of the city, but the Maccabees were able to seize the Temple.

Judas Maccabeus proceeded to rededicate the Temple,

purifying it from its Seleucid profanation. He chose priests who had never compromised with the Seleucid authorities, tore down the altar on which swine had been sacrificed to Zeus, and buried the stones. A new altar was built, new vessels supplied, and proper sacrifices performed. The anniversary of the dedication of the Temple in 165 B.C. is celebrated to this day by the Jews as the eight-day feast of Hanukkah (dedication').

Judas Maccabeus by no means considered this a final victory. It was merely an item. He had as his ambition the liberation of all Jews everywhere in the land that had once been Canaan. He led his army across the Jordan and northward, while his brother Simon, with another troop, took the route northward along the coast. Both defeated Seleucid contingents, enrolled fighters from among the Jewish population, and established strongpoints. By 163 B.C. the Seleucid power south of Damascus had been reduced to tatters, and far off, in what is now central Iran, Antiochus IV died, possibly from tuberculosis. Despite his very real ability, his reign had been a disaster.

The death of Antiochus IV did not end Seleucid attempts to repress the Maccabean revolt. Antiochus' nine-year-old son reigned as Antiochus V, with Lysias as his minister. In 162 B.C. yet another Seleucid army advanced to the attack. It was the strongest yet, and once again it attacked from the south, moving through Beth-zur. It had at least one elephant moving with it.

In a battle at Beth-zechariah, five miles north of Beth-zur, the Maccabeans were forced back. Eleazar, one of the brothers of Judas, fought his way to the elephant, thinking that it carried the king in person. He stabbed it in the abdomen and killed it, but the dying elephant fell on Eleazar and crushed him – and it did not, after all, carry the young king.

Eleazar's feat did not turn the tide of battle, and for the first time, in the face of overwhelming strength, Judas was defeated. He brought what he could save of his forces back to the Gophna hills, where he and his family had first

sought refuge five years before, and the Seleucid forces
reoccupied Jerusalem. This time, however, they were careful to make no attempt to interfere with the Temple services. Lysias' moderation was the result of trouble at
home. Other generals were trying to seize control of the
kingdom from Lysias, while Demetrius, a nephew of
Antiochus IV, was grabbing at the throne itself.

Lysias therefore, in an effort to end the Judean revolt
which was sapping his strength, offered a compromise. He
would grant the Jews complete religious freedom if they
would accept Seleucid political sovereignty. The Hassidim,
who were interested only in Judaism as a religion, accepted
this and retired from the battle. This meant that Lysias
had gained his point, for, without the Hassidim, Judas' remaining forces were too weak to offer resistance and he
could only maintain himself in the Gophna hills and await
events.

In the Seleucid wars that followed, both Antiochus V
and Lysias were killed, and Demetrius I ruled in their
place. With Judea quiet, he attempted to restore the situation as it had once been, with the appointment of a high
priest who would control Judaism in the Seleucid interest
– at least to a reasonable degree. He appointed Eliakim as
high priest; Eliakim, a Hellenizer, preferred to be known
by the Greek name of Alcimus. Since Eliakim-Alcimus
was of the old Zadokite line of priests, the Hassidim
accepted him.

Now there was left only the small band of irreconcilables
in the Gophna hills. Demetrius might have ignored them,
but apparently Judas was attempting to interest Rome in
the Jewish plight, and the Seleucid king decided to clean
them out before it occurred to Rome to interfere.
Demetrius therefore sent his general Bacchides with a
strong force from Jerusalem towards the Gophna hills.

Battle was joined eight miles north of Jerusalem in 161
B.C. Judas, whose forces now were less than a thousand
strong, was overwhelmed. He himself died on the battlefield and the few survivors scattered. Two of his brothers

509

Jonathan and Simon, who were among those survivors, managed to take Judas' body away from the battlefield and bury him in the family tomb at Modin. Thus died the most remarkable Jewish fighter since the time of David eight centuries before.

The Maccabean revolt appeared over. A few men lurked in the southern desert with Jonathan, the younger brother of Judas Maccabeus, but they were powerless and could be ignored. The moderate policy of Lysias and Demetrius I had worked where the stern force of Antiochus IV had failed.

The revolt had nevertheless accomplished one purpose: the Temple was Jewish again and the Seleucids made no attempt ever again to interfere with the ritual. This meant that Judaism had been saved and that – alone – meant that Judas' stand, though it had ended in defeat and death, was nevertheless of crucial importance to world history.

On the other hand, the danger was not entirely over. Judaism might have been saved only to die more slowly. The high priest, Alcimus, did all he could to Hellenize the religion. He died in 159 B.C. – the last high priest who was in any way Zadokite – but Hellenization continued after him. And it might have succeeded had the Seleucid kingdom remained a stable and effective governing force. What prevented the withering of Judaism was not so much what the surviving Maccabees could do, but the continuing dynastic struggle among the Seleucids. Demetrius I was constantly fighting rivals for the throne, and, when he was forced to pull soldiers out of Judea, Jonathan and his small band automatically began to increase in numbers and expanded to fill the vacuum.

Demetrius made the best of it. In 157 B.C. he appointed Jonathan to the post of royal governor and allowed him to enter Jerusalem and rule Judea, provided he acknowledged Seleucid sovereignty. Jonathan agreed to that, accepting the reality of power and letting the appearance
o.

In 152 B.C. an imposter, Alexander Balas, who claimed to be a son of Antiochus IV, obtained the backing of Ptolemaic Egypt and launched a civil war against Demetrius I. Jonathan remained shrewdly uncommitted for a while, allowing both sides to bid for his services. Demetrius offered Jonathan rule over wider areas, and Balas offered to appoint him high priest. Jonathan accepted both offers.

In that year of 152 B.C., then, Jonathan donned the robes of the high priesthood, and for the first time in nine centuries an individual who was not descended from Solomon's high priest, Zadok, officiated in the Temple.

Finally, when Jonathan had to choose, he came down on the side of Balas. The choice seemed a good one, for in 150 B.C., in a final battle between the two claimants, Balas was victorious and Demetrius I was killed.

In 147 B.C., however, the son of Demetrius arrived in Syria and attacked Balas. The son was Demetrius II and he, of course, was hostile to the Maccabeans, who had supported – and were, perforce, continuing to support – Balas. An army loyal to Demetrius encamped in what was once the land of the Philistines and challenged Jonathan to battle. Jonathan, in that same year, accepted the challenge, and the battle was fought in Azotus, the biblical Ashdod.

For the first time the Maccabean army was large enough to fight as something more than a guerrilla force – to fight an organized battle rather than instituting a surprise attack from ambush – and it won. The Maccabees under Jonathan now controlled land on both sides of the Jordan over an area of some 800 square miles.

In 145 B.C. Demetrius II finally defeated Balas in battle and drove him to flight and eventual death, but by then the Seleucid monarchy was a worthless toy. The civil wars that had been nearly continuous since the death of Antiochus IV, eighteen years before, had seen a steady shrinkage of the dominions of Antioch. All the east, including the Tigris-Euphrates valley, was now part of the independent kingdom of Parthia (ruled by a people akin to the Persians). Only Syria remained to the Seleucids.

Demetrius II found his power so limited that he could no longer mount a real offensive against the Maccabean forces. In fact, he needed help against his own enemies. Jonathan offered such help, suggesting he would send a band of seasoned Jewish mercenaries to serve Demetrius if the king would hand over the fortified posts surrounding Jerusalem. Demetrius agreed, accepted the forces, used them to establish his power firmly in Antioch, and then refused to give up the fortified posts.

The angry Jonathan waited for the inevitable – more dynastic troubles. In 143 B.C. a general named Tryphon, making use of a young boy who was hailed as the son of Balas and given the title Antiochus VI, rebelled against Demetrius II. Jonathan threw his support to the new claimant at once.

But Tryphon wearied of the indirection of having to act under cover of a boy and planned to kill Antiochus VI. To do so, however, might have risked the good will of Jonathan, who was, at the moment, his strongest supporter. Tryphon therefore planned to plunge the Maccabean power into confusion in the most direct possible way first. He invited Jonathan to a conference in the royal city of Ptolemais, eighty-five miles north of Jerusalem. Jonathan, apparently flattered to be treated with considerable respect by the Seleucid power, allowed himself to be lured into the city with a very small band of men. He was captured and killed in 142 B.C.

But one Maccabean brother remained – Simon. He reclaimed Jonathan's body and buried it in the family tomb, then once more approached Demetrius II, who still maintained a force against Tryphon. Simon offered him an alliance against Tryphon in exchange for recognition of complete Judean independence. The deal was made, and 142 B.C. marked the moment when, for the first time since Nebuchadnezzar's destruction of Jerusalem, 445 years before, there was an independent Jewish state. Simon ruled

both as king (though he did not use the title) and high
priest.

Almost at once Simon began to strengthen himself. In
141 B.C. he took over the fortified posts in Jerusalem so
that at least the capital city was entirely free of the foreign
soldiery. He also took the coastal city of Joppa to give the
newly independent kingdom a foothold at sea.

*From a material standpoint my history books do not do
particularly well. For instance, they have never moved into
paperback editions. That doesn't matter to me, however,
since I enjoy writing them, and my income is high enough
to let me please myself in this respect.*

*Houghton Mifflin might object, to be sure, but they
don't. Perhaps that is because they don't want to hurt my
feelings and see a look of troubled sadness come into my
eyes . . . So, among the second hundred, they loyally published two books of mine on medieval history:* Con-
stantinople *(Book 106) in 1970, and* The Shaping of France
(Book 126) in 1972.

*From the latter book, here is a passage in which France,
having suffered disastrous defeats at the hands of the
smaller nation of England, meets with an even worse
enemy.*

from THE SHAPING OF FRANCE *(1972)*

But once disasters begin to come, they come in battalions.
France had suffered a disaster at sea at the Battle of Sluys,
and a far worse disaster on land at the Battle of Crécy.
Now there came a disaster worse than either, worse than
both together, worse than anything mere medieval armies
could do; something that placed not only France but
England, too, and all Europe under a terror beyond that
which mere armies could create.

It was the plague.

The plague is essentially a disease of rodents and is spread from rodent to rodent by fleas. Every once in a while, however, when the fleas spread the disease to rodents such as house rats, which live in close conjunction with human beings, the disease spreads also to men. Sometimes it affects the lymph nodes, particularly in the groin and the armpits, causing them to swell into painful 'buboes' – hence 'bubonic plague'. Sometimes the lungs are affected ('pneumonic plague') and that is even worse, for then contagion proceeds from man to man via the air and there is no need for the intervention of rats and fleas.

Sometime in the 1330s, a new strain of plague bacillus made its appearance somewhere in central Asia; a strain to which human beings were particularly susceptible. Men began to die, and even while Edward and Philip fought their trivial battle over who was to rule France, the grinning spectre of death was striding closer to Europe. By the time Calais fell, the plague had reached the Black Sea.

In the Crimea, the peninsula jutting into the north-central Black Sea, there was a seaport called Kaffa where the Genoese had established a trading post. In October 1347, a fleet of twelve Genoese ships just managed to make it back to Genoa from Kaffa. The few men on board who were not already dead were dying – and thus the plague entered western Europe. In early 1348 it was in France and in mid-1348 it had reached England.

Sometimes one caught a mild version of the disease, but very often it struck virulently. In the latter case, the patient was almost always dead within one to three days after the first symptoms. Because the extreme stages were marked by haemorrhagic spots that turned dusky, the disease was called the Black Death.

In a world innocent of hygiene, the Black Death spread unchecked. It is thought to have killed some 25 million people in Europe before it died down (more because all the most susceptible people were dead than because anyone did anything) and many more than that in Africa and Asia. About a third of the population of Europe died, perhaps

more, and it took a century and a half before natural multiplication restored European population to what it had
been at the time of the Battle of Crécy. It was the greatest
natural disaster to strike mankind in recorded history.

Its short-term effects were marked by the abject terror it
inspired among the populace. It seemed as though the
world were coming to an end, and everyone walked in fear.
A sudden attack of shivering or giddiness, a mere headache, might mean that death had marked you for its own
and had given you a couple dozen hours to live.

Whole towns were depopulated, with the first to die
lying unburied while the initial survivors fled – only to
spread the disease to wherever it was they fled to. Farms
lay untended; domestic animals (who also died by the
millions) wandered about uncared for. Whole nations
(Aragon, for instance) were afflicted so badly that they
never truly recovered.

Distilled liquors (alcoholic drinks produced by distilling
wine, thus producing a stronger solution of alcohol than
could be formed by natural fermentation) had first been
developed in Italy about 1100. Now, two centuries later,
they grew popular. The theory was that strong drink acted
as a preventive against contagion. It didn't, but it made
the drinker less concerned, which was something. The
plague of drunkenness settled down over Europe to match
the plague of disease and remained behind after the
disease was gone.

Everyone suffered, with those who lived in crowded
quarters the worst, of course. Towns suffered more than
the countryside, and indeed the gradual urbanization of the
west received a setback from which it did not recover for
a century Monastic communities were also particularly
hard hit, and the quality of monastic life in some ways
never recovered.

Even the highest were vulnerable. In 1348 and 1349,
three archbishops of Canterbury died of the plague. In the
papal capital of Avignon, five cardinals and a hundred
bishops died. A daughter of Edward III, Joan, was on her

way to Castile to marry the son of King Alfonso XI. She died of plague in Bordeaux on her way there. And in Castile, so did King Alfonso. In France, Philip's queen, Joan of Burgundy, died.

The terrified populace had to take action. Knowing nothing of the germ theory or of the danger of fleas, unable to keep clean in a culture which was rather suspicious of cleanliness and considered it unholy, they could do nothing useful. They could, however, find a scapegoat, and for that there were always Jews available.

The theory arose that the Jews had deliberately poisoned wells in order to destroy Christians. The fact that Jews were dying of the plague on equal terms with Christians was not allowed to interfere with the theory, and the Jews were slaughtered without mercy. Of course this did nothing at all to diminish the scourge.

Viewed from a longer range, the Black Death (which kept recurring at intervals – though never again as bad – after the first attack had died out in 1351) destroyed the medieval optimism of the thirteenth century. It placed a kind of gloom on the world and bred a growth of fatalistic mysticism that took a long time to dispel.

It also helped destroy the economic structure of feudalism. There had never been a surplus of labour in the fields and the towns, but with the devastation of the plague (which fell more violently upon the low-born than upon the aristocracy) there was a sudden extreme shortage. Savage laws were promulgated by governments in order to keep serfs and artisans from taking advantage of the suddenly increased value of their muscles and skills, but no laws could counter the economic facts of life.

Serfs who recognized the great need for their services dickered for better treatment and greater privileges and often got them. Artisans charged higher prices. Prices and wages rose, and to the difficulties produced by war and plague were added those of economic dislocation and inflation.

Under the double blow of the Battle of Crécy and the

Black Death, the very basis of feudalism, both military and economic, was destroyed. In western Europe, it had to die. It took its time, but there was never a question of its surviving after the mid-fourteenth century; only of how long it would take before human beings realized that it was dead.

Then, half a century later, after the French had suffered civil war and additional defeats and the ever-victorious English were laying siege to Orléans with final victory at hand, here is what happened:

from THE SHAPING OF FRANCE *(1972)*

On February 12, 1429, when the siege was completing its fourth month, a column of French tried to intercept a wagon train being sent to the English from Paris. This included many barrels of dried herrings, for it was the Lenten season and fish was in high demand. The supply train was under the command of Sir John Fastolfe, who had fought well at Agincourt and in Normandy.

As soon as Fastolfe was aware of the oncoming French, he took vigorous measures for the defence. He drew his wagons into a line that served as an impromptu fortification. From behind the shelter of those wagons, he placed his English longbowmen at one flank, and Parisian crossbowmen (the Parisians were still hotly pro-Burgundy and anti-Armagnac) on the other.

The French fought well, but there was little they could do against the wagon-protected bowmen, and the English won again. Burst barrels strewed herring all over the field, so the action is known as the Battle of the Herrings.

The French relieving forces were particularly disheartened at this repulse because it seemed one more in an endless string of victories won in the field by the English. There seemed no use in fighting at all, so what was left of those forces marched hastily away. No other forces were

sent with any intention of battle. Orléans was left to its
fate, and, after two more months had passed, it seemed
that Orléans must fall and that the Bastard, whatever his
resolution and ability, would simply have to surrender.

And then a very strange thing happened, one of the
strangest in history, and something that would have been
derided as incredible if it had appeared in a work of
fiction.

A peasant girl appeared on the scene.

Her name was Jeanne Darc and she was born about
1412 at the village of Domrémy, at the eastern borders of
France, 160 miles east of Paris. After the Treaty of Troyes,
Domrémy lay in that part of France which had been
handed over to the overlordship of the English king.

Jeanne Darc, or Joan Darc in English, is never known
by that name. Her last name has been misspelled as d'Arc,
as though she were of the nobility, so that in English she
is invariably known as Joan of Arc, although there is no
place called Arc from which she came or over which she
had some claim.

In her teens she was experiencing visions, hearing voices
and imagining herself called on to save France. In 1429,
these visions and voices finally drove her to action. Charles
VII had still not been crowned at Reims, though six full
years had passed since the death of his father. What's more,
the siege of Orléans might end in another English victory,
and that might defeat him forever. It seemed to Joan that
her mission had to start at once, that she had to relieve the
siege and crown Charles.

In January 1429, Joan left for Vaucouleurs, twelve miles
north of Domrémy, where there was a fortified outpost that
still held out for Charles VII. Its captain was sufficiently
impressed by her (or perhaps sufficiently eager to get rid
of her) to send her on to Charles VII with an escort of six
men. Charles VII was then at Chinon, 90 miles south-west
of Orléans and 270 miles from Domrémy. Joan had to
cross English-controlled territory to reach Chinon, and so
she dressed in a man's costume to avoid the kind of

trouble a young girl might have if encountered by soldiers. She arrived at Chinon on February 24, 1429, two weeks after the Battle of the Herrings had ended French attempts to do anything active about the siege of Orléans.

It was a superstitious age. When a girl announced herself as a miraculous maid sent by God, she might be taken for exactly that – or as a dangerous witch sent by the Devil for the ensnarement of men. It was not easy to tell which. Charles VII actually received Joan, and she was then questioned by learned theologians for three weeks in order to determine whether she was of divine or diabolical inspiration.

It may well be that some of the worldly men around Charles were not really concerned with which she was, and perhaps didn't believe she could be either. They might have been trying to decide whether she would be accepted by the soldiers as a miracle maid or not. If the French and (even more) the English could be made to believe that God was fighting on the side of the French, that could have an important effect on morale on either side.

The decision arrived at was (theologically) that Joan was sent by God and (practically/politically) that this attitude would carry conviction. She was therefore sent to Orléans with an escort of about three thousand soldiers under John, Duke of Alençon, who had led the French forces at the lost Battle of Verneuil and had been in captivity for a while as a result. On April 29, 1429, Joan and her escort slipped into the city.

It is important to understand that by now the defending force within the city was quite substantial and, indeed, they outnumbered the thin line of besieging English. What kept the French from emerging to do battle was not the lack of means, but the lack of will. The French were simply unable to believe they could win. What's more, the English had suffered considerably in the course of a half-year siege, and all that kept them to their task was that they were simply unable to believe they could lose.

It was only a matter of morale that kept the situation

going, against the military sense of it all. Once the news
arrived that a miraculous maid was coming to the aid of
the French, the situation with respect to morale changed
suddenly and dramatically and what followed was almost
inevitable. While few events in history have seemed so
miraculous as what Joan of Arc accomplished, it is not
really as miraculous as it seemed.

Very likely, the Bastard of Orléans counted on Joan's
effect on the morale on both sides, and, within a week of
her arrival, he launched an attack, on May 4, on the fortified posts set up by the English at the eastern approaches
of the city. He did not even bother telling her about it. On
learning of the fighting, however, Joan hastened to the
eastern walls. The French soldiers, heartened at her appearance, fought the more savagely, and the English fell
back.

The first sign of French victory set in motion a vicious
cycle for the English. If the French advanced more than
was their wont, it was a sign that Joan was heaven-sent or
hell-sent but, in either case, of miraculous help to the
French and not something mere men could fight against.
The English were all the readier to retreat further, and
to accept that further retreat as further evidence.

When Joan was struck by an arrow, the English cheered,
but it was a superficial wound and, when she appeared on
the battlements again, it was easy to believe that she was
invulnerable. And the English fell back still more readily.

By May 8, the English had abandoned the siege, leaving
their strongpoints, their artillery, their dead and wounded.
They made all haste to get out of the reach of Joan's influence.

Orléans was the Stalingrad of the Hundred Years' War.
The siege of Orléans had been the high point of the English
advance into France. The myth of English invincibility was
broken, the hot glare of Agincourt dimmed; and from here
on in, there could be only recession for the English forces.

Then, having written about ancient and medieval history,

*on and off, for about ten years, I grew eager to tackle
modern history. Since by now the bicentennial year of
1976 was approaching, why not a history of the United
States?*

*It seemed a shrewd idea to me, but I forgot to count
words in my eagerness to write. Houghton Mifflin had provided that the histories run no more than 75,000 to 80,000
words each, since they were primarily aimed at a teenage
audience (though adults, I am firmly convinced, can also
profit from reading my histories).*

*I began my history of the United States with the Indians
and with the discovery and settling of North America by
Europeans, and when the allotted wordage was done, I was
dismayed to find I was only up to 1763. I stopped, called
the book* The Shaping of North America *(Book 137), and
it was published in 1973.*

*I continued, then, with a second book but found I could
only squeeze some fifty years into that . . . and another
fifty years into a third . . . and another fifty years into a
fourth.* The Birth of the United States *(Book 149), published in 1974, took the history from 1763 to 1816;* Our
Federal Union *(Book 161), published in 1975, took it from
1816 to 1865; and* The Golden Door *(Book 189), published
in 1977, took it from 1865 to 1918. I had passed the bicentennial year and I had at least one more volume to do.*

*From the last of these books, here is my description of
the Spanish-American War, perhaps the least important
war we fought:*

from THE GOLDEN DOOR *(1977)*

The Americans had fewer ships than the Spanish, but
those ships were new and beautifully designed. For once,
the United States was ready for war, at least on the seas.

This was partly because of the work of the American
naval officer Alfred Thayer Mahan (born in West Point,
New York, on September 27, 1840). The son of a pro-

fessor at West Point, he himself went to the Naval Academy at Annapolis. He served on blockade duty during the Civil War and remained in the Navy till his retirement as a rear admiral in 1896.

He was a great military theoretician, writing *The Influence of Sea Power upon History, 1660–1783* in 1890, *The Influence of Sea Power upon the French Revolution and Empire, 1793–1812* in 1892, and *The Interest of America in Sea Power, Present and Future* in 1897.

The thesis was this: The ocean is continuous and worldwide; the land, discontinuous and consisting of isolated portions. A landlocked military power can occupy regions adjacent to the home base, but must stop at the coast if it lacks a navy. A naval power, if separated from the military power by the ocean, can isolate itself and, by means of its navy, attack the enemy at every coastal point, safeguard its trade, and blockade its enemy. A sea power would have the world as its supply source and would, in the end, defeat a continental power. It was in this way, Mahan pointed out, that Great Britain had finally defeated all her enemies, including Napoleon, and had gained her world empire.

No nation could grow strong any longer without a navy, Mahan said. As for the United States, which had no powerful nations sharing land boundaries with it and which had two wide oceans on either side, it could be particularly strong, even invulnerable, if it had an effective navy. Mahan pointed out the necessity of a base in Hawaii and coaling stations on smaller islands since the Pacific Ocean was so much wider than the Atlantic. He also advocated the building of a canal across the isthmus of Panama, so that the United States could, in need, quickly concentrate its navy in either ocean.

Following Mahan, the Americans worked hard at developing an efficient navy, and though at the time the war with Spain came, there was no canal across the isthmus, there were American ships in each ocean.

The Pacific Fleet was particularly well placed through a

historical accident. The secretary of the navy, John Davis
Long (born in Buckfield, Maine, October 27, 1838) was
away from his desk, and his assistant secretary served
briefly in his place as acting secretary. That assistant secretary was Theodore Roosevelt, who was a great admirer
of Mahan's* and very keen on using the navy properly.
He ordered six warships in the Pacific to proceed to Hong
Kong in order to be ready to act against the Philippines the
moment war was declared. Secretary Long, when he returned, was furious, but he did not countermand the order.

If the United States had a serviceable navy, it had virtually no army at all. Spain had 155,000 soldiers in Cuba
at the time, while the United States had a total of 28,000
soldiers altogether, and these had fought no one but
Indians for a generation.

Volunteers were called up, but the new, enlarged army
units were not stiffened by scattering veterans throughout
them. Instead, the veterans were kept intact and the
rookies were left to themselves. Furthermore, the supply
organization of both food and medical care was abysmally
poor – the last war in which the United States permitted
itself this disgrace.†

As soon as news of the declaration of war was received
in Hong Kong, the American squadron, under Commodore

---

* Another admirer of Mahan's was Kaiser Wilhelm II of Germany. A month before the Spanish-American War started,
Germany, aware of Mahan's theories, began the building of a
modern navy designed eventually to surpass that of Great Britain.
Great Britain was already suspicious of German ambitions, and
this hit at the very heart of its strength. Great Britain and Germany became deadly enemies and sixteen years later they were on
the opposite sides of a great war.

† It was also the last major war fought with gunpowder, which
had been the mainstay of battle for five centuries and had fouled
the guns, choked the gunners, and hidden the battlefield with its
endless smoke. In 1891, the British chemists James Dewar and
Frederick Augustus Abel had invented cordite, the first of the
smokeless powders and a substance more powerful and shattering
than gunpowder. Future wars would be fought with such smokeless powders.

George Dewey (born in Montpelier, Vermont, on December 26, 1837), a veteran of the Civil War, had to leave, as otherwise Hong Kong's status as a neutral port would be in question. That suited Dewey. His orders were to go to Manila, 1,050 kilometres to the south-east.

Dewey had six ships under his command – four cruisers and two gunboats – and on April 27, 1898, after having put all his ships in complete battle readiness, he sailed for Manila. Waiting for him were ten Spanish ships together with Spanish shore batteries. The Europeans in Hong Kong, imagining the Spaniards to be what they once had been, were certain that Dewey was steaming to his destruction; but there was really no chance of that. Dewey's ships were of the latest design and in tiptop shape. The Spanish ships were little more than hulks, and the Spanish admiral was expecting defeat.

The Spanish admiral lined up seven of his ships just off Manila in order to protect the city, but there was nothing to protect the ships. Dewey reached Manila Bay, saw nothing to prevent his entering, did so, and reached the neighbourhood of Manila itself on the night of April 30.

When daybreak of May 1, 1898, revealed the two opposing fleets to each other, the Spaniards fired high and did no damage. At 5.40 a.m. Dewey said quietly to Captain Charles Vernon Gridley (born in Logansport, Indiana, on November 24, 1844), captain of the flagship, *Olympia*, 'You may fire when ready, Gridley.'

The American ships paraded back and forth before the Spanish fleet, firing steadily. They pulled off briefly at 7.30 so that the men could have a quiet breakfast, then returned to work. By 11.00 a.m. the Spanish fleet was destroyed. Every ship had been sunk or beached and 381 Spaniards had been killed. In the process, Dewey lost not a man. Eight sailors had received minor wounds, that was all. And when the American ships moved in to bombard Manila itself, the Spaniards agreed to silence the shore batteries.

Despite the total victory at sea, Dewey could not take Manila. For that he needed a land force, and he had none.

On May 19, he brought in Aguinaldo from Hong Kong so that he might lead his Filipino insurgents against the Spaniards on land and keep them occupied and incapable of taking any aggressive action against the ships. Even that didn't give Dewey the wherewithal to take the city, and he had to wait for the arrival of American soldiers.

The wait wasn't particularly comfortable. He was isolated and far from any friendly port, and, by June 12, British, French, and German ships had arrived. They were there, ostensibly, to guard the lives and properties of *their* nationals but were clearly hoping to pick up some pieces if the fall of Spanish power in the Philippines created a vacuum there. The Germans were especially aggressive in their provocations, and at one point the desperate Dewey was forced to tell a German officer, 'Tell your admiral if he wants war I am ready.'

But the Germans didn't actually want war; they just wanted whatever they could get without war. With Dewey ready (and the worth of his ships having been dramatically exhibited), and with the United States finally making it clear that, whatever happened to the Philippines, no other nations would be allowed a look-in, the German ships sailed off. Dewey settled down to maintain his blockade and wait for his soldiers.

Meanwhile, in the Atlantic, Spain's fleet had reached the West Indies, and by that time they were completely out of fuel. They could not possibly fight before getting into some Cuban port in order to load coal. The American Navy knew this, and it was only a matter of finding the fleet while it was in port and keeping it there. (From their Florida base, the American ships had to go only a few hundred kilometres to reach any part of the Cuban coast, so they had no fuel problem.)

On May 19, the Spanish fleet reached Santiago, on Cuba's south-eastern coast, and entered. On May 29, the American fleet, under Rear Admiral William Thomas Sampson (born in Palmyra, New York, on February 9, 1840) — who had been head of the board of inquiry in connection with the sinking of the *Maine* — located the Spanish fleet there and instantly blockaded the harbour.

If the American fleet could have entered the harbour, as Dewey had entered Manila Bay, they would surely have destroyed the Spanish ships. However, the channel entrance was narrow and was littered with mines, and the United States did not wish to lose any of its modern and expensive ships if that could be avoided. Yet something had to be done, for as long as the Spanish ships were intact, there was always the possibility that they might do some damage.

It was decided to leave the American fleet outside the harbour and to invade Cuba with a land force that could attack Santiago from the rear. On June 10, marines landed in Guantánamo Bay, sixty-five kilometres east of Santiago, to establish a foothold. (During some preliminary skirmishes, one American commander – a Confederate veteran – forgot who the enemy was and shouted, 'Come on, boys, we've got the damn Yankees on the run.')

More than that was needed though, and the main American army, gathering in Tampa, Florida, had been ordered to Cuba on May 30. It was under General William Rufus Shafter (born in Galesburg, Michigan, on October 16, 1835). He was a veteran of the Civil War and had fought bravely and well, but he now weighed 310 pounds and did not know how to organize a large command.

It took eleven days before embarkation could get started and four days to complete the embarkation – everything done in complete chaos, with Shafter doing virtually nothing. By June 20, the transports reached the vicinity of Santiago. Shafter decided not to attempt a direct attack on the city but to land at a point thirty kilometres east of Santiago. In this, he followed the advice of General Calixto Garcia,* who commanded the Cuban rebels in this area.

* In the course of the war, an American officer, Lieutenant Andrew Summers Rowan, had made contact with Garcia in order to co-ordinate action. In 1899, the American journalist Elbert Green Hubbard wrote a moralistic essay entitled 'A Message to Garcia', exalting this action and using it as a lesson to 'get things

The disembarkation was even more ragged and disorganized than the embarkation had been, and had the Americans faced an efficient and well-commanded enemy, most of them would probably have met their end. As it was, the Spanish command was bad enough to make even Shafter look good, and the Americans were placed on Cuban soil without opposition and without casualties resulting from enemy action.

By June 30, the Americans were ready to march on Santiago. On July 1, two battles were fought – one at El Coney, 8 kilometres north-east of Santiago, and the other at San Juan Hill, about 1.5 kilometres east of Santiago. Both were American victories, and it was in the latter that Theodore Roosevelt distinguished himself.

At the outbreak of the war Roosevelt resigned and joined the First Volunteer Cavalry unit, as a lieutenant colonel. He wasn't its commander, but he was always spectacularly visible, and in the popular mind the unit was Roosevelt's Rough Riders. At San Juan Hill, the Americans were pinned by fire from Spaniards holding the heights and the Rough Riders weren't riding, roughly or otherwise, for they were dismounted. Fighting on foot, they led the charge under enemy fire, though it wasn't actually much of a charge since they moved up the heights slowly and with difficulty. But they moved, and drove the Spaniards off.

It was Roosevelt's only chance at the military glory he longed for. (As he said, 'It wasn't much of a war, but it was all we had.') And it was better than nothing, for he made the most of it in later years. The American satirist Finley Peter Dunne (born in Chicago on July 10, 1867) had his famous Irish-dialect hero, Mr Dooley, remark that when Roosevelt wrote up his Spanish-American experien-

done' through what seems suspiciously like mindless obedience. The essay gained tremendous popularity and was read and memorized by uncounted hordes of schoolchildren – including the author of this book. who, even as a child, disagreed with its simplistic philosophy, but thought it the better part of valour not to say so.

ces he should have entitled it 'Alone in Cuba'.

Once on the heights, the Americans were in a position to bombard the city of Santiago and the Spanish fleet from land. The Spanish admiral, whose orders forbade surrender, had no choice but to try to break out of the harbour. On July 3, he made the attempt and the American ships pounced at once. In four hours, every Spanish ship was destroyed, 474 Spaniards were killed or wounded, and 1,750 were taken prisoner. The American loss was 1 killed and 1 wounded.

'Straight' history is not the only history there is, of course, and one of my interests has long been the history of science. In my first hundred books, the most important example of that is Asimov's Biographical Encyclopedia of Science and Technology *(published by Doubleday), which covered all of science from the time of ancient Egypt to the present in a thousand biographical entries.*

In the course of writing my second hundred books, I revised and enlarged that book to the point where I considered the result, published in 1972, the equivalent of a new book and listed it as Book 118.

I also did a history of the telescope for Houghton Mifflin – Eyes on the Universe (Book 165). Here is the tale of the invention of the telescope from it:

from EYES ON THE UNIVERSE *(1975)*

You might even imagine a piece of glass that was symmetrical, a convex surface on both sides meeting in a line all around the edge. You can imagine it best, perhaps, as two plano-convex pieces of glass placed together flat side to flat side. The result is a 'biconvex' piece of glass.

The biconvex piece of glass has the shape of a lentil seed, and it came to be called by the Latin version of that name. It was a 'lens'. Strictly speaking, only the biconvex piece of glass has a right to the name, but its use has spread to all kinds of transparent objects with smoothly curved surfaces. You can speak of a 'plano-convex lens', for instance, even though there are no lentil seeds with a plano-convex shape.

Crude lenses have been unearthed in Crete and in Asia Minor, and some may date as far back as 2000 B.C. Alhazen's writing on light and refraction mentioned lenses and his books began to be translated into Latin about 1170. They served to stimulate thought and experiment in a Europe that was beginning to grow interested in science.

The first systematic studies of lenses in Europe were made by the English scholar Robert Grosseteste (1175–1253) and his pupil Roger Bacon (1220–1292). Neither knew what was happening to light, but they could observe the magnification. Bacon used lenses to magnify letters on a page and to aid himself in reading. He suggested the wearing of lenses to aid vision, and about 1300 spectacles came into use in Italy.

The first spectacles were made of biconvex lenses, which enlarged objects and which were particularly useful to old people, who are often far-sighted.

It is also possible to have a 'biconcave' lens – one in which the glass is thick at the edge of the lens all around and in which the curve on each side bellies inward, so that the glass is thinner as one moves inward from the edge and is thinnest at the centre. With such a lens, light is bent away from the centre and the effect is just the opposite of that of a biconvex lens. Objects viewed through it seem smaller.

It may seem that such a lens is useless. What is the good in seeing things smaller? The fact is, however, that biconcave lenses are useful in correcting near-sightedness, and spectacles for that purpose began to be used about 1450.

The making of spectacles became an important industry in early modern times, particularly in the Netherlands, where men grew skilled in the manufacture of lenses.

Thus, rather than making lenses either biconvex or biconcave, men could make them convex on one side and concave on the other, so that the resulting 'concavo-convex lens' is thinner and more delicate than either the biconcave or the biconvex lenses. If the curves are so chosen that the centre of the concavo-convex lens is thinner than the edges, such a lens will correct near-sightedness; if the centre is thicker than the edges it will correct far-sightedness.

The shop of a Dutch spectacles-maker, with lenses of every variety lying about, is an invitation to play games, for no one has ever had lenses available to him without at once beginning to peer through them at various objects. A magnification effect is most interesting, and it is only natural to attempt to make the magnification as great as possible.

Two English mathematicians, Leonard Digges (1510?–1571?) and John Dee (1527–1608), even experimented with combinations of lenses in an attempt to increase the magnifying effect, but reported no successes.

When the discovery came, according to the most often repeated version of the story, it came by accident.

Hans Lippershey (1570?–1619?) was a spectacles-maker in the city of Middelburg, in the Dutch province of Zeeland, about eighty miles south-west of Amsterdam. What is supposed to have happened is that an apprentice of his, idling away his time in the absence of his master, amused himself by looking at the world through the lenses that had been left in his care. Eventually, he took two lenses and held them both before his eyes, one nearby and one far off, and found, to his astonishment, that a distant weather-vane appeared to be much larger and closer.

With considerable excitement, he showed this to Lippershey when he returned to the shop. It may be that the apprentice was not beaten for wasting time, for Lippershey seems to have caught the significance of the finding at once.

Lippershey realized that one could not expect to stand about holding two lenses in appropriate positions, one in each hand. He therefore devised a metal tube into which the two lenses could be fitted in the proper place, and he had what he called (in Dutch) a 'looker', something one could look through.

It came to be called, more pretentiously, an 'optic tube' or 'optic glass' or 'perspective glass'. In the first book of *Paradise Lost*, published in 1667, John Milton still refers to such a device as an optic glass. In 1612, however, a Greek mathematician, Ioannes Dimisiani, who was secretary to an Italian cardinal, suggested the word 'telescope', from the Greek words meaning 'to see at a distance'. By about 1650 this word began to gain ground and eventually drove out all others. We can say, then, that Lippershey had invented the first telescope.

But did he? Once the instrument became famous, other Dutchmen lay claim to having been first in the field. This is very possible, for given a supply of lenses, anyone could invent it by accident. One with a particularly good case is another optician of Middelburg, a neighbour of Lippershey's named Zacharias Janssen (1580–1638?). He claimed to have constructed a telescope in 1604, and he may have; Lippershey may have borrowed the idea and made up the story of his apprentice to cover the theft.

Nevertheless, Lippershey deserves credit whether he originated the telescope in the strict sense of the word or not. All his competitors for the honour did nothing with their telescopes, as far as we know, except indulge in viewing for their own amusement. Lippershey made the world conscious of the instrument by offering it to the Dutch government as a war weapon.

At that time, the Netherlands had been fighting a bitter war of independence against Spain for forty years, and all that was keeping the small nation alive against the superior military power of Spain was the Dutch navy. An instrument that would allow ships of the Dutch fleet to see the approach of an enemy long before that enemy could be aware of the Dutch would place the Netherlands in a strong position.

Maurice of Nassau, the capable man who was then stadholder of the Dutch republic, was interested in science and saw the importance of the device at once. He paid Lippershey 900 florins and ordered him to produce for the government telescopes of a binocular variety, ones that could be looked through with both eyes at once.

Maurice tried to keep the telescope a secret, but that was impossible; the device was too simple. The mere rumour that such a thing existed meant that any ingenious man could duplicate it at once. Telescopes were offered to Henry IV of France before 1608 was over, but King Henry, while amused, was not interested.

The secret war weapon, then, was no secret – but the Dutch did not lose too much. In 1609, a truce with Spain was worked out and the Dutch were never in real danger (from Spain, at least) thereafter. The telescope could go its way, then, with not even the sketchiest attempt to keep it secret – and it did.

By all odds, though, the most unusual bit of history included in my second hundred books is fictional. In 1973, the Saturday Evening Post, *aware of the coming bicentennial suggested that I write a fantasy about Benjamin Franklin, one in which I would talk to him, perhaps, and get the advice of the wise old sage with respect to our contemporary problems.*

I thought it was a fascinating idea, and I felt I could handle it since I had already written The Shaping of North America *and* The Birth of the United States *in addition to* The Kite That Won the Revolution, *a book specifically on Franklin, which was included in my first hundred.*

I therefore wrote a story called 'The Dream' and it was published in the January–February 1974 Saturday Evening Post.

As so often happens, though, the publishers' appetite was only whetted and they came after me again. They wanted more dream conversations with Franklin, and I

*wrote three more before mounting one of my all-too-rare
rebellions against such things and refusing to do any more.*

*I called the additional stories simply 'Second Dream',
'Third Dream', and 'Fourth Dream', but the* Saturday
Evening Post *called them 'Benjamin's Dream', 'Party by
Satellite', and 'Benjamin's Bicentennial Blast'.*

*Then, in January 1976, the printers' union of New York
held its annual banquet on Franklin's birthday (he being
the patron saint of American printers). It was their custom
to put out a small booklet of Frankliniana, and on this
occasion, with my permission they put out a collection of
three of the Dreams. (For some reason, they left out the
third.)*

*It was a privately printed book, beautifully done, and
longer than some of my children's books. What's more, it
contained stories of mine that were not otherwise collected
in book form, so I placed it on my list as Book 170 (with
the most inconvenient name of all the books in my entire
two hundred). From it, here is 'The Dream', the first in the
series, in its entirety:*

'The Dream' *(1974)*

'I'm dreaming,' I said. It seemed to me that I had said it
aloud. I know that I was in bed. I was aware of the bedclothes. I was aware of the scattered city lights peeping
through the slats of the Venetian blinds.

Yet he was there. As alive – as living – as real –

I could reach out and touch him, but I dared not move.

I recognized him. I've seen enough pictures of him, and
so has everyone. He did not look quite like his pictures,
for he was old, very old. White hair fringed his head. I
recognized him. I simply knew who he was.

He said, 'I'm dreaming.'

We stared at each other and all the world faded away –
the bed and the bedclothes and the room. I said. 'You're
Benjamin Franklin.'

He smiled slowly and said, 'It may be that this is not a dream only. I stand close to death and perhaps the dying may have their wishes answered, if the wish be sufficiently earnest. Of what year are you?'

I felt panic rise. It might be a dream, but it might be madness. 'I am dreaming!' I insisted wildly.

'Of course, you are, after a fashion, dreaming,' said Franklin – what else could I call him? 'And I as well. How is it conceivable that you and I could speak but by something outside reality? And how does man transcend reality but in dreams? Of what year are you, my good sir?'

I was silent. He waited patiently and then shook his head.

'Then I will speak first,' he said. 'I am old enough to have naught to fear. It is New Year's Eve of the Year of our Lord 1790, in the fourteenth year of the Independence of the United States, and in the first year of the presidency of George Washington. And in the last year of poor Benjamin Franklin, too. I will not last the new year. I know that.

'I do not die prematurely. In a fortnight and a few days I will mark my eighty-fourth birthday. A good old age, for it has made my life long enough to see my native land become a new nation among the nations of the earth, and I have had something to do with that. We have a Constitution that was hammered out, not without pain, and will perhaps serve. And General Washington is spared to lead us.

'Yet will our nation last? The great monarchies of Europe remain hostile and there are dissensions among ourselves. British forces still hold our frontier posts; Spain threatens in the south; our trade languishes; the party spirit grows. Will our nation last?'

I managed to nod my head.

He chuckled almost noiselessly. 'Is that all you can say? A nod? I asked for two hundred years. With this new year coming in, my last year, I asked what the United States might be like on its two hundredth birthday. Are these, then, the only tidings I am vouchsafed?'

'Almost,' I managed to say. 'Almost. It is almost the bicentennial.'

Franklin nodded. 'You two centuries is a long time. It is two centuries since the first Englishmen stepped ashore on Roanoke Island; two centuries since Spain's invincible Armada was smashed. I fear the many inevitable changes two more centuries will bring.'

He paused and then his voice seemed stronger, as though he were preparing to face whatever might be. 'You speak of the bicentennial as though you accept the idea casually. The United States, then, still exists in your time?'

'Yes!'

'In what condition? Still independent? Still with the princely domain we won from Great Britain?'

'Still independent,' I said, and I felt myself grow warm with the pleasure of bringing great news. 'And far larger. It is a land as large as all of Europe, with a population of more than two hundred million drawn from every nation. Fifty states stretch from the Atlantic to the Pacific, with the fiftieth leaping the sea to the Hawaiian Islands of the mid-Pacific.'

His eyes lightened with joy. 'And Canada?'

'Not Canada. That remains under the British crown.'

'Great Britain is still a monarchy then?'

'Yes. Queen Elizabeth II is on the throne, but Great Britain is our friend and has been for a long time.'

'Let the Creator be praised for that. Does the nation prosper?'

'The richest on earth. The strongest.'

Now Franklin paused. Then: 'You say that because you think to please me, perhaps. Richer than Great Britain? Stronger than France?'

'If you asked to have the future revealed to you, would it be lies you would hear? The time has not been all bliss. If we are a mighty union of states now, under our thirty-seventh President in unbroken succession from George Washington, it is because we have survived a long and bloody war between the states. In this present century, we have fought war after war overseas. We have had periods of economic disaster and periods of political corruption. It has not been the best of all possible worlds, but we have survived, and, as we approach the bicentennial, we are the richest and strongest nation on earth.'

The old man seemed restless. He stirred in his bed and said, 'I feel that I would like to walk about. I am not yet so old as to be bedridden. Yet I fear it will break the vision. It grows stronger, do you not feel that?'

'Yes,' I said. It was as though we two alone, separated by two centuries, were all that existed in a universe closed tightly about us.

Franklin said, 'I feel your thoughts without asking. I begin to grow in you, or you in me. I sense your world – the world that is to come.'

There was a tickling in my skull – not a tickling, either – a sensation I could not describe and still cannot. It was another mind which, even in great old age, was more powerful than my own and had gently inserted itself into the interstices of my own.

Franklin said, with infinite satisfaction, 'Yours is an age in which natural philosophy, then, is highly advanced, I see.'

'We call it science now,' I said, 'and you are right. We fly through the air and can circle the globe in less time than it took you to go from Boston to Philadelphia. Our words streak at the speed of light and reach any corner of the globe in a fraction of a second. Our carriages move without horses and our buildings tower a quarter of a mile into the air.'

He was silent and for a time seemed to be attempting to absorb what might have seemed like wild fantasy.

I said, 'Much of it stems from you. You were the first to penetrate the nature of electricity, and it is electricity that now powers our society. You invented the lightning rod, the first device, based on the findings of pure science, to defeat a natural calamity. It was with the lightning rod that men first turned to science for help against the universe.'

He said, 'You make it unnecessary for an old man to praise himself. I am too old to play at the game of modesty. I look back at my life and my eyes are not so blind as to fail to show me something of my true worth. Do you think, then, the lightning rod is my greatest invention?'

'One of them, certainly,' I said.

'Not at all,' said Franklin seriously, 'for my greatest invention is the United States, which I see is fated to increase so mightily in strength and wealth. But you think I exaggerate?'

'Well,' I said, 'you were a member of the committee that wrote the Declaration of Independence –'

'Tom Jefferson did the writing,' interrupted Franklin, 'though I suggested a passage or two.'

'And you were a member of the Constitutional Convention –'

'Where I devoted myself to quieting tempers. None of that. I invented the United States over a score of years before it was born. Have you forgotten that in your time?'

'I am not certain –'

'The French!' he said, impatiently. 'Have the Americans of the future forgotten the day when France controlled Canada and Louisiana and reached out to take the Ohio Valley, too. The day when they would have penned us between the mountains and the sea, to take us at their leisure later?'

'We remember,' I said. 'We remember Wolfe and the capture of Quebec.'

'But that was victory, in 1759. Cast your mind back to 1754. The French were at Fort Duquesne, only two hundred fifty miles from Philadelphia. Young George Washington's mission to the French – and he was Young George then, a lad of twenty-one – had failed. Yet the colonies would not take action against the menace. The Pennsylvania proprietary government was torpid. The British were concerned with Europe, not with us. And even the

Iroquois, our old Indian allies, were threatening to transfer their friendship to the French. Do you remember all that?'

'Only dimly, sir.'

'So Governor De Lancey of New York called a congress of the colonies to meet and confer about the common danger. On June 19, 1754, twenty-five delegates from seven colonies – the four of New England, plus New York, Pennsylvania, and Maryland – met at Albany. We comforted the Iroquois and held them firm, and then, on June 24, I presented my plan of union to the Albany Congress.'

He paused dramatically, then said, 'I suggested the colonies be governed by a governor-general, appointed and paid by the British crown. Partner with him was to be a grand council in which delegates from the various colonies, in number proportional to population, would sit. The grand council would deal with American affairs, and the governor-general would see to it that the interests of the empire were preserved. The congress accepted it – on July 4. It might have saved the colonies for Great Britain.

I nodded. 'It might have. Canada finally came to much the same arrangement and is still under the British crown, though it rules itself.'

'Ah! But the colonies ignored my plan because it gave too much power to the crown, and Parliament ignored it because it gave too much power to the colonies. But the idea of union, which was *mine*, did not die, you see. And what I suggested, moulded into modified form by time, came to pass, so that my intention became the United States of America. And,' he added with deep satisfaction, 'I lived to see it and to play my small – no, my *large* part.'

I nodded again.

'And now,' he said, 'you live in a great world that has grown curiously small, a world far smaller than my thirteen colonies of 1754. Around the world in a day, you say? Words at the speed of light? The astronomer royal, Mr Bradley, had worked that out to be some 180,000 miles per second.'

'That is right; 186,282 miles per second.'

'Even to the exact mile? And yet your world is as divided as our American states once were.'

'More divided, I fear.'

'I catch a dim view of devices that make war deadly,' he said.

'We have bombs that can destroy –'

But old Franklin waved his hand. 'Do not tell me. I see enough. And yet with the chance of universal destruction, there remains no certainty of peace?'

'The nations are armed and hostile.'

'The United States arms also?'

'Certainly. It is the strongest nuclear power.'

'Then man does not advance in wisdom as he does in power?'

I shrugged. What could I say?

Franklin said, 'Are there no enemies against which the nations can unite? We tried to unite against France, but relied too greatly on Great Britain to feel the absolute need. We did unite against Great Britain, at last, when we stood alone.'

I said, 'There is no power against whom the nations of the world feel the need to unite. There is no enemy from beyond the earth to threaten us with universal defeat and slavery.'

'Are there no enemies other than those who are living beings?' asked Franklin angrily. 'Is there not ignorance? Is there not misery? Is there not hunger and disease, and hatred and bigotry, and disorder and crime? Has your world changed so much that these things do not exist?'

'No. We have them. Not all of man's material advance has ended the threat of those things you mention. We multiply still in great number – nearly four billion the world over – and that multiplies our problems and may even destroy us all.'

'And mankind will not combine against this immaterial foe?'

I said, 'No more than the colonies combined against

France or even against Great Britain until bloodshed in New England brought them a clear and present danger.'

Franklin said, 'Can you wait for a clear and present danger? What you call a nuclear war would make it too late at once. If matters advanced to the point where your complex society broke down, then even in the absence of war you could not prevent catastrophe.'

'You are correct, sir.'

'Is there no way, then, to dramatize the –' His head bent in thought. He said, 'You spoke of a war between the states. Are the states still at enmity? Is the nation still divided?'

'No, the wounds are healed.'

'How? In what manner?'

'That is not easy to explain. For one thing, in the years after that war, the nation was engaged in building the West. In this great colonizing venture, all the states, north and south, combined. In that common task, and in the further task of strengthening the nation, smaller enmities were forgotten.'

'I see,' said Franklin. 'And is there no great venture in which the world is engaged in your time. Is there nothing so grand that in it all the nations may find a common goal and, as you say, forget the smaller enmities?'

I thought for a moment. 'Space, perhaps.'

'Space?'

'Both ourselves and the Soviet Union – which used to be the Russian Empire – have sent out exploring vessels as far as the planets Mars and Jupiter.'

For a moment Franklin seemed speechless. Then he said, 'With men on board?'

'No, unmanned. But six vessels, carrying three men each, have travelled to the moon. Twelve Americans have walked on the moon. A seventh vessel miscarried but brought its crew safely back to earth.'

Franklin said, 'And with so majestic a feat at the disposal of mankind, the nations of the world can yet quarrel?'

'I am sorry, but it is so.'

'Is the venture, perhaps, merely a useless show?'

'No. Not at all. Vessels bearing instruments circle earth. They help in our planetary communications. They serve as navigational aids. They report on our cloud cover and help us predict the weather. They investigate the properties of space and help us understand our universe. Through their observations we can plot earth's resources, pinpoint earth's physical problems of pollution, understand the planet as a whole in ways we never could before. We can add to our knowledge in an as yet unsuspected fashion that will help us in —'

'And *still* the nations quarrel?'

'Yes.'

Franklin's eyes began to blaze at this. One arm reached out tremblingly towards me. 'Then there must be further dramatization. Tell me, is it an American venture only — those vessels to the moon — or are other nations involved?'

'It is strictly American.'

'Ah. And the bicentennial approaches. Then cannot the United States establish a birthday party that will be the greatest birthday party of all time by making it a celebration for mankind?'

'In what way, sir?'

'Launch one of your vessels on the bicentennial,' he said energetically. 'Or, if there is not time for that, announce one to be launched by the united aid of all the nations of the world. Let there be a celebration of the Fourth, not as the bicentennial of a single nation, but as a glorification of the principle of the union of political entities against a common foe and for a common purpose.

'Let there be the largest birthday cake in the world, if you will; the decoration of whole cities; the saluting of a thousand guns; the playing of ten thousand bands — but let it be for mankind. Let the leaders of all nations assemble to praise the union of mankind. Let them all plan their own part in the launching of vessels into space under the auspices of a united planet. Let the conquest of space be the source of pride for nothing smaller than mankind. Let it be that in which all men can find a common glory, and in which all men can forget small enmities.'

I said, 'But the problems of mankind will remain. They will not disappear.'

Franklin's figure seemed to waver, grow less substantial. 'Do you want everything at once? The American union did not solve all problems for Americans. But it made it possible for solutions to be sought, and sometimes found.'

He grew dimmer still, wraithlike, and then vanished in a fading smoke. And I woke up.

If it were a dream, it was Franklin's dream, too. And a greater dream still – of a union beyond our Union.

But what could I do? I do not make policy.

Yet I am a writer. With help, I might make myself heard. With help!

So I picked up the telephone and called a certain editor, for, in addition to the lightning rod and the United States, hadn't Benjamin Franklin also invented the *Saturday Evening Post*?

PART 9

The Bible

Among my first hundred books is the two-volume Asimov's Guide to the Bible. *What could I do for an encore?*

One thing I could do was to write articles on biblical subjects for people who were impressed with the Guide. *Reader's Digest Books asked me to contribute essays to an elaborate book they were compiling about men and women in the Bible. I wrote articles for them on Jacob, Ruth, and so on.*

Although I was well paid, I didn't particularly enjoy the task since the editors had their ideas and they were not mine. Eventually, when the book came out, I found that everyone who had had anything to do with the book was carefully acknowledged – the editors, photographers, paper cutters, office boys, garbage collectors – everyone but the writers. The written words, it could only be assumed, had been carved on Sinai by direct revelation.

I was furious. Although I had contributed a substantial portion of the book, I refused to include it in my list – not if my authorship were in no way acknowledged. In fact, I didn't even keep the book.

It was not, however, an effort that had been entirely wasted. My biography on Ruth got me to thinking about the subject, and for Doubleday I wrote a book for young people called The Story of Ruth *(Book 127). It was published in 1972.*

I repeated the thesis of this book in an F & SF *essay, 'Lost in Non-Translation', which appeared in March 1972 and was then included in my essay collection* The Tragedy of the Moon *(Book 144), published by Doubleday in 1973. The essay is included here in full.*

'Lost in Non-Translation' *(1972)*

At the Noreascon (the Twenty-ninth World Science Fiction Convention), which was held in Boston on the Labor Day weekend of 1971, I sat on the dais, of course, since, as the Bob Hope of science fiction, it is my perennial duty to hand out the Hugos. On my left was my daughter, Robyn – sixteen, blonde, blue-eyed, shapely, and beautiful. (No, that last adjective is not a father's proud partiality. Ask anyone.)

My old friend Clifford D. Simak was guest of honour, and he began his talk by introducing, with thoroughly justified pride, his two children, who were in the audience. A look of alarm instantly crossed Robyn's face.

'Daddy,' she whispered urgently, knowing full well my capacity for inflicting embarrassment, 'are you planning to introduce *me*?'

'Would that bother you, Robyn?' I asked.

'Yes, it would.'

'Then I won't,' I said, and patted her hand reassuringly.

She thought a while. Then she said, 'Of course, Daddy, if you have the urge to refer, in a casual sort of way, to your beautiful daughter, that would be all right.'

So you can bet I did just that, while she allowed her eyes to drop in a charmingly modest way.

But I couldn't help but think of the blond, blue-eyed stereotype of Nordic beauty that has filled Western literature ever since the blond, blue-eyed Germanic tribes took over the western portions of the Roman Empire, fifteen centuries ago, and set themselves up as an aristocracy.

... And of the manner in which that stereotype has been used to subvert one of the clearest and most important lessons in the Bible – a subversion that contributes its little bit to the serious crisis that today faces the world, and the United States in particular.

In line with my penchant for beginning at the beginning,

come back with me to the sixth century B.C. A party of Jews had returned from Babylonian exile to rebuild the Temple at Jerusalem, which Nebuchadnezzar had destroyed seventy years before.

During the exile, under the guidance of the prophet Ezekiel, the Jews had firmly held to their national identity by modifying, complicating, and idealizing their worship of Yahweh into a form that was directly ancestral to the Judaism of today. (In fact Ezekiel is sometimes called 'the father of Judaism'.)

This meant that when the exiles returned to Jerusalem, they faced a religious problem. There were people who, all through the period of the exile, had been living in what had once been Judah, and who worshipped Yahweh in what they considered the correct, time-honoured ritual. Because their chief city (with Jerusalem destroyed) was Samaria, the returning Jews called them Samaritans.

The Samaritans rejected the newfangled modifications of the returning Jews, and the Jews abhorred the old-fashioned beliefs of the Samaritans. Between them arose an undying hostility, the kind that is exacerbated because the differences in belief are comparatively small.

In addition there were, also living in the land, those who worshipped other gods altogether – Ammonites, Edomites, Philistines, and so on.

The pressures on the returning band of Jews were not primarily military, for the entire area was under the more or less beneficent rule of the Persian Empire; they were social pressures, and perhaps even stronger for that. To maintain a strict ritual in the face of overwhelming numbers of non-believers is difficult, and the tendency to relax that ritual was almost irresistible. Then, too, young male returnees were attracted to the women at hand and there were intermarriages. Naturally, to humour the wife, ritual was further relaxed.

But then, possibly as late as about 400 B.C., a full century after the second Temple had been built, Ezra arrived in Jerusalem. He was a scholar of the Mosaic law, which had been edited and put into final form in the course of the exile. He was horrified at the backsliding and put through a tub-thumping revival. He called the people together, led them in chanting the law and expounding on it, raised their religious fervour, and called for confession of sins and renewal of faith.

One thing he demanded most rigorously was the abandonment of all non-Jewish wives and their children. Only so could the holiness of strict Judaism be maintained, in his view. To quote the Bible (and I will use the recent New English Bible for the purpose):

'Ezra the priest stood up and said, "You have committed an offence in marrying foreign wives and have added to Israel's guilt. Make your confession now to the Lord the God of your fathers and do his will, and separate yourselves from the foreign population and from your foreign wives." Then all the assembled people shouted in reply, "Yes; we must do what you say . . ." ' (Ezra 10 : 10–12).

From that time on, the Jews as a whole began to practise an exclusivism, a voluntary separation from others, a multiplication of peculiar customs that further emphasized their separateness; and all of this helped them maintain their identity through all the miseries and catastrophes that were to come, through all the crises, and through exiles and persecutions that fragmented them over the face of the earth.

The exclusivism, to be sure, also served to make them socially indigestible and imparted to them a high social visibility that helped give rise to conditions that made exiles and persecutions more likely.

Not everyone among the Jews adhered to this policy of exclusivism. There were some who believed that all men were equal in the sight of God and that no one should be excluded from the community on the basis of group identity alone.

One who believed this (but who is forever nameless) attempted to present this case in the form of a short piece of historical fiction. In this fourth-century-B.C. tale the heroine was Ruth, a Moabite woman. (The tale was presented as having taken place in the time of the judges, so the traditional view was that it was written by the prophet Samuel in the eleventh century B.C. No modern student of the Bible believes this.)

Why a Moabite woman, by the way?

It seems that the Jews, returning from exile, had traditions concerning their initial arrival at the borders of Canaan under Moses and then Joshua, nearly a thousand years before. At that time, the small nation of Moab, which lay east of the lower course of the Jordan and of the Dead Sea, was understandably alarmed at the incursion of tough desert raiders and took steps to oppose them. Not only did they prevent the Israelites from passing through their territory, but, tradition had it, they called in a seer, Balaam, and asked him to use his magical abilities to bring misfortune and destruction upon the invaders.

That failed, and Balaam, on departing, was supposed to have advised the king of Moab to let the Moabite girls lure the desert raiders into liaisons, which might subvert their stern dedication to their task. The Bible records the following:

'When the Israelites were in Shittim, the people began to have intercourse with Moabite women, who invited them to the sacrifices offered to their gods; and they ate the sacrificial food and prostrated themselves before the gods of Moab. The Israelites joined in the worship of the Baal of Peor, and the Lord was angry with them' (Numbers 25 : 1–3).

As a result of this, 'Moabite women' became the quintessence of the type of outside influence that by sexual attraction tried to subvert pious Jews. Indeed, Moab and the neighbouring kingdom to the north, Ammon, were singled out in the Mosaic code:

'No Ammonite or Moabite, even down to the tenth generation, shall become a member of the assembly of the Lord . . . because they did not meet you with food and water on your way out of Egypt, and because they hired Balaam . . . to revile you . . . You shall never seek their welfare or their good all your life long' (Deuteronomy 23:3–4, 6).

And yet there were times in later history when there was friendship between Moab and at least some men of Israel, possibly because they were brought together by some common enemy.

For instance, shortly before 1000 B.C., Israel was ruled by Saul. He had held off the Philistines, conquered the Amalekites, and brought Israel to its greatest pitch of power to that point. Moab naturally feared his expansionist policies and so befriended anyone rebelling against Saul. Such a rebel was the Judean warrior David of Bethlehem. When David was pressed hard by Saul and had retired to a fortified stronghold, he used Moab as a refuge for his family.

'David . . . said to the king of Moab, "Let my father and mother come and take shelter with you until I know what God will do for me." So he left them at the court of the king of Moab, and they stayed there as long as David was in his stronghold' (1 Samuel 22:3–4).

As it happened, David eventually won out, became king first of Judah, then of all Israel, and established an empire that took in the entire east coast of the Mediterranean, from Egypt to the Euphrates, with the Phoenician cities independent but in alliance with him. Later, Jews always looked back to the time of David and of his son Solomon as a golden age, and David's position in Jewish legend and thought was unassailable. David founded a dynasty that ruled over Judah for four centuries, and the Jews never stopped believing that some descendant of David would yet return to rule over them again in some idealized future time.

Yet, on the basis of the verses describing David's use of Moab as a refuge for his family, there may have arisen a tale to the effect that there was a Moabite strain in David's ancestry. Apparently, the author of the Book of Ruth determined to make use of this tale to point up the doctrine of non-exclusivism by using the supremely hated Moabite woman as his heroine.

The Book of Ruth tells of a Judean family of Bethlehem – a man, his wife, and two sons – who are driven by famine to Moab. There the two sons marry Moabite girls, but after a space of time all three men die, leaving the three women – Naomi, the mother-in-law, and Ruth and Orpah, the two daughters-in-law – as survivors.

Those were times when women were chattels, and unmarried women, without a man to own them and care for them, could subsist only on charity. (Hence the frequent biblical injunction to care for widows and orphans.)

Naomi determined to return to Bethlehem, where kinsmen might possibly care for her, but urged Ruth and Orpah to remain in Moab. She does not say, but we might plausibly suppose she is thinking, that Moabite girls would have a rough time of it in Moab-hating Judah.

Orpah remains in Moab, but Ruth refuses to leave Naomi, saying, 'Do not urge me to go back and desert you . . . Where you go, I will go, and where you stay, I will stay. Your people shall be my people, and your God my God. Where you die I will die, and there I will be buried. I swear a solemn oath before the Lord your God: nothing but death shall divide us' (Ruth 1:16–17).

Once in Bethlehem, the two were faced with the direst poverty, and Ruth volunteered to support herself and her mother-in-law by gleaning in the fields. It was harvest time, and it was customary to allow any stalks of grain that fell to the ground in the process of gathering to remain there to be collected by the poor. This gleaning was a kind of welfare programme for those in need. It was, however, backbreaking work, and any young woman, particularly a Moabite, who engaged in it underwent certain obvious risks at the hands of the lusty young reapers. Ruth's offer was simply heroic.

As it happened, Ruth gleaned in the lands of a rich Judean farmer named Boaz, who, coming to oversee the

work, noticed her working tirelessly. He asked after her,
and his reapers answered, 'She is a Moabite girl . . . who
has just come back with Naomi from the Moabite country'
(Ruth 2:6).

Boaz spoke kindly to her and Ruth said, 'Why are you
so kind as to take notice of me when I am only a
foreigner?' (Ruth 2:10). Boaz explained that he had heard
how she had forsaken her own land for love of Naomi
and how hard she worked to take care of her.

As it turned out, Boaz was a relative of Naomi's dead
husband, which must be one reason why he was touched
by Ruth's love and fidelity. Naomi, on hearing the story,
had an idea. In those days, if a widow was left childless,
she had the right to expect her dead husband's brother to
marry her and offer her his protection. If the dead husband
had no brother, some other relative would fulfil the task.

Naomi was past the age of childbearing, so she could
not qualify for marriage, which in those days centred
about children; but what about Ruth? To be sure, Ruth
was a Moabite woman and it might well be that no Judean
would marry her, but Boaz had proven kind. Naomi
therefore instructed Ruth how to approach Boaz at night
and, without crudely seductive intent, appeal for his
protection.

Boaz, touched by Ruth's modesty and helplessness,
promised to do his duty, but pointed out that there was a
kinsman closer than he and that, by right, this other
kinsman had to have his chance first.

The very next day, Boaz approached the other kinsman
and suggested that he buy some property in Naomi's
charge and, along with it, take over another responsibility.
Boaz said, 'On the day when you acquire the field from
Naomi, you also acquire Ruth the Moabitess, the dead
man's wife . . .' (Ruth 4:5).

Perhaps Boaz carefully stressed the adjectival phrase
'the Moabitess', for the other kinsman drew back at once.
Boaz therefore married Ruth, who in time bore him a son.
The proud and happy Naomi held the child in her bosom

and her women friends said to her, 'The child will give you new life and cherish you in your old age; for your daughter-in-law who loves you, who has proved better to you than seven sons, has borne him' (Ruth 4:15).

In a society that valued sons infinitely more than daughters, this verdict of Judean women on Ruth, a woman of the hated land of Moab, is the author's moral – that there is nobility and virtue in all groups and that none must be excluded from consideration in advance simply because of their group identification.

And then, to clinch the argument for any Judean so nationalistic as to be impervious to mere idealism, the story concludes: 'Her neighbours gave him a name: "Naomi has a son," they said; "we will call him Obed." He was the father of Jesse, the father of David' (Ruth 4:17).

Where would Israel have been, then, if there had been an Ezra present to forbid the marriage of Boaz with a 'foreign wife'?

Where does that leave us? That the Book of Ruth is a pleasant story, no one will deny. It is almost always referred to as a 'delightful idyll', or words to that effect. That Ruth is a most successful characterization of a sweet and virtuous woman is beyond dispute.

In fact everyone is so in love with the story and with Ruth that the whole point is lost. It is, by right, a tale of tolerance for the despised, of love for the hated, of the reward that comes of brotherhood. By mixing the genes of mankind, by forming the hybrid, great men will come.

The Jews included the Book of Ruth in the canon partly because it is so wonderfully told a tale but mostly (I suspect) because it gives the lineage of the great David, a lineage that is *not* given beyond David's father, Jesse, in the soberly historic books of the Bible that anteceded Ruth. But the Jews remained, by and large, exclusivistic and did not learn the lesson of universalism preached by the Book of Ruth.

Nor have people taken its lesson to heart since. Why should they, since every effort is made to wipe out that lesson? The story of Ruth has been retold any number of ways, from children's tales to serious novels. Even movies have been made of it. Ruth herself must have been pictured in hundreds of illustrations. And in every illustration I have ever seen, she is presented as blonde, blue-eyed, shapely, and beautiful – the perfect Nordic stereotype I referred to at the beginning of the article.

For goodness' sake, why shouldn't Boaz have fallen in love with her? What great credit was there in marrying her? If a girl like that had fallen at your feet and asked you humbly to do your duty and kindly marry her, you would probably have done it like a shot.

Of course she was a Moabite woman, but so what? What does the word 'Moabite' mean to you? Does it arouse any violent reaction? Are there many Moabites among your acquaintances? Have your children been chased by a bunch of lousy Moabites lately? Have they been reducing property values in your neighbourhood? When was the last time you heard someone say, 'Got to get those rotten Moabites out of here. They just fill up the welfare rolls'?

In fact, judging by the way Ruth is drawn, Moabites are English aristocrats and their presence would raise property values.

The trouble is that the one word that is *not translated* in the Book of Ruth is the key word 'Moabite', and as long as it is not translated, the point is lost; it is lost in non-translation.

The word 'Moabite' really means 'someone of a group that receives from us and deserves from us nothing but hatred and contempt'. How should this word be translated into a single word that means the same thing to, say, many modern Greeks? . . . Why, 'Turk'. And to many modern Turks? . . . Why, 'Greek'. And to many modern white Americans? . . . Why, 'black'.

To get the proper flavour of the Book of Ruth, suppose we think of Ruth not as a Moabite woman but as a black woman.

Reread the story of Ruth and translate 'Moabite' to 'black' every time you see it. Naomi (imagine) is coming back to the United States with her two black daughters-in-law. No wonder she urges them not to come with her. It *is* a marvel that Ruth so loved her mother-in-law that she was willing to face a society that hated her unreasoningly and to take the risk of gleaning in the face of leering reapers who could not possibly suppose they need treat her with any consideration whatever.

And when Boaz asked who she was, don't read the answer as, 'She is a Moabite girl,' but as, 'She is a black girl.' More likely, in fact, the reapers might have said to Boaz something that was the equivalent of (if you'll excuse the language), 'She is a nigger girl.'

Think of it that way and you find the whole point is found in translation and only in translation. Boaz' action in being willing to marry Ruth because she was virtuous (and not because she was a Nordic beauty) takes on a kind of nobility. The neighbours' decision that she was better to Naomi than seven sons becomes something that could have been forced out of them only by overwhelming evidence to that effect. And the final stroke that out of this miscegenation was born none other than the great David is rather breathtaking.

We get something similar in the New Testament. On one occasion a student of the law asks Jesus what must be done to gain eternal life, and he answers his own question by saying, 'Love the Lord your God with all your heart, with all your soul, with all your strength, and with all your mind; and your neighbour as yourself' (Luke 10:27).

These admonitions are taken from the Old Testament, of course. That last bit about your neighbour comes from a verse that says, 'You shall not seek revenge, or cherish anger towards your kinsfolk; you shall love your neighbour as a man like yourself' (Leviticus 19:18).

(The New English Bible translation sounds better to me here than the King James's: 'Thou shalt love thy neighbour as thyself.' Where is the saint who can truly feel another's pain or ecstasy precisely as he feels his own? We must not ask too much. But if we simply grant that someone else is 'a man like yourself', then he can be treated with decency at least. It is when we refuse to grant even this, and talk of another as our inferior, that contempt and cruelty come to seem natural, and even laudable.)

Jesus approves the lawyer's saying, and the lawyer promptly asks, 'And who is my neighbour?' (Luke 10:29). After all, the verse in Leviticus first speaks of refraining from revenge and anger towards *kinsfolk*; might not, then, the concept of 'neighbour' be restricted to kinsfolk, to one's own kind, only?

In response, Jesus replies with perhaps the greatest of the parables – of a traveller who fell in with robbers, who was mugged and robbed and left half dead by the road. Jesus goes on, 'It so happened that a priest was going down by the same road; but when he saw him, he went past on the other side. So too a Levite came to the place, and when he saw him went past on the other side. But a Samaritan who was making the journey came upon him, and, when he saw him, was moved to pity. He went up and bandaged his wounds, bathing them with oil and wine. Then he lifted him on to his own beast, brought him to an inn, and looked after him there' (Luke 10:31–34).

Then Jesus asks who the traveller's neighbour was, and the lawyer is forced to say, 'The one who showed him kindness' (Luke 10:37).

This is known as the Parable of the Good Samaritan, even though nowhere in the parable is the rescuer called a *good* Samaritan, merely a Samaritan.

The force of the parable is entirely vitiated by the common phrase 'good' Samaritan, for that has cast a false light on who the Samaritans were. In a free-association test, say 'Samaritan' and probably every person being tested will answer, 'Good'. It has become so imprinted in all our brains that Samaritans are good that we take it for granted that a Samaritan would act like that and wonder why Jesus is making a point of it.

We forget who the Samaritans were, in the time of Jesus!

To the Jews, they were *not* good. They were hated, despised, contemptible heretics with whom no good Jew would have anything to do. Again, the whole point is lost through non-translation.

Suppose, instead, that it is a white traveller in Mississippi who has been mugged and left half dead. And suppose it was a minister and a deacon who passed by and refused to 'become involved'. And suppose it was a black sharecropper who stopped and took care of the man.

Now ask yourself: Who was the neighbour whom you must love as though he were a man like yourself if you are to be saved?

The Parable of the Good Samaritan clearly teaches that there is nothing parochial in the concept 'neighbour', that you cannot confine your decency to your own group and your own kind. All mankind, right down to those you most despise, are your neighbours.

Well, then, we have in the Bible two examples – in the Book of Ruth and in the Parable of the Good Samaritan – of teachings that are lost in non-translation, yet are terribly applicable to us today.

The whole world over, there are confrontations between sections of mankind defined by a difference of race, nationality, economic philosophy, religion, or language, so that one is not 'neighbour' to the other.

These more or less arbitrary differences among peoples who are members of a single biological species are terribly dangerous, and nowhere more so than here in the United States, where the most perilous confrontation (I need not tell you) is between white and black.

Next to the population problem generally, mankind faces no danger greater than this confrontation, particularly in the United States.

It seems to me that more and more, each year, both whites and blacks are turning, in anger and hatred, to violence. I see no reasonable end to the steady escalation but an actual civil war.

In such a civil war, the whites, with a preponderance of numbers and an even greater preponderance of organized power, would in all likelihood 'win'. They would do so, however, at an enormous material cost and, I suspect, at a fatal spiritual one.

And why? Is it so hard to recognize that we are all neighbours, after all? Can we, on both sides – on *both* sides – find no way of accepting the biblical lesson?

Or if quoting the Bible sounds too mealy-mouthed, and if repeating the words of Jesus seems too pietistic, let's put it another way, a practical way:

Is the privilege of feeling hatred so luxurious that it is worth the material and spiritual hell of a white–black civil war?

If the answer is really yes, then one can only despair.

PART 10

Short-Shorts

I've always liked short-short stories.

First, since they are brief and can be read quickly, you can get the value of one even if you only have five minutes to spare – while waiting for a telephone call or while drinking a cup of coffee. It can fill in a disregarded corner of the day.

Second, there can be no frills. You've got to have the story distilled down to 1,500 words or less, and ideally that leaves room only for the point; and that point, when the story is well done, can jab itself into your mind and never be forgotten.

Third, writing one is a challenge, and I enjoy challenges.

In May 1973, the Saturday Evening Post *asked me to write a short-short science fiction story for them and I did. I meant to write a lighthearted robot story and even called it 'Light Verse', intending a pun. Alas, the story squirmed in my hands (even short-shorts can do that) and became rather more tragic than I had intended.*

I included it eventually in my short-story collection Buy Jupiter and Other Stories *(Book 164), which Doubleday published in 1975. Here it is in full:*

'Light Verse' *(1973)*

The very last person anyone would expect to be a murderer was Mrs Avis Lardner. Widow of the great astronaut-martyr, she was a philanthropist, an art collector, a hostess *extraordinaire*, and, everyone agreed, an artistic genius. But above all, she was the gentlest and kindest human being one could imagine.

Her husband, William J. Lardner, died, as we all know,

of the effects of radiation from a solar flare, after he had deliberately remained in space so that a passenger vessel might make it safely to Space Station 5.

Mrs Lardner had received a generous pension for that, and she had then invested wisely and well. By late middle age she was very wealthy.

Her house was a showplace, a veritable museum, containing a small but extremely select collection of extraordinarily beautiful jewelled objects. From a dozen different cultures she had obtained relics of almost every conceivable artefact that could be embedded with jewels and made to serve the aristocracy of that culture. She had one of the first jewelled wristwatches manufactured in America, a jewelled dagger from Cambodia, a jewelled pair of spectacles from Italy, and so on almost endlessly.

All was open for inspection. The artefacts were not insured, and there were no ordinary security provisions. There was no need for anything conventional, for Mrs Lardner maintained a large staff of robot servants, all of whom could be relied on to guard every item with imperturbable concentration, irreproachable honesty, and irrevocable efficiency.

Everyone knew of the existence of those robots, and there is no record of any attempt at theft, ever.

And then, of course, there was her light-sculpture. How Mrs Lardner discovered her own genius at the art, no guest at her many lavish entertainments could guess. On each occasion, however, when her house was thrown open to guests, a new symphony of light shone throughout the rooms; three-dimensional curves and solids in melting colour, some pure and some fusing in startling, crystalline effects that bathed every guest in wonder and somehow always adjusted itself so as to make Mrs Lardner's blue-white hair and soft, unlined face gently beautiful.

It was for the light-sculpture more than anything else that the guests came. It was never the same twice and never failed to explore new experimental avenues of art. Many people who could afford light-consoles prepared light-sculptures for amusement, but no one could approach Mrs Lardner's expertise. Not even those who considered themselves professional artists.

She herself was charmingly modest about it. 'No, no,' she would protest when someone waxed lyrical. 'I wouldn't call it "poetry in light". That's far too kind. At most, I would say it was mere "light verse".' And everyone smiled at her gentle wit.

Though she was often asked, she would never create light-sculpture for any occasion but her own parties. 'That would be commercialization,' she said.

She had no objection, however, to the preparation of elaborate holograms of her sculptures so that they might be made permanent and reproduced in museums of art all over the world. Nor was there ever a charge for any use that might be made of her light-sculptures.

'I couldn't ask a penny,' she said, spreading her arms wide. 'It's free to all. After all, I have no further use for it myself.' It was true! She never used the same light-sculpture twice.

When the holograms were taken, she was co-operation itself. Watching benignly at every step, she was always ready to order her robot servants to help. 'Please, Courtney,' she would say, 'would you be so kind as to adjust the stepladder?'

It was her fashion. She always addressed her robots with the most formal courtesy.

Once, years before, she had been almost scolded by a government functionary from the Bureau of Robots and Mechanical Men. 'You can't do that,' he said severely. 'It interferes with their efficiency. They are constructed to follow orders, and the more clearly you give those orders, the more efficiently they follow them. When you ask with elaborate politeness, it is difficult for them to understand that an order is being given. They react more slowly.'

Mrs Lardner lifted her aristocratic head. 'I do not ask for speed and efficiency,' she said. 'I ask goodwill. My robots love me.'

The government functionary might have explained that robots cannot love, but he withered under her hurt but gentle glance.

It was notorious that Mrs Lardner never even returned a robot to the factory for adjustment. Their positronic brains are enormously complex, and once in ten times or so the adjustment is not perfect as it leaves the factory. Sometimes the error does not show up for a period of time, but whenever it does, U. S. Robots and Mechanical Men, Inc., always makes the adjustment free of charge.

Mrs Lardner shook her head. 'Once a robot is in my house,' she said, 'and has performed his duties, any minor eccentricities must be borne. I will not have him man-handled.'

It was the worst thing possible to try to explain that a robot was but a machine. She would say very stiffly, 'Nothing that is as intelligent as a robot can ever be *but* a machine. I treat them like people.'

And that was that!

She kept even Max, although he was almost helpless. He could scarcely understand what was expected of him. Mrs Lardner denied that strenuously, however. 'Not at all,' she would say firmly. 'He can take hats and coats and store them very well, indeed. He can hold objects for me. He can do many things.'

'But why not have him adjusted?' asked a friend once.

'Oh, I couldn't. He's himself. He's very lovable, you know. After all, a positronic brain is so complex that no one can ever tell in just what way it's off. If he were made perfectly normal there would be no way to adjust him back to the lovability he now has. I won't give that up.'

'But if he's maladjusted,' said the friend, looking at Max nervously, 'might he not be dangerous?'

'Never,' laughed Mrs Lardner. 'I've had him for years. He's completely harmless and quite a dear.'

Actually he looked like all the other robots – smooth, metallic, vaguely human, but expressionless.

To the gentle Mrs Lardner, however, they were all

individual, all sweet, all lovable. It was the kind of woman she was.

How could she commit murder?

The very last person anyone would expect to be murdered would be John Semper Travis. Introverted and gentle, he was *in* the world but not *of* it. He had that peculiar mathematical turn of mind that made it possible for him to work out in his head the complicated tapestry of the myriad positronic brainpaths in a robot's mind.

He was chief engineer of U. S. Robots and Mechanical Men, Inc.

But he was also an enthusiastic amateur in light-sculpture. He had written a book on the subject, trying to show that the type of mathematics he used in working out positronic brain-paths might be modified into a guide to the production of aesthetic light-sculpture.

His attempt at putting theory into practice was a dismal failure, however. The sculptures he himself produced, following his mathematical principles, were stodgy, mechanical, and uninteresting.

It was the only reason for unhappiness in his quiet, constrained, and secure life, and yet it was reason enough for him to be very unhappy indeed. He *knew* his theories were right, yet he could not make them work. If he could but produce *one* great piece of light-sculpture –

Naturally, he knew of Mrs Lardner's light-sculpture. She was universally hailed as a genius, yet Travis knew she could not understand even the simplest aspect of robotic mathematics. He had corresponded with her, but she consistently refused to explain her methods, and he wondered if she had any at all. Might it not be mere intuition? But even intuition might be reduced to mathematics. Finally he managed to receive an invitation to one of her parties. He simply had to see her.

Mr Travis arrived rather late. He had made one last attempt at a piece of light-sculpture and had failed miserably.

He greeted Mrs Lardner with a kind of puzzled respect and said, 'That was a peculiar robot who took my hat and coat.'

'That is Max,' said Mrs Lardner.

'He is quite maladjusted, and he's a fairly old model. How is it you did not return it to the factory?'

'Oh, no,' said Mrs Lardner. 'It would be too much trouble.'

'None at all, Mrs Lardner,' said Travis. 'You would be surprised how simple a task it was. Since I am with U.S. Robots, I took the liberty of adjusting him myself. It took no time and you'll find he is now in perfect working order.'

A queer change came over Mrs Lardner's face. Fury found a place on it for the first time in her gentle life, and it was as though the lines did not know how to form.

'You adjusted him?' she shrieked. 'But it was *he* who created my light-sculptures. It was the maladjustment, the *maladjustment*, which you can never restore, that – that –'

It was really unfortunate that she had been showing her collection at the time and that the jewelled dagger from Cambodia was on the marble tabletop before her.

Travis's face was also distorted. 'You mean if I had studied his uniquely maladjusted positronic brain-paths I might have learned –'

She lunged with the knife too quickly for anyone to stop her and he did not try to dodge. Some said he came to meet it – as though he *wanted* to die.

Short-shorts need not be fiction. On occasion I am asked to do short non-fiction articles for one outlet or another, and I particularly enjoy doing them for TV Guide, since there the opportunity exists for immersing myself in any of a wide variety of subjects.

There was a television special on various reputed monsters, for instance, such as the abominable snowman, Bigfoot, the Loch Ness monster, and so on. I view reports of such objects with the deepest scepticism, and when TV

uide *asked for a 'backgrounder' on the programme, I
produced an article entitled 'The Monsters We Have Lived
With', which brought me angry letters from some readers
who didn't want their monsters taken away from them
just because they didn't exist.*

As it happens, Doubleday occasionally publishes collections of miscellaneous essays of mine that have appeared in places other than F & SF. My second hundred books contain three of these collections, of which the latest is *The Beginning and the End* (*Book 187*), published in 1977. It includes my monster backgrounder, which is here reproduced in full.

The Monsters We Have Lived With' *(1974)*

Mankind has always lived with monsters. That fact dates back, no doubt, to the time when the early ancestors of man moved about in constant fear of the large predators around them. Fearful as the mammoths, sabre-toothed tigers, and cave bears may have been, it is the essence of the human mind that still worse could be imagined.

The dread forces of nature were visualized as super-animals. The Scandinavians imagined the sun and the moon to be pursued forever by gigantic wolves, for instance. It was when these caught up with their prey that eclipses took place.

Relatively harmless animals could be magnified into errors. The octopuses and squids, with their writhing tentacles, were elaborated into the deadly Hydra, the many-headed snake destroyed by Hercules; into Medusa with her snaky hair and her glance that turned living things to stone; into Scylla with her six heads, whom Ulysses encountered.

Perhaps the most feared animal was the snake. Slithering unseen through the underbrush, it came upon its victim unawares. Its lidless eyes, its cold and malignant stare, its sudden strike, all served to terrorize human beings. Is it

any wonder that the snake is so often used as the ver
principle of evil – as, for instance, in the tale of the Garde
of Eden.

But imagination can improve even on the snake. Snake
can be imagined who kill not by bite, but merely by a look
and this is the 'basilisk' (from the Greek word meanir
'little king').

Or else make the snake much larger, into what th
Greeks called Python, and it can represent the origina
chaos which had to be destroyed by a god before th
orderly universe could be created. It was Apollo who kille
the Python in the early days of the earth, according to th
Greek myths, and who then established the oracle
Delphi on the spot.

Another Greek word for a large snake was 'drakon
which has become our 'dragon'. To the snaky length
the dragon were added the thicker body and stubby le;
of that other dread reptile, the crocodile. Now we have th
monster Tiamat, which the Babylonian god Marduk ha
to destroy in order to organize the universe.

Symbolize the burning bite of the venomous snake an
you have the dragon breathing fire. Dramatize the swi
and deadly strike of the snake and you have the drago
flying through the air.

Some monsters are, of course, animals that have bee
misunderstood into beauty rather than horror. The on
horned rhinoceros may have contributed to the myth
the unicorn, the beautiful one-horned horse. And the hor
of the mythical unicorn is exactly like the tooth of th
real-life narwhal.

The ugly sea cow with its flippered tail, rising half ou
of the sea and holding a newborn young to its breast i
the human position, may have dazzled shortsighted sailo
into telling tales of beautiful mermaids.

Throughout history, of course, man's greatest enem
was man, so it is not surprising that man himself serve
as the basis for some of the most fearful monsters – th
giants and cannibalistic ogres of all sorts.

It may well be that the origin of such stories lies in the fact that various groups of human beings made technological advances in different directions and at different times. A tribe of warriors armed with stone axes, meeting an army of soldiers in bronze armour and carrying bronze-tipped spears, will be sent flying in short order with many casualties. The Stone Age survivors may well have the feeling that they have met an army of man-eating giants.

Thus, the primitive Israelite tribes, on first approaching Canaan and encountering walled cities and well-armed soldiers, felt the Canaanites to be a race of giants. Traces of that belief remain in the Bible.

Then, too, a high civilization may fall and those who follow forget the civilization and attribute its works to giants of one kind or another. The primitive Greeks, coming across the huge, thick walls that encircled the cities of the earlier, highly civilized Mycenaeans, imagined those walls to have been built by giant Cyclopes.

Such Cyclopes were later placed in Sicily (where Ulysses encountered them in the tales told in the *Odyssey*) and were supposed to have but one eye. They may have been sky gods, and the single eye may represent the sun in heaven. It may also have arisen from the fact that elephants roamed Sicily in prehuman times. The skull of such an elephant, occasionally found, would show large nasal openings in front which might be interpreted as the single eye of a giant.

There can be giants in ways other than physical. Thus medieval Englishmen had no notion of how or why the huge monoliths of Stonehenge had been erected. They blamed it on Merlin's magic. He caused the stones to fly through the air and land in place. (The Greeks also had tales of musicians who played so beautifully that, captivated by the sweet strains, rocks moved into place and built a wall of their own accord.)

But as man's knowledge of the world expanded, the room available for the dread or beautiful monsters he had invented shrank, and belief in them faded. Large animals were discovered – giant whales, moose, Komodo lizards, okapis, giant squids, and so on. These were, however, merely animals and lacked the super-terror our minds had created.

What is left then?

The giant snakes and dragons that once fought with the gods and terrorized mankind have shrunk to a possible sea serpent reported to be cowering at the bottom of Loch Ness.

The giants, the ogres, the monstrous one-eyed cannibals that towered over our puny race of mortals, have diminished to mysterious creatures that leave footprints among the snows of the upper reaches of Mount Everest or show their misty shapes fugitively in the depths of our shrivelling forests.

Even if these exist (which is doubtful), what a puny remnant they represent of the glorious hordes man's mind and imagination have created.

PART 11

Humour

I discussed in OPUS 100 my struggles to achieve a bit of humour in my writing. I may have succeeded there, for reviewers often mentioned my sense of humour (as revealed in my writing) and seemed to do so with approval.

That may be, but it was not till my second hundred books that I produced volumes that dealt with humour per se *or that were specifically humorous books rather than other kinds of books that just happened to have a bit of humour as seasoning.*

The first book of this sort that I wrote was Isaac Asimov's Treasury of Humor *(Book 114), a large compendium of jokes and comments on humour and joke-telling. Houghton Mifflin published it in 1971.*

How I came to write it is described in the introduction to that book, and this is given here:

from ISAAC ASIMOV'S TREASURY OF HUMOR *(1971)*

For nearly all my life I have been swapping jokes. At almost every friendly gathering that I have attended, there have been two or three people present with a large repertoire of funny stories and the ability to tell them with finesse, and so joke-swapping was almost inevitable. Modesty compels me to refrain from saying that of all those present I generally had the largest repertoire of jokes and could tell them with the most finesse, but if I weren't modest I would say so.

This has led to my having been asked, on occasion, why someone like myself, with pretensions to intellect, should content himself with endless joke-telling while shunning the ardent discussions of politics, philosophy, and literature that might be proceeding in another corner of the room.

To this my answer is threefold, in order of increasing importance:

1) I spend most of my day being intellectual at my typewriter, and telling jokes on an evening now and then helps balance the situation.

2) Jokes of the proper kind, properly told, can do more to enlighten questions of politics, philosophy, and literature than any number of dull arguments.

3) I like to.

Then, too, as it happens, this whole business of joke-telling saved my life not too long ago –

In June 1969, my wife and I, along with another couple, Howard and Muriel Hirt, were off on a motor trip that was to end in a vacation. As it happens, vacations send me into deep melancholy and I had been achingly apprehensive of this one for weeks. It was only to last for a weekend but it was to be at an elaborate hotel of a type that I detested beyond measure.

With doom hastening closer at every turn of the whirling wheels, I tried to fight off my gathering misery by telling jokes in feverish succession.

Muriel was kind enough to laugh quite a bit, and then she said, 'Listen, Isaac, why don't you write a jokebook?'

That made it my turn to laugh.

'Who would publish it?' I asked.

She said, 'I thought you said you could get someone or other to publish anything you wrote.'

I do say things like that when I am feeling more than ordinarily megalomaniac, but that was not what suddenly began to circle wildly through the tortuous meshes of my mind.

A new thought arose –

Suppose that while I was ostensibly vacationing, and while everyone around me was going through the horrifying ritual of lying in the sun and volleyballing and hiking and doing whatever other forms of refined torture are supposed to be fun, I was secretly writing down jokes and, in that way, working on a book.

I would then be having no vacation at all! (Oh, magic words!)

As soon as we had registered and unpacked, therefore, I approached the desk and said, 'I would like to check out a typewriter for the weekend.'

This hotel, you must understand, is marvellously equipped. I do not remember the exact figures, but the impression I have is that the hotel possesses three swimming pools, four golf links, seventeen tennis courts, twenty-eight miles of hiking trails, and seventy-five thousand reclining beach chairs in serried ranks and files, each one laden with a vacationer slowly frying in his own juice. It also has an enormous nightclub, fourteen buildings, and sixty miles of corridors.

With a hotel that has everything, I had no hesitation in asking for a typewriter.

I was quickly disabused. The desk clerk said, 'You want to check out a *what*?'

'A typewriter!' I said.

He looked blank, and I could see he was wondering if a typewriter might be anything like a set of golf clubs.

I said, 'Well, then, do you have writing paper?'

He handed me a sheet of writing paper in which the monogram of the hotel took up half the area, leaving just enough room to write a message to a friend that might go: 'Here I am at the X Hotel, dying.'

I said, 'Give me about fifty.'

He handed them over, and for the next two and a half days, wherever we were – tramping the corridors, lying in the sun, sitting in the shade, waiting for food at the table, enduring the unbelievable, dinning mayhem at the nightclub – I quietly scribbled jokes on paper while carefully maintaining a fixed smile on my face to indicate how much I was enjoying the vacation.

Occasionally, I would overhear someone at a neighbouring table say, 'Watch out, Sadie, and be careful what you say. That fellow there is writing down every word he hears.'

It was undoubtedly all that kept me alive.

I finished the vacation with a sheaf of handwritten jokes, which I converted into typescript and brought to Houghton Mifflin as a sample.

And eventually the book was completed and published, and here it is!

It would scarcely be suitable to let it go at that. The book contains 640 jokes (almost all of them quite clean), and I include several of them here.

from ISAAC ASIMOV'S TREASURY OF HUMOR (1971)

Moskowitz had bought a parrot and one morning found the bird at the eastern side of the cage, with a small prayer shawl over its head, rocking to and fro and mumbling. Bending low to listen, Moskowitz was thunderstruck to discover the parrot was intoning prayers in the finest Hebrew.

'You're Jewish?' asked Moskowitz.

'Not only Jewish,' said the parrot, 'but Orthodox. So will you take me to the synagogue on Rosh Hashanah?'

Rosh Hashanah, the Jewish New Year, was indeed only two days off, and it would as always usher in the high-holiday season which would end with Yom Kippur, the Day of Atonement, ten days later.

Moskowitz said, 'Of course, I'll take you, but can I tell my friends about you? It isn't a secret, I hope?'

'No secret at all. Tell anyone you want to.' And the parrot returned to his praying.

Moskowitz went to all his friends, full of the story of his Jewish parrot. Of course no one believed him, and in no time at all Moskowitz was taking bets. By Rosh Hashanah, he had a hundred dollars, all told, riding on the parrot.

Grinning, Moskowitz brought the parrot to the synagogue in its cage. He put him in a prominent place and everyone turned to watch, even as they mumbled their prayers. Even the rabbi watched, for he had seven dollars that said the parrot could not pray.

Moskowitz waited. Everyone waited. And the parrot did nothing. Moskowitz carefully arranged the prayer shawl over the bird's head, but the parrot ducked and the shawl fell off.

After the services, Moskowitz's friends, with much mockery, collected their money. Even the rabbi snickered as he took his profit of seven dollars.

Utterly humiliated, Moskowitz returned home, turned viciously on the parrot, and said, 'Prepare to die, you little monster, for I'm going to wring your neck. If you can pray, now's the time.'

Whereupon the parrot's voice rang out clearly: 'Hold it, you dumb jerk. In ten days it's Yom Kippur, when all Jews will sing the tragic, haunting Kol Nidre. Well, bet everybody that I can sing the Kol Nidre.'

'Why? You didn't do anything today.'

'Exactly! So for Yom Kippur, just think of the odds you'll get!'

A young man is reported to have approached the renowned composer Wolfgang Amadeus Mozart (one of the great musical prodigies of all time) and asked, 'Herr Mozart, I have the ambition to write symphonies, and perhaps you can advise me how to get started.'

Mozart said, 'The best advice I can give you is to wait until you are older and more experienced, and try your hand at less ambitious pieces to begin with.'

The young man looked astonished. 'But, Herr Mozart, you yourself wrote symphonies when you were considerably younger than I.'

'Ah,' said Mozart, 'but I did so without asking advice.'

Young Leah, in the old days of eastern Europe, was the sole support of her mother, and had been fortunate enough to marry a substantial young man, despite the miserable state of her dowry. Leah was happy and her mother was ecstatic.

Imagine her mother's shock then, when, on the morning after the wedding, Leah returned in misery and announced she would not return to her husband. 'I love him madly,' she said, 'but I had to leave him.'

Stubbornly, she refused to give the reason, but, from what she said, it was apparent that the young man had made some rather sophisticated sexual demands on her.

As the days passed, both mother and daughter grew more and more miserable, the former out of frustrated finances, the latter out of frustrated love. Finally, the mother suggested that they visit the town rabbi, the beloved Rabbi Joshua of Khaslavich. After all, in such matters one needed guidance.

They were granted an audience, and when the rabbi demanded the details and Leah hung back, Rabbi Joshua said kindly, 'Whisper it into my ear, my daughter. No one will know but we ourselves and God.'

She did so, and as she whispered, the rabbi's kindly brow furrowed, and lightning flashed from his mild eyes.

'My daughter,' he thundered, 'it is not fitting for a Jewish girl to submit to such vile indignities. It would be a deadly sin, and because of it a curse would be laid on our whole town.'

Back went mother and daughter, disconsolate, and after a week of continued privation, the mother said, 'You know, our rabbi is a wonderful man, but it is sometimes wise to get a second opinion. Why not consult Rabbi Samuel of Krichev? He is very highly spoken of as a man of learning.'

Why not, indeed? They got into the wagon and bumped their way to the next town. As Leah whispered the tale

into Rabbi Samuel's ear, the old man's earlocks uncurled
and turned distinctly greyer. He said in strangled tones,
'My daughter, it was for sins such as this that the Holy
One, blessed be He, sent down upon the earth a flood in
days of yore. You must not agree to his demands.'

Again mother and daughter returned, and now, for a
long time, the dreary round of day-to-day living continued,
until the mother said, 'Let us make one final attempt to
obtain guidance. Let us go to the Grand Rabbi of Vilna.
There is no one in the whole world as wise as he and as
learned. And whatever he says we may accept as the final
word.'

They bought their railway tickets, which seriously
depleted their meagre savings, and rode to Vilna. For the
third time, Leah whispered her story into a rabbinical ear.
The Grand Rabbi listened with equanimity and then
said, 'My daughter, be guided by your husband. He is a
young and vigorous man, and it is fitting that you both
enjoy yourselves. Have no qualms concerning this thing.'

Leah was thunderstruck. She said, 'But, Grand Rabbi,
how can you say this? Rabbi Joshua of Khaslavich said
it would bring a curse upon our town. Rabbi Samuel of
Krichev said such sins caused the flood.'

But the Grand Rabbi merely stroked his white beard
and smiled. 'My daughter,' he said, 'what do those small-
town rabbis know about big-city sex?'

Among the Germans, Berlin is considered the very
epitome of Prussian brusqueness and efficiency, while
Vienna is the essence of Austrian charm and slipshoddery.

The tale is told of a Berliner visiting Vienna who was
lost and in need of directions. What would such a Berliner
do? He grabbed at the lapel of the first passing Viennese
and barked out, 'The post office? Where is it?'

The startled Viennese carefully detached the other's
fist, smoothed his lapel, and said in a gentle manner, 'Sir,
would it not have been more delicate of you to have
approached me politely and to have said, "Sir, if you

have a moment and happen to know, could you please direct me to the post office?" '

The Berliner stared in astonishment for a moment, then growled, 'I'd rather be lost!' and stamped away.

That very same Viennese was visiting Berlin later that year, and it turned out that now it was he who had to search for the post office. Approaching a Berliner, he said politely, 'Sir, if you have a moment and happen to know, could you please direct me to the post office?'

With machine-like rapidity, the Berliner replied, 'About face, two blocks forward, sharp turn right, one block forward, cross street, half-right under arch, sharp left over railroad tracks, past news-stand, into post office lobby.'

The Viennese, more bewildered than enlightened, nevertheless murmured, 'A thousand thanks, kind sir –'

Whereupon the Berliner snatched furiously at the other's lapel and shouted, 'Never mind the thanks! *Repeat the instructions!*'

Pierre was celebrating his silver wedding, and while all were unrestrainedly merry over the ample liquor provided by the host, Pierre himself remained in the corner, nursing a drink and following one of the guests with baleful eyes.

A friend noticed this strange action, all the more strange on so happy an occasion, and said, 'At whom are you glaring, Pierre my friend?'

'At my lawyer, may his soul rot.'

'But why are you so angry with him?'

'It is a sad tale. After I had been married ten years, I decided I had had enough and that the cleanest solution would be to kill my wife. Painlessly, of course, for I am no monster. Being a methodical man, I approached my lawyer – that one there – and asked him of the possible consequences. He told me that whereas killing a husband is, here in France, a mere misdemeanour, killing a wife is a felony, and that even with a most skilful defence I would have to count on fifteen years in jail. He urged me not to do it and I let myself be guided by his advice.'

'Well, then, why are you angry?'

'Because,' said Pierre, 'if I had not listened to his idiotic advice, on this very day I would have been a free man at last.'

Although Isaac Asimov's Treasury of Humor *was the first humorous book I wrote, it was not the first I published.*

On March 12, 1971, I had lunch with Beth Walker and Millicent Selsam of Walker and Company to discuss my ABC's of the Earth. *When that was done, the two editors talked shop and the conversation veered to* The Sensuous Woman *and* The Sensuous Man, *two sleazy books that were making money out of prurience.*

Beth turned to me and said, 'Why don't you write a dirty book, Isaac?'

I thought of my own propensities and said dryly, 'What do you want me to write? The Sensuous Dirty Old Man?'

That turned out to be a dreadful thing to say, for Beth fell in love with the title and hounded me into doing the book. She then raced it into print and it appeared less than ninety days after my original mocking suggestion, appearing as Book 112.

In no way, of course, was The Sensuous Dirty Old Man *merely sex. I should hope that I don't have to stoop to try to write and sell a book on the basis of salacity alone. It was satire and was intended, at all points, to be more humorous than salacious.*

Don't get me wrong. I don't eschew the salacious. I merely insist that humour be primary. Thus:

from THE SENSUOUS DIRTY OLD MAN *(1971)*

Sometime during the 1930s, women, having stripped off enough layers of frontal textile, discovered that insufficient material was left to protect the delicate tissues of the

bosom. To protect these, modern engineering devised a
structure that served to compress the bosom into firm
cone-shaped objects which, far from requiring protection,
could allow unlimited manoeuvre without danger. Un-
avoidably it caught the masculine eye – or some other part
of the male anatomy if he weren't careful, leaving a nasty
bruise.

The service performed to womankind by this new
garment cannot easily be exaggerated. It was first designed
by an organization of bio-engineers who, although individually anonymous, have become world famous by the
corporate title of Bosom Rehabilitation Associates. The
garment they engineered possessing the small initials BRA
on the strap quickly became known, in consequence, as
the 'bra'.

The gentlemen of B.R.A. carefully laboured to give
each woman that firmly jutting profile one would naturally
associate with strength of will and character, and it
worked. Many a woman who in her natural unprotected
state would have slunk into a room, abashed and uncertain,
could, with her bra firmly in place, walk in, shoulders back
and chest thrown out, proudly aware that every man in the
place would at once note and admire her strength of
character.

Every woman felt uplifted by the experience, so the
industry began to speak of the 'uplift bra'.

And yet the uplift bra had its troubles. For one thing,
the designers had unaccountably placed its hooks in the
back. In addition, the straps cut the shoulders, and in hot
weather there were such matters as heat, perspiration, and
skin rashes.

Little by little the thought came that it might be
possible to eliminate the bra and allow the contents to
find their natural level; or, as President Nixon so succinctly
put it in discussing this very problem, the time had come
for America to adopt a lower profile.

Certain of the more excitable women determined not
merely to eliminate the bra but to burn it as a gesture of

contempt. The slogan arose: LET'S IGNITE BRAS. This was abbreviated to L.I.B. and in no time at all Women's Lib was a power in the land.

The result was, in the light of hindsight, inevitable. The ladies found themselves back where they had been in the 1930s and, indeed, worse off than ever. The sturdier fabrics of a much earlier day, the taffeta dress and corduroy blouse, had given way to sheer synthetics. What had earlier been hidden and protected by the bra was hidden and protected no longer by virtually anything. Indeed, the tender caress of the soft synthetic irritated the delicate bosom surface till every unevenness was accentuated and softly revealed.

At a time when President Nixon was making one point very, very clear, the average young girl on the streets of New York was doing exactly twice as well.

And dirty old men, on those same streets, found that they had a new target – and new hazards. Without the constriction of the bra, the average young lady, moving forward in a healthy free-swinging stride, presents what can only be described as a moving target.

It is therefore difficult for the dirty old man to get to the point; for the point shifts. It moves wildly at the slightest bodily motion. It jiggles, wobbles, and dangles; heaves, yaws, and rolls; vibrates, oscillates, and undulates.

The dirty old man may find himself trying to follow every movement by use of eye muscles, head muscles, or both. This is not advisable. Aside from the fact that in the attempt to concentrate too entirely on the target he may walk into a wall, the constant movement of eyes or head or both will induce dizziness, headache, nausea, and even that dread affliction of the inveterate leerer, watering eyes. The whole complex of symptoms makes up the syndrome of 'mammamobilism'.

Mammamobilism is known to the medical profession by the euphemistic phrase 'nipple shock', but in this book I have no use for euphemisms and do not intend to employ them. The general public, the taxi driver, the construction

worker, everyone, says 'mammamobilism', and that's what
I shall say, too.

The Italians, far wiser than we in their attitude towards
sex, have no compunctions about using the phrase. You
will recall that in the great opera *Rigoletto* the Duke,
when Gilda runs past him jiggling, claps his hand to his
brow and begins the brilliant tenor aria: 'Oh, mamma-
mobile –'

Although you can see that the disease played so important a part in the opera written by Joe Green* a
century and a quarter ago, thanks to the extraordinary
equipment of the pasta-consuming coloratura soprano of
his day, it did not strike the American public till just a
few short years ago. Mammamobilism is not amenable
to penicillin or to any of the other antibiotics. Prevention,
then, is the key. Do *not* try to follow the moving target.
Fix the eye rather upon some key portion of the dress
pattern and allow the sense of sight to be titillated
sporadically.

*Oddly enough, a new career (if you want to call it that)
started for me quite unexpectedly in 1974.*

*I was returning by ship (I don't fly) from a visit to
Great Britain, and things were a little dull. At the table
at luncheon, as conversation flagged and as I looked aim-
lessly at the ocean outside the window from my seat in the
Queen's Grill of the* Queen Elizabeth II, *a limerick
occurred to me.*

*I had made up an occasional limerick in my life but
had never paid much attention to them. This time, though,
the limerick flowed into my mind so easily that I found
myself unable to resist quoting it. I began, without warning, by saying, 'There was a young girl from Decatur.'*

What conversation there was stopped, and everyone at

* Green, having emigrated to Italy, adopted the Italian version
of his name, Giuseppe Verdi. For reasons known only to opera
buffs, the Italian name is actually better known today than the
name he was born with in Poughkeepsie, New York.

the table turned to look at me.

'Who went out to sea on a freighter,' I said, *and now attention was focused on me with an almost painful intensity.*

'She was screwed by the Master – an utter disaster,' said I, *and paused a little to let the suspense gather, and then I added, 'But the crew all made up for it later.'*

There was an explosion of laughter.

I was very pleased and, for the first time, took the trouble to write down one of my own limericks.

That was fatal, for from that moment on, every time I made up a limerick I wrote it down. What's more, I began to concentrate on constructing them. By the time I had sixteen, I brought them to Walker and Company with the glad tidings that when I had a hundred I would make a book out of them, which Walker might then publish. Sam Walker winced at that but, like a good sport, agreed.

I then got to work seriously, using the same criterion I had used for The Sensuous Dirty Old Man. *A limerick could be as salacious as necessary, provided it was more funny than salacious. And I added another rule: it could never be physically repulsive.*

Before I was through, I had not only a hundred limericks and a published book (complete with lengthy introduction and commentary on each limerick) but four hundred and forty-four limericks and four *published books.*

These were: Lecherous Limericks *(Book 166), in 1975;* More Lecherous Limericks *(Book 177), in 1976; Still More Lecherous Limericks (Book 185), in 1977; and* Limericks: Too Gross *(Book 196), in 1978. The limericks were numbered consecutively through the three volumes, from 1 to 300, and the happy tale of the young girl from Decatur was, very appropriately, given pride of place as number 1.*

Here are two limericks from each of the first three books:

from LECHEROUS LIMERICKS *(1975)*

Well, Hardly Ever

There was an old maid of Peru
Who swore that she never would screw
    Except under stress
    Of forceful duress
Like, 'I'm ready, dear, how about you?'

Impatience

There was a young couple from Florida
Whose passion grew steadily torrider.
    They were planning to sin
    In a room in an inn.
Who can wait? So they screwed in the corridor.

from MORE LECHEROUS LIMERICKS *(1976)*

Shutting the Barn Door

There was an effete lazy fop
Who preferred all his women on top.
    He said, 'I'm no jerk,
    Let *them* do the work,
But if I get pregnant, I'll stop.'

You Mean

A young fellow, divinely endowed,
Once said, very haughty and proud,
    When a girl, much too free,
    Placed her hand on his knee,
'That isn't my knee, Miss McCloud.'

from STILL MORE LIMERICKS *(1977)*

Reasons Enough

The virginal nature of Donna
Had for many long years been a goner.
    When asked why she screwed,
    She replied, 'Gratitude,
Politeness – and just 'cause I wanna.'

Emily Post

There was a young man of Connecticut
Who tore off a young woman's petticoat.
    Said she, with a grin,
    'You will have to get in.
For to do nothing more isn't etiquette.'

PART 12

Social Sciences

Until now I have carefully followed the order of the sections as originally given in Opus 100: from Part 1, Astronomy, to Part 11, Humour.

I would hate, though, to have you think that, having established a certain diversity in my writings in my first hundred books, I would allow that diversity to stand, that I would seek out no new fields for my second hundred. That is not so. There are no less than four additional sections in this present book.

First, the social sciences. This, I must admit, is not my forte, and consequently I have done very little writing in this field. It is important, after all, for any versatile writer to have a keen perception of his limitations. Otherwise, the ease with which he may hop from subject to subject, and his vanity over being able to do so, may lure him to write on something he knows nothing about with disastrous consequences.

To be sure, some of my F & SF essays deal with one aspect or another of the social sciences – the essays that I refer to as 'controversials' in my correspondence with my editor, Edward L. Ferman. There, however, I am writing informally to an audience of friends and giving only my opinions, making no pretence of speaking authoritatively.

In one instance during my second hundred books, however, I allowed myself to be talked into doing a book that edges rather far into the social.

Frances Schwartz of Abelard-Schuman phoned me in 1973 and asked me to do a book on population aimed at an audience of young people. It is a subject near to my heart, for I firmly believe that if the world does not master the population problem, civilization is very likely going to *collapse within half a century.*

I agreed to do the book therefore, and it appeared in 1974 under the imprint of the John Day Company, which by then was a sister house of Abelard-Schuman. The title is Earth: Our Crowded Spaceship *and it is Book 156. Here is an excerpt:*

from EARTH: OUR CROWDED SPACESHIP *(1974)*

There are many people who are educated and who know about the world population and the way it is growing but think there is no danger. They tell themselves that people who talk of the danger are foolish and wrong.

People who don't believe there is a crisis can point to the Netherlands, for instance. They say that the Netherlands is prosperous and yet is much more densely populated than the world average. They say that it would do no harm to let the whole world become that densely populated. They don't seem to realize that the Netherlands is prosperous because it has fertile soil and much water; that it makes use of a great deal of industrial products like fertilizer and insecticides; that it imports a great deal of oil and that it has no forests to speak of.

There just isn't enough fertile soil and enough water to make the entire world into one gigantic Netherlands. There isn't enough fertilizer and insecticides and oil, and we don't really want to cut down all the forests. Besides, it won't take very long for the earth to be as densely populated all over as the Netherlands is now, and if it could be done, how would we stop the population increase at that point?

Some people think that science will solve all problems. They say that more people will just mean more scientists working on those problems. They don't realize that the problems get worse and worse, faster and faster, and that sooner or later – probably sooner – science just won't be able to keep up the pace.

Some people even think that population means strength. They think that large nations with many people can conquer neighbouring nations with fewer people. They think that many people means a large, powerful army. They think that if their own nation does not increase its population, a neighbouring nation which *does* increase its population will conquer them. For this reason, some nations think that they must have more and more babies, more and more people, if they are to remain strong and free.

Even if war is not involved, some people think a nation with a large population can keep its own customs, languages, and attitudes better than a nation with a small population. If a neighbouring nation grows faster, they think, that neighbouring nation might impose *its* customs, language, and attitudes on the smaller one, just by outnumbering them.

Actually, this is not so. Very often in history, small nations have conquered large ones. It's not so much the size of the army as its organization and the technical level of its weapons. Thus, Greece took over Persia in the 300s B.C., Mongolia took over China in the 1200s, and Great Britain took over India in the 1700s, even though Persia, China, and India were far more populous than Greece, Mongolia, and Great Britain.

Then, too, the Greek language and culture in ancient times and the English language and culture in modern times spread over the world even though those languages were spoken by few people to begin with.

If a nation wishes to avoid being dominated by its neighbours, its best chance is to raise its standard of living and its level of technology. This can be done best by not allowing its population to grow to such a point that it is sunk in misery and poverty. In fact, the worst way in which a nation can try to avoid being dominated by its neighbour is to increase its population to the point of misery and poverty.

If every nation tries to compete with its neighbours by

raising its population, then the whole world will be sunk in misery and poverty. The nations will all decline in a catastrophe that will leave nothing behind that is worth dominating. No one will have gained anything. Everyone will have lost everything.

Once all this is understood, and people generally agree that population growth must not be allowed to continue, they must also come to understand how that growth can be stopped. Population grows because more people are being born than are dying. There are two ways, then, in which the growth can be stopped. You can increase the number of people who die until it matches the number of people who are being born. Or else you can decrease the number of people who are born until it matches the number of people who are dying.

The first method – increasing the death rate – is the usual way in which population is controlled in all species of living things other than ourselves. It is the method by which human populations have been controlled in the past. It is the 'natural' method. If there are too many people, some starve or die of disease or by violence. If we don't do anything now, it will be the way population will be controlled in the future. Billions will die.

Must we let that happen because it is the 'natural' way?

Through all the history of mankind, the human brain has been bending nature to its will. If we had really decided that the 'natural' way was the right way, we would never have begun to make tools or build fires or develop agriculture or study science. It is because mankind has bent nature to its will that there are now many, many people who live more comfortably and better than people ever have before. We must continue to work out ways to be more comfortable by using the intelligent way, and not just the 'natural' way.

The 'natural' way to control population is by raising the death rate, but we don't want that, for catastrophe lies that way. The intelligent way is to reduce the birth rate. If, say, 40,000,000 people die each year, then not more than 40,000,000 people should be born each year. In fact, we may want to *reduce* the world population to some reasonable value, in which case, if 40,000,000 people die each year, we may want only 30,000,000 people to be born, or only 20,000,000, till the desired population level is reached.

But how can the birth rate be reduced?

One way is for people to stop mating. This, however, is not very practical, since people enjoy it too much to stop. A better way is to let mating continue but to use methods that keep it from resulting in babies.

There are a number of different ways in which the birth rate can be made to drop without interfering with people's pleasure. In the last twenty years, the birth rate in the United States and in some other countries has dropped because more and more women are using pills to keep from having babies they don't want.

To make sure that mating doesn't result in babies is called 'birth control'. It is by adopting methods of birth control that population growth can be stopped with the least damage.

There are many difficulties here. Certain religious organizations are against birth control. Many groups of people have ways of life that would not fit in easily with birth control. Then, too, even if birth control were desired, there are many places in the world where people are so poor they can't afford to buy the materials that make it possible.

So you see, it comes down to education again. People not only have to be taught that a problem exists, they have to be taught exactly how to solve it by birth control and why it is right to do so. And they must be given the necessary materials without charge.

PART 13

Literature

Perhaps the most outrageous books among my second hundred are my annotations of literary classics.

In the first place, it does take a certain amount of overweening self-assurance for a person whose intellectual expertise is in the sciences to decide to do large and complicated books on a subject that may easily be mistaken for literary criticism. Literary critics (who are bound to be asked to review the books) are sure to be annoyed at this invasion of their home turf.

Secondly, the books tend to be elaborate and expensive and Doubleday (whom I stuck with the publication thereof) was sure to be forced to risk considerable sums on them that they might not earn back. (Doubleday has never uttered a word of complaint in the matter, but that doesn't stop me from worrying about it.)

After my two-volume Asimov's Guide to the Bible, *it was inevitable that I would plan* Asimov's Guide to Shakespeare.

What I did, in the latter case, was to take up each of Shakespeare's plays in turn, go through it carefully, describing as much of the plot as was necessary for my purposes, and quoting those passages that contained historical, mythological, biographical, or geographical allusions. Since these might not be plain to the reader and might get in the way of a proper understanding of the text, I explained each one.

I did not in the least attempt to discuss the plays as dramatic vehicles or indulge in true literary criticism.

Asimov's Guide to Shakespeare *appeared in two volumes in 1970 as Books 104 and 105, and here is my treatment of the opening soliloquy from* Richard III, *in volume 2:*

from ASIMOV'S GUIDE TO SHAKESPEARE *(1970)*

Richard III deals with events that immediately follow
Henry VI, Part 3, and it is very likely that Shakespeare
began work on it as soon as he was through with the
Henry VI trilogy. It was probably completed by 1593
at the latest.

At that time Shakespeare was still at the beginning of
his career. He had written two narrative poems, a number
of sonnets, a couple of light comedies, and the *Henry VI*
trilogy, all popular and successful, but none, as yet, a blockbuster. With *Richard III* Shakespeare finally made it big.

It is a play after the manner of Seneca, like *Titus
Andronicus*, which Shakespeare was also working on at
the time, but infinitely more successful.

Indeed, *Richard III* was so full of harrowing and
dramatic episodes, and Richard III himself was so successful a character, so wonderful a villain, with so much
bravery and dry humour mingled with his monstrous
behaviour, that the play pleased all and made it quite plain
that Shakespeare was a new star of brilliant magnitude on
the literary scene. Indeed, despite the fact that the play is
quite raw compared to the polished mastery of Shakespeare's later plays, it is still one of his most popular and
successful plays today.

The play opens with Richard of Gloucester, youngest
brother of King Edward IV, alone on the stage. He sets
the time of the scene by saying:

> *Now is the winter of our discontent*
> *Made glorious summer by this sun of York;*
> (Act 1, scene 1, lines 1–2)

This ties in well with the final speech in *Henry VI*, Part
3, in which Edward IV says happily that the troubles are
all over and that only joy is left.

It was in 1471 that the last serious Lancastrian threat
was smashed at Tewkesbury. Old King Henry VI and his
son, Prince Edward, were dead immediately after that

battle, and no one was left to dispute the right of King Edward to the throne.

The 'sun of York' (and a sun was one of the symbols of the Yorkist house) was indeed shining.

The sun of York does not satisfy Richard, however. In a speech that resembles one he had made in the earlier play, he explains that he is so physically deformed that the joys of peace, such as dancing and lovemaking, are beyond him. He will therefore confine himself to the joys of ambition, and labour to make himself a king. After all, in *Henry VI*, Part 3, he waxed lyrical over the joys of being a king, and it is not to be wondered at that he should want those joys.

In order to become a king, he must get out of the way those who have a prior right to the throne. Among them, of course, is his older brother George of Clarence. Richard explains in his soliloquy:

> *Plots have I laid, inductions* [beginnings] *dangerous,*
> *By drunken prophecies, libels, and dreams,*
> *To set my brother Clarence and the king*
> *In deadly hate the one against the other;*
> *And if King Edward be as true and just*
> *As I am subtle, false, and treacherous,*
> *This day should Clarence closely be mewed up*
> *About a prophecy which says that G*
> *Of Edward's heirs the murderer shall be.*
>
> (Act 1, scene 1, lines 32–40)

Shakespeare is here condensing time, for George of Clarence's final break with his royal brother came in 1477, six years after the climactic Battle of Tewkesbury, despite the appearance in the first two lines of the soliloquy that it is the very morrow of the battle that is in question.

Why did the break between the brothers come? Well, it required no plot on the part of Richard, really, for George of Clarence had some of the characteristics in reality that Richard was later slanderously described as having.

It was George who was ambitious and faithless. He had deserted Edward and sided with Warwick in 1469, and had come back to his allegiance to York, we may be sure, only out of a feeling that Warwick was going to lose and that he himself would gain more by a second double-cross.

Edward had forgiven the twice faithless George, but that did not prevent George from continuing to scheme for his own aggrandizement in such a way that the king was bound, eventually, to suspect his brother of aiming at the throne.

George did his best, for instance, to keep his hands on the whole enormous Warwick estate. This may have been out of mere avarice, but it may also have been out of a realization of how useful wealth would be in planning a revolt. He had married Warwick's elder daughter, Isabella, in the days when he and Warwick had been friends and allies. The younger daughter, Anne, had been married to Edward, prince of Wales, the son of old King Henry. Prince Edward was now dead and Anne was a widow; and George was determined to keep her a widow, lest some new husband insist on a half share in the Warwick estate. While Anne remained a widow, George controlled it all, and he kept the poor lady a virtual prisoner to see to it that the situation would continue.

This intentness on wealth at all costs would naturally disturb Edward.

Then there arose a new matter. Charles the Bold of Burgundy died in battle in 1477, leaving behind a twenty-year-old daughter, Mary, as his only heir. (Charles's wife had been Margaret of York, the sister of George of Clarence, but Mary was his daughter by a previous wife.)

Burgundy had, for over half a century, been the wealthiest nation in Europe, and under Charles it had reached its political peak, for Charles had almost defeated France and made an independent kingdom of his land. Now, with only a young woman to rule Burgundy, its days seemed numbered under the pressure of France to the

est and the Holy Roman Empire to the east. Unless,
that is, some strong independent prince quickly married
Mary and carried on where Charles the Bold had left off.
George of Clarence was now a widower and he saw him-
self as husband of Mary and as the new duke of
Burgundy.

King Edward thoroughly disapproved of this scheme.
It seemed to him that if his ambitious, faithless brother
became duke of Burgundy, with all the resources of
Burgundy at his call, he would be a source of endless
trouble. He would have the money to finance plots against
Edward and scheme at a double throne.

Edward therefore forbade the marriage and the two
brothers became open enemies. It did not take much more
for Edward to begin to suspect George of plotting his
death. Two of George's henchmen were accused of trying
to bring about that death by sorcery, and when George
insisted they were innocent, Edward angrily had his
brother arrested and thrown in the Tower of London.

Whether George was actually plotting Edward's death
we cannot say, but certainly his past and his character
gave cause for suspicion, and in those troubled times that
was enough.

And what had been Richard's record through all this?
Well, for one thing, he had remained utterly faithful to
Edward in the hard times when Warwick had temporarily
hurled him from the throne. He had fought with bravery
and distinction at the battles of Barnet and Tewkesbury.
He had done Edward's dirty work (probably) in arranging
the death of old King Henry VI in the Tower. In all
respects, Richard was as much the loyal brother as George
was the faithless one.

This helps explain the frustrating manner in which the
characters in *Richard III* fall prey to villainous Richard,
though his villainy is made to appear patent to all. In
actual history, you see, he *wasn't* a villain.

Thus, consider the prophecy that helped set the king
against his brother: that someone with the initial *G* would

be a traitor to him. (Undoubtedly, there were prophecie
extant of this sort, and of every other too, for there ar
astrologers and prophets everywhere and at all times, ever
in our own country now, and only those prophecies tha
come true or seem to come true are later remembered.
The king felt this applied to George of Clarence; bu
why not to Richard of Gloucester? The king suspecte
George because George deserved it; he did not suspec
Gloucester because the real Gloucester's unshakeabl
loyalty left no room for suspicion.

We can also ask ourselves whether Richard really had
hand in raising Edward's suspicions against George. Ther
is no evidence of that at all until the later anti-Richar
polemicists got to work. They say that he spoke openly i
favour of his brother to the king in order to hide his secre
manoeuvrings. The 'manoeuvrings', however, are a late
invention presented even by the polemicists as only
matter of suspicion, whereas the one *fact* they admit i
that Richard defended his brother Clarence openly – whic
took courage.

By the time Asimov's Guide to Shakespeare *had come ou
my marriage had broken up and I found myself in New
York in a two-room hotel suite and rather at a loss.*

*For the first time in my life I needed to consult no one'
taste but my own, so I went to lower Fourth Avenue t
poke around the secondhand bookstores, something I ha
always wanted to do.*

*I came across a Modern Library edition of Lord Byron'
great comic epic* Don Juan, *which I had read (or ha
at least, begun to read) in my college days. I brought
home in triumph, feeling that I could now have somethin
to read at night when I couldn't sleep (and I wasn't sleep
ing very well in my lonely hotel apartment).*

*The first night, I had hardly managed to read th
seventeen-stanza dedication and the very beginnin
of the first canto before all was lost. I put the boo*

side and spent the rest of the night in restless waiting
r the morning so that I could begin to annotate it.

I did annotate it, and, unlike my treatment of the Bible
nd Shakespeare, I quoted the entire epic along with the
nnotations. I managed to persuade Doubleday to publish
(which they eventually did – their own idea – in a very
eautiful and expensive edition).

Asimov's Annotated 'Don Juan' (Book 130) was pub-
shed in 1972, and I have rarely had such fun writing a
ook. Here is the first verse of the first canto just to give
ou a notion of what I was doing:

om ASIMOV'S ANNOTATED 'DON JUAN' (1972)

I want a hero: an uncommon want,
> When every year and month sends forth a new one,
Till, after cloying the gazettes with cant,[1]
> The age discovers he is not the true one:
Of such as these I should not care to vaunt,
> I'll therefore take our ancient friend Don Juan [2] –
We all have seen him, in the pantomime,
Sent to the devil somewhat ere his time.[3]

Canto 1 was written between September 6 and November
, 1818, in Venice, Italy.

1. The gazettes were not then, as now in the American
nse of the word, simply newspapers. They were official
eekly journals, publishing statistics of governmental
terest: movements of the royal family, lists of honours
ranted, those killed in battle, and so on. Byron refers to
e gazettes now and then in *Don Juan*, chiefly in order
bestow a sardonic glance at their role as a military
bituary list.

2. Don Juan is an 'ancient friend' because he was a
ell-known figure out of Spanish folklore. He first received
cognized literary presentation in the drama *El Burlador*
e Sevilla, written in 1630 by the Spanish dramatist Gabriel

Téllez (who wrote under the pseudonym Tirso de Molina)

In the original folk tale, Don Juan was the epitome o the licentious man, who aspired (usually successfully) t make love to every woman he met, and who did so wit utter disregard for any law. The climax of his story is hi liaison with a noblewoman and its consequences. He kill the woman's father in a duel. The father is buried and a effigy of him is placed over the tomb. Don Juan, seein, that effigy, mockingly invites it to dinner. The stone figur duly arrives at the meal and drags the rake and blaspheme to Hell.

Various versions of this legend had already appeared i Spain and elsewhere by Byron's time. Molière had writte a play on the theme and Mozart, an opera. Byron, wit no compunction whatever, utterly altered the plot in hi own version. In fact, all that Byron left of the traditiona Don Juan is his name and birthplace; *nothing more!* Do Juan's character is utterly changed. From a heartles blasphemer, seducer, and libertine (as the world viewe Byron), he becomes an innocent, far more sinned agains than sinning (as Byron viewed himself). Even the hero' name was tampered with, for Byron abandoned th universal 'Don Wahn' and called him, with sturdy Englis disregard for the eccentric pronunciations of foreigners 'Don Joo'un', as we can tell by the fact that he rhyme Juan with 'new one' and 'true one'.

3. Don Juan was also a favourite in pantomimes an puppet shows, particularly one adapted from the play *Th Libertine* by Thomas Shadwell. The climax of such show invariably came at the point where Don Juan, defiant t the last, is dragged down to Hell by the devil to th screaming enthusiasm of the audience.

Nor did working on Don Juan *in the least sate me. Whil it was in press, I did the same for Milton's great tragi epic* Paradise Lost, *throwing in* Paradise Regained *fo good measure. In this case, too, I quoted the entire wor along with the annotations.*

Doubleday did Asimov's Annotated 'Paradise Lost' *also, and without a murmur. It was published in 1974 as Book 154.*

I had thought, when I first began to work on Paradise Lost, *that it would be hard work since I was under the firm impression that I didn't like Milton's style. I changed my mind, however. Once I immersed myself in it, I found I loved the long and rolling sonority of those magnificent Latinate sentences of his. Here's the very first sentence in the epic, one that rumbles on for sixteen lines of iambic pentameter – together with my annotations, of course.*

from ASIMOV'S ANNOTATED 'PARADISE LOST' *(1974)*

> Of Man's First disobedience,[1] and the Fruit
> Of that Forbidden Tree,[2] whose mortal taste
> Brought Death into the World, and all our woe,
> With loss of Eden,[3] till one greater Man [4]
> Restore us, and regain the blissful Seat,
> Sing, Heav'nly Muse,[5] that on the secret top
> Of Oreb, or of Sinai,[6] didst inspire
> That Shepherd, who first taught the chosen Seed,[7]
> In the Beginning how the Heav'ns and Earth [8]
> Rose out of Chaos:[9] Or if Sion Hill [10]
> Delight thee more, and Siloa's Brook that flow'd
> Fast by the Oracle of God;[11] I thence
> Invoke thy aid to my advent'rous song,
> That with no middle flight intends to soar
> Aboe th' Aonian Mount,[12] while it pursues
> Things unattempted yet in Prose or Rhyme.

1. The epic poem *Paradise Lost* begins immediately with a statement of purpose. Its story is that told in the second and third chapters of the biblical book of Genesis: that of Eve's, then Adam's, disobedience to God and their violation of the one negative command given them after

their creation. Since Adam and Eve were the first (and, till then, the only) human beings to exist, according to the biblical account, and since this was their first disobedience, it was the first disobedience of mankind generally.

2. It was this tree that was involved in the one negative command given to Adam: 'And the Lord God commanded the man, saying, "Of every tree of the garden thou mayest freely eat: But of the tree of the knowledge of good and evil, thou shalt not eat of it; for in the day that thou eatest thereof thou shalt surely die"' (Genesis 2:16–17).

The quotation I have just given is from the Authorized Version of the Bible (generally known as the King James Bible), which was first published in 1611, fifty-six years before the publication of *Paradise Lost*. It has been the traditional Bible of English-speaking Protestant, both in Milton's time and now, so I will use it for quotations throughout these notes.

3. It was the land of Eden in which Adam and Eve existed before their disobedience and from which they were evicted afterwards, as the poem will describe in great detail. Specifically it was in a garden in that region in which they dwelt: 'And the Lord God planted a garden eastward in Eden; and there he put the man whom he had formed' (Genesis 2:8).

It is common, but not correct, to refer to the garden itself as Eden, as Milton does here. This is not to say that Milton did not know better, of course. In the constricting bounds of poetry, the necessities of rhyme, rhythm, or imagery may require a certain departure from strict accuracy. This is tolerated as 'poetic licence'.

4. The 'greater Man' is Jesus. The New Testament worked out the doctrine that there was a symmetry in the story of man. By the sin of one man, Adam, all mankind was condemned, and by the virtue of one man, Jesus, all mankind was saved again: 'For as by one man's disobedience many were made sinners, so by the obedience of one shall many be made righteous' (Romans 5:19).

5. Milton draws his sources not only from the Bible

but from Greek and Latin literature, primarily the great epic poems: Homer's *Iliad* and *Odyssey* and Virgil's *Aeneid*. *Paradise Lost* is quite obviously and undeniably an imitation of all these, particularly the last. Indeed, so densely packed with classical allusion is Milton's epic, so reverent is its treatment of classical myths, and so slavish (almost) is its picture of angels as Homeric heroes, that we are bound to consider *Paradise Lost* a pagan translation (and a gloriously majestic one) of the biblical creation tale.

It was customary for the pagan epic poets to invoke the Muse at the start of their poem, the Muse being the spirit of poetic inspiration. Homer and Virgil both did so and Milton does so as well.

6. There is a limit, of course, to how pagan the rigidly Puritan Milton can allow himself to be. The Muse must therefore be identified with the revealing and inspiring Spirit of God.

One place where the divine Spirit revealed itself was at 'the secret top of Oreb' (Mount Horeb). Thus the Bible tells us that Moses, while still in exile in Midian, 'led the flock to the backside of the desert, and came to the mountain of God, even to Horeb. And the angel of the Lord appeared unto him in a flame of fire out of the midst of a bush' (Exodus 3:1–2).

After Moses went to Egypt, at the behest of God, and then led the Israelites out of Egypt, he brought them to Mount Sinai: 'And the Lord came down upon Mount Sinai, on the top of the mount: and the Lord called Moses up to the top of the mount; and Moses went up' (Exodus 19:20).

Many biblical commentators decided that Horeb and Sinai are alternative names for the same mountain, and that is how Milton treats them here.

7. It is Moses who is 'that Shepherd' who received the message of God on Mount Horeb, or Sinai. Though raised in the palace of Egypt's pharaoh, he had killed an Egyptian and been forced to flee the land. He reached Midian and

married the daughter of an important man of the region, one with large herds of sheep. 'Now Moses kept the flock of Jethro his father in law, the priest of Midian' (Exodus 3:1).

The teachings of Moses were addressed to the Israelites, who believed themselves divinely chosen to keep God's commandments and to worship him in the correct manner. Thus: 'O ye seed of Israel his servant, ye children of Jacob, his chosen ones' (1 Chronicles 16:13). Hence the reference to 'the chosen Seed'.

8. It was Moses, according to a Jewish tradition adopted by the Christians, who wrote the first five books of the Bible, under the inspiration of God. In particular, he was supposed to have written the first verse, which opens with the phrase used here by Milton: 'In the beginning God created the heavens and the earth' (Genesis 1:1).

9. In the Hebrew tradition, it is stated in the very first biblical verse that heaven and earth were created. The implication was that, before the creation, *nothing* existed.

In the Greek tradition, however, chaos existed to begin with, and even antedated the gods. Chaos was viewed as matter in formless disorder, so the creation of the universe in the Greek view consisted of imposing form on formlessness and extracting order out of disorder.

Milton accepts the pagan view when he speaks of 'how the Heav'ns and Earth/Rose out of Chaos'. He is not, however, entirely without biblical authority, for the Bible goes on to say after the initial verse, 'And the earth was without form, and void' (Genesis 1:2). In other words, even though heaven and earth were created out of nothing, they appeared as chaos to begin with, and it was out of that that God, in six days, extracted form and order.

10. 'Sion hill' is Mount Zion, which was the height about which the city of Jerusalem was built. It was the fortified centre of the city, the site of the ruler's palace, the place of last defence. It was David's capture of Mount Zion that placed Jerusalem in Israelite hands: 'Nevertheless David took the strong hold of Zion' (2 Samuel 5:7). It

was on Mount Zion that David's son, Solomon, built the
Temple. Zion therefore became the religious centre of
the kingdom as well. It was on Mount Zion, with its
Temple, that the Spirit of God might be thought to be
resting.

11. Siloa ('Siloam', in the Greek form) is a tunnel in
Mount Zion through which water was conducted. The
water formed a pool at the base of the mountain and
served as a water supply. Its connection with divine
inspiration comes in a tale of the manner in which Jesus
cured a blind man by placing saliva-caked soil on his eyes,
'And said unto him, "Go, wash in the pool of Siloam" '
(John 9:7). Since the pool was at the base of the mount
on which the Temple stood, it 'flow'd Fast by the Oracle
of God'.

12. Milton never stays long with biblical allusions, but
always finds himself irresistibly drawn back to the classical.
He moves now from biblical to pagan sources of inspiration. Aonia is an alternative name for the Greek district
known as Boeotia. The 'Aonian Mount' is Helicon, a
mountain in Boeotia sacred to the Muses and therefore
symbolizing a source of poetic inspiration.

In 1975, I had lunch with James Fixx of Horizon *over the
possibility of my doing a piece for it. Fixx was astonished
at the variety of my writing, and since I don't suffer from
overdeveloped humility, I cheerfully described some of the
books I had done and rather emphasized my annotations –
of which I am inordinately proud.*

*He hadn't heard of them and asked if I could annotate
a poem for* Horizon. *I agreed readily, even jubilantly, and
decided to do Rudyard Kipling's 'Recessional'.*

Alas Horizon *rejected it with, I suspect, something akin
to horror. Fixx had got the idea, I think, that my annotations were satirical or humorous and, of course, they are
completely serious.*

I shrugged off the rejection, and since I am strongly

averse to letting anything I have written go to waste, I annotated three dozen other poems and persuaded Doubleday to publish Familiar Poems Annotated *in 1977 (Book 181). From that book, here is my originally rejected annotation of 'Recessional':*

from FAMILIAR POEMS ANNOTATED *(1977)*

Recessional [1]

by RUDYARD KIPLING [2]

God of our fathers, known of old, [3]
    Lord of our far-flung battle line, [4]
Beneath whose awful hand we hold
    Dominion over palm and pine – [5]
Lord God of Hosts, [6] be with us yet,
Lest we forget – lest we forget! [7]

The tumult and the shouting dies,
    The captains and the kings depart: [8]
Still stands Thine ancient sacrifice,
    An humble and a contrite heart. [9]
Lord God of Hosts, be with us yet,
Lest we forget – lest we forget!

Far-called, our navies melt away; [10]
    On dune and headland sinks the fire: [11]
Lo, all our pomp of yesterday
    Is one with Nineveh [12] and Tyre! [13]
Judge of the Nations, [14] spare us yet,
Lest we forget – lest we forget!

If, drunk with sight of power, we loose
    Wild tongues that have not Thee in awe,
Such boastings as the Gentiles [15] use,
    Or lesser breeds without the Law – [16]
Lord God of Hosts, be with us yet,
Lest we forget – lest we forget!

For heathen heart [17] that puts her trust
  In reeking tube and iron shard,[18]
All valiant dust [19] that builds on dust,[20]
  And, guarding, calls not Thee to guard –
For frantic boast and foolish word,
Thy Mercy on Thy People, Lord! [21]

1. By 1897, the year 'Recessional' was written, Great Britain was at the peak of its power. Victoria had been queen for sixty years – sixty years that had seen the nation advancing steadily in population, prosperity, prestige, and power. Now the nation was celebrating the Diamond Jubilee, the sixtieth anniversary of Victoria's accession to the throne.

Great Britain ruled over an empire that had been expanding throughout the nineteenth century and was still expanding. To symbolize British glory and success, Victoria had been promoted to a higher title and had been made empress of India in 1876. Small though Great Britain might be in area, she ruled nearly a quarter of the world directly, and dominated virtually all the rest financially.

And yet the most famous literary work to emerge from this ecstatic celebration turned out to be this sombre poem. Its very name indicates the manner in which its mood went precisely contrary to that of the happy nation.

A recession is an act of retiring or withdrawing, and a recessional is a piece of music played at the end of some performance or ceremony, as the audience is leaving. The poem, therefore, deals with the possible decline of the empire; its departure, so to speak, from the stage of history.

2. Joseph Rudyard Kipling was born in Bombay, India, on December 30, 1865, and India was the very epitome of imperial success. It was India that was the most populous, the most historic, the most exotic, and the most impressive of all British possessions. It was of India that the British monarch became empress. In the years Kipling spent in

India, he grew interested in Indian life and culture but always from the viewpoint of a member of a master race.

Kipling came to be viewed as the outstanding literary spokesman for imperialism – that is, for the view that men of European descent (and of British descent in particular) had a kind of natural right·to rule over non-Europeans, and that it was even their duty to do so. Yet in the midst of the frantic Jubilee celebration, a chill foretaste of the nemesis of imperialism seemed to come over him.

He died in London on January 18, 1936.

3. The poem is biblical in tone and flavour. The British, in Kipling's view, were God's chosen people, destined for world rule, and it was impossible for him not to hark back to that other chosen people, the Israelites. Throughout the poem, the British are made into the contemporary equivalent of biblical Israel.

Thus, when Moses came to the Israelite slaves in Egypt with the news that God would rescue them, he had to assure them that it was no invention of his own that he was bringing, no unknown deity, but an ancestral God of proven work, one that was known of old. God's instructions to Moses were: 'Thus shalt thou say unto the Children of Israel, the Lord God of your fathers, the God of Abraham, the God of Isaac, and the God of Jacob, hath sent me unto you' (Exodus 3:15).

And so Kipling, in addressing God, stresses the same historic continuity, the same ancestral respectability, to lend a more sombre note to the prayer.

4. 'Far-flung' indeed! The empires of the past had been limited in size. The largest had been that of the Mongols, who from 1240 to 1340 had ruled over most of Asia and half of Europe. Even that empire had been contiguous, however, with all parts land-connected; it was not truly intercontinental; not truly a world empire.

It was only after the opening of the age of exploration that world empires became possible. In the course of the sixteenth century, Portugal and Spain each established trading posts on every continent and took over large land areas in the Americas. Indeed, from 1580 to 1640 Spain took over Portugal and combined both empires. These Iberian empires could only be held together feebly, however, in the days of sailing ships, especially since the home nations were in the grip of a depressed and declining economy.

It was with the coming of industrialization that a real gap opened between those nations that could impose colonialization and those that must suffer it. Great Britain, which was the first to industrialize, forged on to outstrip the earlier world empires in extent, far outstrip them in population, and far, far outstrip them in power.

Of the previous world empires, it had been said that the sun never set upon them. At every moment during earth's rotation some region forming part of the empire was on the day-lit portion of the globe. The earlier examples were forgotten, however, in the greater example of the newer empire. Throughout the nineteenth century, it was common to say that 'the sun never set upon the British Empire'. And it was easy to begin to believe this in the figurative sense, too – that the sun of history and power would never set and that the British Empire would remain basking in an eternal noon.

5. Again a reference to the wide extent of the British Empire. The palm is a characteristic tree of the tropics, and the pine the characteristic tree of the northernmost forests. The palm trees of India and the pine forests of Canada were both under the rule of the government in London. (Canada had dominion status and considerable self-rule, to be sure.)

6. The ancient peoples all had war gods, lords of the hosts (armies), and why not? When did a people need their god more than when they were meeting their enemies in battle (and when, presumably, the enemies were busily calling upon *their* gods for help). Kipling specifically recognizes the role of God as generalissimo when he refers to him earlier as 'Lord of our far-flung battle line'.

In the Bible, the Creator is sometimes spoken of as 'God of hosts' or 'Lord of hosts' when the divine role on the battlefield, or as an agent of destruction, is to be emphasized. Thus, when the Bible describes the manner in which God will inflict military defeat upon the Egyptians, it says, 'And the Egyptians will I give over into the hand of a cruel lord; and a fierce king shall rule over them, saith the Lord, the Lord of hosts' (Isaiah 19:4).

Again, in a plea to reverse the civil war that is giving the enemy an opportunity to destroy Israel, we have, 'Turn us again, O Lord God of hosts, cause thy face to shine; and we shall be saved' (Psalms 80:19).

7. To the biblical writers, the military defeat and physical destruction of a land are the direct result of forgetting what is due to God, since God's people cannot suffer defeat except as punishment by an angry and forgotten God. Thus, the Bible quotes God as saying: 'For Israel hath forgotten his Maker, and buildeth temples; and Judah hath multiplied fenced cities, but I will send a fire upon his cities, and it shall devour the palaces thereof' (Hosea 8:14).

8. Tumult and shouting evoke a picture of the clamour of battle, and 'captains' and 'kings' are the leaders of armies. There is a biblical passage describing the war horse that is reminiscent of these lines: 'He saith among the trumpets, Ha, ha; and he smelleth the battle afar off, the thunder of the captains and the shouting' (Job 39:25).

But the noise dies and the warriors depart. Military glory *alone* is insufficient, for the wars end and there must be something to maintain the nation afterwards.

These two lines also evoke the 'tumult and the shouting' of the Jubilee, the gathering of royalty and of military notables from every European nation. The noise of the Jubilee has to die, too, and the celebrants must depart, and what then?

9. It is a common biblical notion that it is not the proud, the powerful, and the arrogant who are cared for by God, but the humble, the repentant, and the unassum-

ing. The former are too apt to be tempted into feeling they have no need of God and are therefore likely to forget Him. The latter cannot forget Him because they have nowhere else to turn.

Thus: 'The Lord is nigh unto them that are of a broken heart; and saveth such as be of contrite spirit' (Psalms 34:18). Again: 'The sacrifices of God are a broken spirit: a broken and a contrite heart, O God, thou wilt not despise' (Psalms 51:17).

10. Great Britain's prime defence was its navy. It was through its navy's defeat of the Spanish Armada in 1588 that England became an important power on the stage of the modern world. It was because its navy patrolled and controlled the waters about itself that Great Britain was held inviolate from the armies of Philip II of Spain and of Louis XIV and Napoleon of France – armies that would have destroyed the nation, could they have but set foot on it.

What's more, it was British control of the sea beyond its own waters that controlled the trade of the world, poured wealth into the unblockaded island, and, in the end, wore out and frustrated all the Continental conquerors and left their land victories useless.

But what if Great Britain, foolishly vainglorious, attempted tasks too great for her, or entered into tasks without careful forethought and planning? The navy, 'far-called' (that is, spread thin over the waters of a worldwide empire, too thin) would melt away. The links binding the empire would be broken, and the homeland itself would be left defenceless before the attack of armies that could not be prevented from landing.

11. Dunes are sandy ridges common along seashores. Headlands are spits and capes, bits of land jutting out into the sea. Lighthouses on such places guide incoming ships at night or in fogs. They are necessary for a maritime nation, whose ships are its life line. They are unnecessary once a navy no longer exists, since trade can no longer be protected once the life line is cut. And with the life

line cut, the sinking of the fire in the lighthouses becomes a symbolic way of representing the dying of the nation.

12. Nineveh was the capital of the Assyrian Empire in the seventh century B.C. during the days of its greatest glory. Under Ashurbanipal, it became not only the military centre of western Asia, but the cultural centre as well. It might have seemed to the proud warrior caste of Assyria that their power and rule were eternal, yet Ashurbanipal died in 627 B.4. with his empire essentially intact, and within twenty-five years it was all gone, forever.

Nineveh fell to Chaldean rebels from within the empire and to Median horsemen from without in 612 B.C. It was never rebuilt, and two centuries later, when a Greek army passed that way, they had to ask what the mounds were.

13. Tyre is a particularly close approximation to Great Britain. It, too, was a naval power, with a citadel on an island that could not be forced while its ships controlled the seas about it. Tyre, too, built up a vast network of trading posts and flung its merchantmen and warships far out, from end to end of the Mediterranean and even into the Atlantic.

Tyre's prosperity declined slowly as it adjusted to the realities of the mighty Asian empires of Assyria and its successors. Finally, in 323 B.C., Tyre was besieged by Alexander the Great, who filled in the sea between the island and the coast. He took the city after nine months and destroyed it. It exists to this day as a small coastal city in Lebanon, but no shadow of its former glory remains.

14. This title, given to God, harks back to the biblical passage in which Abraham attempts to dissuade God from destroying Sodom with indiscriminate anger against its inhabitants. After all, there may be some people of Sodom who are righteous. Abraham said, 'That be far from thee to do after this manner, to slay the righteous with the wicked; and that the righteous should be as the wicked, that be far from thee: Shall not the Judge of all the earth do right?' (Genesis 18:25).

15. It is the wild overweening pride, the 'hubris' of the Jubilee, that makes Kipling uneasy. The behaviour is not British in his opinion, but is more suited to other and inferior people (a viewpoint which is itself an example of hubris, of course).

'Gentiles' are, strictly speaking, related members of a tribe or clan (from the Latin word 'gens', meaning tribe or clan). Any group that considers itself in a special relationship to God, or as having a special significance in history, is likely to lump all other people as Gentiles, as members of the (other) tribes. Thus, to Jews, all non-Jews are Gentiles; and to Mormons, all non-Mormons are Gentiles.

To Kipling, with his attitude that the British are the modern Israelites and the new-chosen of God, all non-British are Gentiles, and therefore inferior beings who know no better than to indulge in vainglorious boasting. That the British should do that as well would be shameful.

16. The agreement, or covenant, by which the Israelites became the chosen of God, required that, in exchange, they obey the Law as delivered to Moses on Mount Sinai. Thus, God says, 'Now, therefore, if ye will obey my voice indeed, and keep my covenant, then ye shall be a peculiar treasure unto me above all people' (Exodus 19:5).

To be 'without the Law', then, is not to be of the elect. Again, there is the flavour of inferiority about those not chosen. They are not British (Israelite), and therefore they are 'lesser breeds'.

17. The word 'heathen' is used in the English translation of the Bible for those who did not worship the God of Israel: 'Why do the heathen rage –' (Psalms 2:1). The word means those of the heath, or backwoods, who are unsophisticated and cling to primitive traditions and worship.

18. The 'reeking tube' is the gun barrel generally, of all sizes, and the 'iron shard' is the bullet or other object fired from it. The trust in force exclusively, without regard to moral justification, is exemplified in a jingle that became

current in Great Britain after the invention of a new and improved machine gun by the American inventor Hiram Stevens Maxim in 1884:

> Whatever happens, we have got
> The Maxim-gun, and they have not.

Ironically enough, even as Kipling wrote, the word 'reeking' became obsolete.

For six hundred years the chemical explosive used on the battlefield to propel bullets and balls had been gunpowder. That had produced smoke, soot, and reeking odours that fouled the guns, choked the gunners, and obscured the battlefield. In the last decades of the nineteenth century, however, smokeless powders were developed. In the wars of the twentieth century, various smokeless powders were used, and though the 'tube' grew steadily more deadly, it was no longer 'reeking'.

19. From the biblical view, man was a creature compounded of dust: 'And the Lord God formed man of the dust of the ground, and breathed into his nostrils the breath of life' (Genesis 2:7). In battle, man might display valour, but that did not dignify his origins; he was merely 'valiant dust', a phrase William Shakespeare uses in *Much Ado About Nothing*.

20. This is a reference to the biblical parable of the 'foolish man, who built his house upon the sand: And the rain descended, and the floods came, and the winds blew, and beat upon that house; and it fell' (Matthew 7:26–27).

21. The last plea is, of course, biblical: 'Be merciful, O Lord, unto thy people Israel –' (Deuteronomy 21:8), and Kipling here directly equates the British with Israel.

Yet God chose *not* to have mercy, for immediately after 1897, the year of the Diamond Jubilee, the British Empire began its decline.

Even while the Jubilee was being celebrated, British imperialism was pressing hard on the independent Boer territories north of British dominions in South Africa. In 1899 this turned into open war, which, to British surprise and humiliation, lasted nearly three years. The British won in the end after they had sufficiently reinforced their armies, but world sympathy was with the Boers.

The British, surprised at being cast in the role of villains, and cast down at finding they had not a friend in the world, lost the euphoria of 1897, and it was never, quite, to return.

One more bit of literature remains to be mentioned, something rather widely removed from the great literary classics I have referred to.

Somehow, almost accidentally, I found myself involved with the Baker Street Irregulars, a group of lovable eccentrics who find no pleasure greater than reading, re-reading, analysing, and discussing the sixty stories and novels that involve Sherlock Holmes plus all the simple and arcane side-issues thereof.

Drawn in, I found myself producing items of Sherlockian interest.

Otto Penzler, a book collector and the proprietor of Mysterious Press, a small house given over to items of specialized interest to mystery fans, suggested in July 1977 that I write sixty limericks, one for each of the items in the Sherlock Holmes canon. Since I was about to make a small trip on the Queen Elizabeth II *and wanted desperately to keep myself busy while doing so (I have an aversion to pure vacationing), I agreed.*

The sixty limericks that resulted, all written on the QE II, *were put together as* Asimov's Sherlockian Limericks (*Book 191*), *which was published on January 6, 1978, Sherlock Holmes's one hundred twenty-fourth birthday (by BSI reckoning) and the day of that year's meeting of the Baker Street Irregulars.*

Here is the last of my Sherlockian limericks:

from ASIMOV'S SHERLOCKIAN LIMERICKS *(1978)*

Farewell, Sherlock! Farewell, Watson, too.
First to last, you've been loyal and true.
Of the human totality
Who've lived in reality
There've been none quite as real as you.

PART 14

Mysteries

Although the list of my second hundred books is disturbingly short on science fiction, things aren't altogether bad. At least, I have begun to write mystery fiction in addition.

This is not to say I was a complete stranger to the mystery story in my first hundred books. A number of my science fiction stories were mysteries, including my two novels The Caves of Steel *and* The Naked Sun.

I wrote only one 'straight' mystery among my first hundred books, The Death Dealers, *but that involved scientists and science all the way through. Even the gimmick was a chemical one. The small number of straight mystery short stories I wrote were similarly saturated with science and scientists.*

From 1971 onwards, however, I have written no less than thirty straight mystery short stories that had nothing to do with science – rather old-fashioned mysteries in the ratiocinative tradition of Agatha Christie and John Dickson Carr. The first twelve of them were collected in Tales of the Black Widowers *(Book 155), which Doubleday published in 1974, and the next twelve in* More Tales of the Black Widowers *(Book 178), which they published in 1976. The remaining six, along with six more yet to be written, will someday (I hope) be included in a third book.*

How I came to write these mysteries I explain in the introduction to Tales of the Black Widowers.

from THE TALES OF THE BLACK WIDOWERS *(1976)*

But then, back in 1971, I received a letter from that gorgeous blonde young lady Eleanor Sullivan, who is managing editor of *Ellery Queen's Mystery Magazine* (or

EQMM, for short), asking if I would consider writing a short story for the magazine. Of course, I jubilantly agreed, because I thought that if they *asked* for one, they couldn't possibly have the cruelty to reject it once written, and that meant I could safely write my own kind of story – very cerebral.

I began revolving plot possibilities in my head rather anxiously, for I wanted something with a reasonable twist to it and Agatha Christie, all by herself, had already used virtually all possible twists.

While the wheels were slowly turning in the recesses of my mind, I happened to be visiting the actor David Ford (who was in both the Broadway and Hollywood versions of *1776*). His apartment is filled with all kinds of interesting oddities, and he told me that he was convinced once that someone had taken something from his apartment, but he could never be sure because he couldn't tell whether anything was missing.

I laughed and all the wheels in my head, heaving a collective sigh of relief, stopped turning. I had my twist.

I then needed a background against which to display the twist, and here we have something else.

Back in the early 1940s, legend has it, a man married a lady who found his friends unacceptable, and vice versa. In order to avoid breaking off a valued relationship, those friends organized a club, without officers or bylaws, for the sole purpose of having a dinner once a month. It would be a stag organization so that the husband in question could be invited to join and his wife legitimately requested not to attend. (Nowadays, with women's lib so powerful, this might not have worked.)

The organization was named the Trap-Door Spiders (or TDS, for short) probably because the members felt themselves to be hiding.

Thirty years have passed since the TDS was organized, but it still exists. It is still stag, though the member whose marriage inspired the organization is long since divorced. (As a concession to male non-chauvinism, a cocktail party was given on February 3, 1973, at which the TDS wives could meet one another – but this did not become an annual custom.)

Once a month the TDS meets, always on a Friday night, almost always in Manhattan, sometimes in a restaurant, sometimes in a member's apartment. Each meeting is co-hosted by two volunteers who bear all the expenses for the occasion and who may each bring a guest. The average attendance is twelve. There are drinks and conversation from 6.30 to 7.30 p.m.; food and conversation from 7.30 to 8.30 p.m.; and just conversation thereafter.

After the meal each guest is grilled on his interests, his profession, his hobbies, his views, and the results are almost always interesting, often fascinating.

The chief among the general eccentricities of the TDS are these: (1) Every member is addressed as 'Doctor' by the others, the title going along with the membership, and (2) each member is supposed to try to arrange for a mention of the TDS in his obituary.

I had been a guest myself on two different occasions, and when I moved to New York in 1970, I was elected to membership.

Well, then, thought I, why not tell my mystery story against the background of the meeting of an organization something like the TDS? My club would be called the Black Widowers and I would cut it in half to make it manageable – six people and one host.

Naturally, there are differences. The members of the TDS have never, in real life, attempted to solve mysteries, and none of them is as idiosyncratic as the members of the Black Widowers. In fact, the members of the TDS are, one and all, lovable people, and there is a mutual affection that is touching to see. Therefore, please be assured that the characters and events in the stories in this book are my own invention and are not to be equated with anyone or anything in the TDS, except insofar as they may seem intelligent or lovable.

In particular, Henry, the waiter, is my own invention

and has no analogue, however remote, in the TDS.

Most of the Black Widowers stories appeared in Ellery Queen's Mystery Magazine (EQMM) *and a few in* F & SF. *Three of the stories in each book, however, did not see prior publication, and I will choose one of them to include here, complete, as a sampling of the group. It is 'Earthset and Evening Star'.*

'Earthset and Evening Star' *(1976)*

Emmanuel Rubin, whose latest mystery novel was clearly proceeding smoothly, lifted his drink with satisfaction and let his eyes gleam genially through his thick-lensed glasses.

'The mystery story,' he pontificated, 'has its rules, which, when broken, make it an artistic failure, whatever success it may have in the marketplace.'

Mario Gonzalo, whose hair had been recently cut to allow a glimpse of the back of his neck, said, as though to no one, 'It always amuses me to hear a writer describe something he scrawls on paper as "art".' He looked with some complacency at the cartoon he was making of the guest for that month's banquet session of the Black Widowers.

'If what you do is the definition of art,' said Rubin, 'I withdraw the term in connection with the writer's craft. One thing to avoid, for instance, is the idiot plot.'

'In that case,' said Thomas Trumbull, helping himself to another roll and buttering it lavishly, 'aren't you at a disadvantage?'

Rubin said loftily, 'By "an idiot plot", I mean one in which the solution would come at once if an idiot investigator would but ask a logical question, or if an idiot witness would but tell something he knows and has no reason to hide.'

Geoffrey Avalon, who had left a neatly cleaned bone

on his plate as the only evidence of the slab of roast beef that had once rested there, said, 'But no skilled practitioner would do that, Manny. What you do is set up some reason to prevent the asking or telling of the obvious.'

'Exactly,' said Rubin. 'For instance, what I've been writing is essentially a short story, if one moves in a straight line. The trouble is the line is so straight, the reader will see its end before I'm halfway. So I have to hide one crucial piece of evidence, and do it in such a way that I don't make an idiot plot out of it. So I invent a reason to hide that piece, and in order to make the reason plausible I have to build a supporting structure around it – and I end with a novel, and a damn good one.' His sparse beard quivered with self-satisfaction.

Henry, the perennial waiter at the Black Widowers' banquets, removed the plate from in front of Rubin with his usual dexterity. Rubin, without turning, said 'Am I right, Henry?'

Henry said softly, 'As a mystery reader, Mr Rubin, I find it more satisfying to have the piece of information delivered to me and to find that I have been insufficiently clever and did not notice.'

'I just read a mystery,' said James Drake in his softly hoarse smoker's voice, 'in which the whole point rested on character one being really character two, because the *real* character one was dead. I was put on to it at once because, in the list of characters at the start, character one was not listed. Ruined the story for me.'

'Yes,' said Rubin, 'but that wasn't the author's fault. Some flunky did that. I once wrote a story that was accompanied by one illustration that no one thought to show me in advance. It happened to give away the point.'

The guest had been listening quietly to all this. His hair was just light enough to be considered blond, and it had a careful wave in it that looked, somehow, as though it belonged there. He turned his rather narrow but clearly good-humoured face to Roger Halsted, his neighbour, and said, 'Pardon me, but since Manny Rubin is my friend,

I know he is a mystery writer. Is this true of the rest of you as well? Is this a mystery writers' organization?'

Halsted, who had been looking with sombre approval at the generous slab of Black Forest torte that had been placed before him as dessert, withdrew his attention with some difficulty and said, 'Not at all. Rubin is the only mystery writer here. I'm a mathematics teacher myself; Drake is a chemist; Avalon is a lawyer; Gonzalo is an artist; and Trumbull is a code expert with the government.

'On the other hand,' he went on, 'we do have an interest in this sort of thing. Our guests often have problems they bring up for discussion, some sort of mystery, and we've been rather lucky –'

The guest leaned back with a small laugh. 'Nothing of the sort here, alas. Of the mystery, the murder, the fearful hand clutching from behind the curtain, there is nothing in my life. It is all very straightforward, alas; very dull. I am not even married.' He laughed again.

The guest had been introduced as Jean Servais, and Halsted, who had attacked the torte with vigour and, in consequence, felt a friendly glow filling him, said, 'Does it matter to you if I call you John?'

'I would not strike you, sir, if you did, but I pray you not to. It is not my name. Jean, please.'

Halsted nodded. 'I'll try. I can manage that *zh* sound, but getting it properly nasal is another thing. Zhohng,' he said.

'But that is excellent. Most formidable.'

'You speak English very well,' said Halsted, returning the politeness.

'Europeans require linguistic talent,' said Servais. 'Besides, I have lived in the United States for nearly ten years now. You are all Americans, I suppose. Mr Avalon looks British somehow.'

'Yes, I think he likes to look British,' said Halsted. And with a certain hidden pleasure he said, 'And it's Avalon. Accent on the first syllable and nothing nasal at the end.'

But Servais only laughed. 'Ah yes, I will try. When I

first knew Manny, I called him "Roo-bang", with the accent on the last syllable and a strong nasalization. He corrected me very vigorously and at great length. He is full of pepper, that one.'

The conversation had grown rather heated by this time over a general dispute concerning the relative merits of Agatha Christie and Raymond Chandler, with Rubin maintaining a rather lofty silence, as though he knew someone who was better than either but would not mention the name out of modesty.

Rubin seemed almost relieved when, with the coffee well in progress and Henry ready to supply the post-prandial brandy, the time came for him to tap the water glass with his spoon and say, 'Cool it, cool it, gentlemen. We are coming now to the time when our guest, Jean Servais, is to pay for his dinner. Tom, it's all yours.'

Tom scowled and said, 'If you don't mind, Mr Servais,' giving the final *s* just enough of a hiss to make his point, 'I'm not going to try to display my French accent and make the kind of jackass of myself that my friend Manny Rubin does. Tell me, sir, how do you justify your existence?'

'Why, easily,' said Servais pleasantly. 'Did I not exist, you would be without a guest today.'

'Please leave us out of it. Answer in more general terms.'

'In general, then, I build dreams. I design things that cannot be built, things I will never see, things that may never be.'

'All right,' said Trumbull, looking glum, 'you're a science fiction writer like Manny's pal what's-his-name – uh – Asimov.'

'No friend of mine,' said Rubin swiftly. 'I just help him out now and then when he's stuck on some elementary scientific point.'

Gonzalo said, 'Is he the one you once said carried *The Columbia Encyclopedia* around with him because he was listed there?'

'It's worse now,' said Rubin. 'He's bribed someone at

the Britannica to put him into the new, fifteenth edition, and these days he drags the whole set with him wherever he goes.'

'The new, fifteenth edition –' began Avalon.

'For God's sake,' said Trumbull, 'will you let our guest speak?'

'No, Mr Trumbull,' said Servais, as though there had been no interruption at all, 'I am no science fiction writer, though I read it sometimes. I read Ray Bradbury, for instance, and Harlan Ellison.' (He nasalized both names.) 'I don't think I have ever read Asimov.'

'I'll tell him that,' muttered Rubin. 'He'll love it.'

'But,' continued Servais, 'I suppose you might call me a science fiction engineer.'

'What does that mean?' asked Trumbull.

'I do not write of lunar colonies. I design them.'

'You *design* them!'

'Oh yes, and not lunar colonies only, though that is our major task right now. We work in every field of imaginative design for private industry, Hollywood, even NASA.'

Gonzalo said, 'Do you really think people can live on the Moon?'

'Why not? It depends on what mankind is willing to do, how large an initial investment it is ready to make. The environment on the Moon can be engineered to the precise equivalent of Earth's, over restricted underground areas, except for gravity. We must be content with a lunar gravity that is one sixth our own. Except for that, we need only allow for original supplies from Earth and for clever engineering – and that is where we come in, my partner and I.'

'You're a two-man firm?'

'Essentially. While my partner remains my partner, of course.'

'Are you breaking up?'

'No, no. But we quarrel over small points. It is not surprising. It is a bad time for him. But no, we will not break up. I have made up my mind to give in to him, perhaps. Of course, I am entirely in the right and it is a pity to lose what I would have.'

Trumbull leaned back in his chair, folded his arms, and said, 'Will you tell us what the argument is all about? We can then state our own preferences, whether for you or for your partner.'

'It would not be a hard choice, Mr Trumbull, for the sane,' said Servais. 'I swear it . . . This is the way it is. We are designing a full lunar colony, in complete detail. It is for a motion picture company and it is for a good fee. They will make use of some of it in a grand science fiction spectacle they are planning. We naturally supply far more than they can use, but the idea is that if they have an overall picture of what may be – and for a wonder they want it as scientifically accurate as possible – they can choose what they wish to use of it.'

'I'll bet they bollix it up,' said Drake pessimistically, 'no matter how careful you are. They'll give the Moon an atmosphere.'

'Oh, no,' said Servais, 'not after six lunar landings. That error we need not fear. Yet I have no doubt they will make mistakes. They will find it impossible to handle low-gravity effects properly throughout, and the exigencies of the plot will force some infelicities.

'Still that cannot be helped and our job is merely to supply them with the most imaginative material possible. This is my point, as you will see in a moment . . . We plan a city, a small city, and it will be against the inner lip of a crater. This is unavoidable because the plot of the movie demands it. However, we have our choice as to the identity and location of the crater, and my partner, perhaps because he is an American, goes for the obvious with an American directness. He wishes to use the crater Copernicus.

'He says that it is a name that is familiar; so if the city is called Camp Copernicus, that alone will breathe the Moon, exotic adventure, and so on. Everyone knows, he says, the name of the astronomer who first placed the Sun at the centre of the planetary system, and moreover it is a name that sounds impressive.

'I, on the other hand, am not impressed with this. As seen from Copernicus, the Earth is high in the sky and stays there. As you all know, only one side of the Moon always faces the Earth, so that from any spot on that side of the Moon's surface the Earth is always more or less in the same spot in the sky.'

Gonzalo said suddenly, 'If you want the lunar city to be on the other side of the Moon so that the Earth *isn't* in the sky, you're crazy. The audience will absolutely want the Earth there.'

Servais held up his hand in agreement. 'Absolutely! I agree. But if it is always there, it is almost as though it is *not* there. One gets too used to it. No, I choose a more subtle approach. I wish the city to be in a crater that is on the boundary of the visible side. From there, of course, you will see the Earth at the horizon.

'Consider what this introduces. The Moon does not keep the same side to the Earth exactly. It swings back and forth by a very small amount. For fourteen days it swings one way and then for fourteen days it swings back. This is called "libration".' He paused here as though to make sure he was pronouncing it correctly in English. 'And it comes about because the Moon does not move in a perfect circle about the Earth.

'Now, you see, if we establish Camp Bahyee in the crater of that name, the Earth is not only at the horizon but it moves up and down in a twenty-eight-day cycle. Properly located, the lunar colonists will see the Earth rise and set, slowly, of course. This lends itself to imaginative exploitation. The characters can arrange for some important action at Earthset, and the different positions of the Earth can indicate the passage of time and raise the suspense. Some terrific special effects are possible, too. If Venus is near the Earth and Earth is in a fat crescent stage, Venus will then be at its brightest; and when Earth sets, we can show Venus, in the airless sky of the Moon, to be a very tiny crescent itself.'

'Earthset and evening star, and one clear call for me,' muttered Avalon.

Gonzalo said, 'Is there really a crater called Bahyee?'

'Absolutely,' said Servais. 'It is, in fact, the largest crater that can be seen from the Earth's surface. It is 290 kilometres across – 180 miles.'

'It sounds like a Chinese name,' said Gonzalo.

'French!' said Servais solemnly. 'A French astronomer of that name was mayor of Paris in 1789 at the time of the Revolution.'

'That wasn't a good time to be mayor,' said Gonzalo.

'So he discovered,' said Servais. 'He was guillotined in 1793.'

Avalon said, 'I am rather on your side, Mr Servais. Your proposal lends scope. What was your partner's objection?'

Servais shrugged in a gesture that was more Gallic than anything he had yet said or done. 'Foolish ones. He says that it will be too complicated for the movie people. They will confuse things, he says. He also points out that the Earth moves too slowly in the Moon's sky. It would take days for the Earth to lift its entire globe above the horizon, and days for it to lower entirely below the horizon.'

'Is that right?' asked Gonzalo.

'It's right, but what of that? It will still be interesting.'

Halsted said, 'They can fudge that. Make the Earth move a little faster. So what?'

Servais looked discontented. 'That's no good. My partner says this is precisely what the movie people will do and this alteration of astronomical fact will be disgraceful. He is very violent about it, finding fault with everything, even with the name of the crater, which he says is ridiculous and laughable so that he will not endure it in our report. We have never had arguments like this. He is like a madman.'

'Remember,' said Avalon, 'you said you would give in.'

'Well, I will have to,' said Servais, 'but I am not pleased. Of course, it is a bad time for him.'

Rubin said, 'You've said that twice now, Jean. I've never met your partner, so I can't judge the personalities involved. Why is it a bad time?'

Servais shook his head. 'A month ago, or a little more, his wife killed herself. She took sleeping pills. My partner was a devoted husband, most uxorious. Naturally, it is terrible for him and, just as naturally, he is not himself.'

Drake coughed gently. 'Should he be working?'

'I would not dare suggest he not work. The work is keeping him sane.'

Halsted said, 'Why did she kill herself?'

Servais didn't answer in words but gestured with his eyebrows in a fashion that might be interpreted in almost any way.

Halsted persisted. 'Was she incurably ill?'

'Who can say?' said Servais, sighing. 'For a while, poor Howard —' He paused in embarrassment. 'It was not my intention to mention his name.'

Trumbull said, 'You can say anything here. Whatever is mentioned in this room is completely confidential. Our waiter, too, before you ask, is completely trustworthy.'

'Well,' said Servais, 'his name doesn't matter in any case. It is Howard Kaufman. In a way, work has been very good for him. Except at work, he is almost dead himself. Nothing is any longer important to him.'

'Yes,' said Trumbull, 'but now something *is* important to him. He wants his crater, not your crater.'

'True,' said Servais. 'I have thought of that. I have told myself it is a good sign. He throws himself into something. It is a beginning. And perhaps all the more reason, then, that I should give in. Yes, I will. It's settled, I will. There's no reason for you gentlemen to try to decide between us. The decision is made, and in his favour.'

Avalon was frowning. 'I suppose we should go on to question you further on the work you do and I suppose, moreover, that we should not intrude on a private misfortune. Here at the Black Widowers, however, no questions are barred, and there is no Fifth Amendment to plead. I am dissatisfied, sir, with your remarks concerning the unfortunate woman who committed suicide. As a happily married man, I am puzzled at the combination of love and suicide. You said she wasn't ill?'

'Actually, I didn't,' said Servais, 'and I am uncomfortable at discussing the matter.'

Rubin struck the empty glass before him with his spoon. 'Host's privilege,' he said vigorously. There was silence.

'Jean,' he said, 'you are my guest and my friend. We can't force you to answer questions, but I made it clear that the price of accepting our hospitality was the grilling. If you have been guilty of a criminal act and don't wish to discuss it, leave now and we will say nothing. If you will talk, then, whatever you say, we will still say nothing.'

'Though if it is indeed a criminal act,' said Avalon, 'we would certainly strongly advise confession.'

Servais laughed rather shakily. He said, 'For one minute there, for one frightened minute, I thought I had found myself in a Kafka novel and would be tried and condemned for some crime you would drag out of me against my will. Gentlemen, I have committed no crime of importance. A speeding ticket, a bit of creative imagination on my tax return – all that is, so I hear it said, as American as apple pie. But if you're thinking I killed that woman and made it look like suicide – please put it out of your heads at once. It *was* suicide. The police did not question it.'

Halsted said, 'Was she ill?'

'All right, then, I will answer. She was not ill as far as I know. But after all, I am not a doctor and I did not examine her.'

Halsted said, 'Did she have children?'

'No. No children. Ah, Mr Halsted, I suddenly remember that you spoke earlier that your guests had problems that they brought up for discussion, and I said I had none. I see you have found one anyway.'

Trumbull said, 'If you're so sure it was suicide, I suppose she left a note.'

'Yes,' said Servais, 'she left one.'

'What did it say?'

'I couldn't quote it exactly. I did not myself see it. According to Howard, she merely apologized for causing unhappiness but said that she could not go on. It was quite banal and I assure you it satisfied the police.'

Avalon said, 'But if it was a happy marriage, and there was no illness and no complications with children, then – Or were there complications with children? Did she want children badly and did her husband refuse –'

Gonzalo interposed. 'People don't kill themselves because they don't have kids.'

'People kill themselves for the stupidest reasons,' said Rubin. 'I remember –'

Trumbull cried out with stentorian rage, 'Damn it, you guys, Jeff has the floor.'

Avalon said, 'Was the lack of children a disturbing influence?'

'Not as far as I know,' said Servais. 'Look, Mr Avalon, I am careful in what I say, and I did *not* say it was a happy marriage.'

'You said your partner was devoted to his wife,' said Avalon gravely, 'and you used that fine old word "uxorious" to describe him.'

'Love,' said Servais, 'is insufficient for happiness if it flows but one way. I did not say that *she* loved *him*.'

Drake lit another cigarette. 'Ah,' he said, 'the plot thickens.'

Avalon said, 'Then it is your opinion that that had something to do with the suicide.'

Servais looked harassed. 'It is more than my opinion, sir. I *know* it had something to do with the suicide.'

'Would you tell us the details?' asked Avalon, unbending just slightly from his usual stiff posture as though to convert his question into a courtly invitation.

Servais hesitated, then said, 'I remind you that you have promised me all is confidential. Mary – Madame Kaufman and my partner were married for seven years and it seemed a comfortable marriage, but who can tell in affairs of this sort?

'There was another man. He is older than Howard and to my eyes not as good-looking – but again, who can tell in affairs of this sort? What she found in him is not likely to be there on the surface, for all to see.'

Halsted said, 'How did your partner take *that*?'

Servais looked up and flushed distinctly. 'He never knew. Surely, you are not of the opinion that I told him this? I am not the type, I assure you. It is not for me to interfere between husband and wife. And frankly, if I had told Howard, he would not have believed me. It is more likely he would have attempted to strike me. And then what was I to do? Present proof? Was I to arrange matters so as to have them caught under conditions that could not be mistaken? No, I said nothing.'

'And he really didn't know?' asked Avalon, clearly embarrassed.

'He did not. It had not been going on long. The pair were excessively cautious. The husband was blindly devoted. What can I say?'

'The husband is always the last to know,' said Gonzalo sententiously.

Drake said, 'If the affair was so well hidden, how did you find out, Mr Servais?'

'Purest accident, I assure you,' said Servais. 'An incredible stroke of misfortune for her, in a way. I had a date for the evening. I did not know the girl well and it did not, after all, work out. I was anxious to be rid of her, but first – what would you have, it would not be gentlemanly to abandon her – I took her home in an odd corner of the city. And, having said good-bye in a most perfunctory manner, I went into a nearby diner to have a cup of coffee and recover somewhat. And there I saw Mary Kaufman and a man.

'Alas, it jumped to the eye. It was late; her husband, I remembered at once, was out of town, her attitude towards the man – Accept my assurances that there is a way a woman has of looking at a man that is completely unmistakable, and I saw it then. And if I were at all unsure, the expression on her face, when she looked up and saw me frozen in surprise, gave it all away.

'I left at once, of course, with no greeting of any kind, but the damage was done. She called me the next day, in agony of mind, the fool, fearful that I would carry stories to her husband, and gave me a totally unconvincing explanation. I assured her that it was a matter in which I did not interest myself in the least, that it was something so unimportant that I had already forgotten it. I am glad, however, I did not have to face the man. Him, I would have knocked down.'

Drake said, 'Did you know the man?'

'Slightly,' said Servais. 'He moved in our circles in a very distant way. I knew his name; I could recognize him. It didn't matter, for I never saw him after that. He was wise to stay away.'

Avalon said, 'But why did she commit suicide? Was she afraid her husband would find out?'

'Is one ever afraid of that in such a case?' demanded Servais, with a slight lifting of his lip. 'And if she were, surely she would end the affair. No, no, it was something far more common than that. Something inevitable. In such an affair, gentlemen, there are strains and risks which are great and which actually add an element of romance. I am not entirely unaware of such things, I assure you.

'But the romance does not continue forever, whatever the story books may say, and it is bound to fade for one faster than for the other. Well then, it faded for the man in this case before it did for the woman, and the man took the kind of action one sometimes does in such affairs. He left – went – disappeared. And so the lady killed herself.'

Trumbull drew himself up and frowned ferociously. 'For what reason?'

'I assume for that reason, sir. It has been known to happen. I did not know of the man's disappearance, you understand, till afterwards. After the suicide I went in search of him, feeling he was in some way responsible, and rather promising myself to relieve my feelings by bloodying his nose – I have a strong affection for my partner, you understand, and I felt his sufferings – but I discovered the fine lover had left two weeks before and left no forwarding address. He had no family and it was easy for him to leave, that blackguard. I could have tracked him down, I suppose, but my feelings were not strong enough to push me that far. And yet, I feel the guilt –'

'What guilt?' asked Avalon.

'It occurred to me that when I surprised them – quite unintentionally, of course – the element of risk to the man became unacceptably high. He knew I knew him. He may have felt that sooner or later it would come out and he did not wish to await results. If I had not stumbled into that diner they might still be together, she might still be alive, who knows?'

Rubin said, 'That is far-fetched, Jean. You can't deal rationally with the ifs of history. But I have a thought –'

'Yes, Manny?'

'After the suicide your partner was very quiet, nothing was important to him. I think you said that. But now he's quarrelling with you violently, though he has never done that before, I gather. Something may have happened in addition to the suicide. Perhaps *now* he has discovered his wife's infidelity and the thought drives him mad.'

Servais shook his head. 'No, no. If you think I have told him, you are quite wrong. I admit I think of telling him now and then. It is difficult to see him, my dear friend, wasting away over a woman who, after all, was not worthy of him. It is not proper to pine away for one who was not faithful to him in life. Ought I not tell him this? Frequently, it seems to me that I should and even must. He will face the truth and begin life anew. But then I think and even *know* that he will not believe me, that our friendship will be broken, and he will be worse off than before.'

Rubin said, 'You don't understand me. Might it not be that someone *else* has told him? How do you know you were the only one who knew?'

Servais seemed a bit startled. He considered it and said, 'No. He would, in that case, certainly have told me the news. And I assure you, he would have told it to me with the highest degree of indignation and informed me that he at once attempted to strike the villain who would so malign his dead angel.'

'Not,' said Rubin, 'if he had been told that *you* were his wife's lover. Even if he refused to believe it, even if he beat the informant to the ground, could he tell *you* the tale under such circumstances And could he be entirely certain? Would he not find it impossible to avoid picking fights with you in such a case?'

Servais seemed still more startled. He said slowly, 'It was, of course, not I. No one could possibly have thought so. Howard's wife did not in the least appeal to me, you understand.' He looked up and said fiercely, 'You must accept the fact that I am telling you the truth about this. It was *not* I, and I will *not* be suspected. If anyone had said it was I, it could only be out of deliberate malice.

'Maybe it was,' said Rubin. 'Might it not be the real lover who would make the accusation – out of fear you would give him away? By getting in his story first –'

'Why should he do this? He is away. No one suspects him. No one pursues him.'

'He might not know that,' said Rubin.

'Pardon me.' Henry's voice sounded softly from the direction of the sideboard. 'May I ask a question?'

'Certainly,' said Rubin, and the odd silence fell that always did when the quiet waiter, whose presence rarely obtruded on the festivities, made himself heard.

Servais looked startled, but his politeness held. He said, 'Can I do anything for you, waiter?'

Henry said, 'I'm not sure, sir, that I quite understand the nature of the quarrel between yourself and your partner. Surely there must have been decisions of enormous complexity to make as far as the technical details of the colony were concerned.'

'You don't know even a small part of it,' said Servais indulgently.

'Did your partner and you quarrel over all those details, sir?'

'N-no,' said Servais. 'We did not quarrel. There were discussions, of course. It is useless to believe that two men, each with a strong will and pronounced opinions, will agree everywhere, or even anywhere, but it all worked out reasonably. We discussed, and eventually we came to some conclusion. Sometimes I had the better of it, sometimes he, sometimes neither or both.'

'But then,' said Henry, 'there was this one argument over the actual location of the colony, over the crater, and there it was all different. He attacked even the name of the crater fiercely and, in this one case, left no room for the slightest compromise.'

'No room at all. And you are right. Only in this one case.'

Henry said, 'Then I am to understand that at this time, when Mr Rubin suspects that your partner is being irritated by suspicion of you, he was completely reasonable and civilized over every delicate point of lunar engineering and was wildly and unbearably stubborn only over the single matter of the site – over whether Copernicus or the other crater was to be the place where the colony was to be built?'

'Yes,' said Servais with satisfaction. 'That is precisely how it was and I see the point you are making, waiter. It is quite unbelievable to suppose that he would quarrel with me over the site out of ill humour over suspicion that I have placed horns on him, when he does not quarrel with me on any other point. Assuredly, he does not suspect me of ill dealing. I thank you, waiter.'

Henry said, 'May I go a little further, sir?'

'By all means,' said Servais.

'Earlier in the evening,' said Henry, 'Mr Rubin was kind enough to ask my opinion over the techniques of his profession. There was the question of deliberate omission of details by witnesses.'

'Yes,' said Servais, 'I remember the discussion. But I did not deliberately omit any details.'

'You did not mention the name of Mrs Kaufman's lover.'

Servais frowned. 'I suppose I didn't, but it wasn't deliberate. It is entirely irrelevant.'

'Perhaps it is,' said Henry, 'unless his name happens to be Bailey.'

Servais froze in his chair. Then he said anxiously, 'I don't recall mentioning it. Sacred – I see your point again, waiter. If it slips out now without my remembering it, it is possible to suppose that, without quite realizing it, I may have said something that led Howard to suspect –'

Gonzalo said, 'Hey, Henry, I don't recall Jean giving us any name.'

'Nor I,' said Henry. 'You did not give the name, sir.'

Servais relaxed slowly and then said, frowning, 'Then how did you know? Do you know these people?'

Henry shook his head. 'No, sir, it was just a notion of mine that arose out of the story you told. From your reaction, I take it his name *is* Bailey?'

'Martin Bailey,' said Servais. 'How did you know?'

'The name of the crater in which you wished to place the site is Bahyee; the name of the city would be Camp Bahyee.'

'Yes.'

'But that is the French pronunciation of the name of a French astronomer. How is it spelled?'

Servais said, 'B-a-i-l-l-y. Great God, *Bailly*!'

Henry said, 'In English pronunciation, pronounced like the not uncommon surname Bailey. I am quite certain American astronomers use the English pronunciation, and that Mr Kaufman does too. You hid that piece of information from us, Mr Servais, because you never thought of the crater in any other way than Bahyee. Even looking at it, you would hear the French sound in your mind and make no connection with Bailey, the American surname.'

Servais said, 'But I still don't understand.'

'Would your partner wish to publicize the name, and place the site of a lunar colony in Bailly? Would he want to have the colony called Camp Bailly, after what a Bailey has done to him?'

'But he didn't *know* what Bailey had done to him,' said Servais.

'How do you know that? Because there's an old saw that says the husband is always the last to know? How else can you explain his utterly irrational opposition to this one point, even his insistence that the name itself is horrible? It is too much to expect of coincidence.'

'But if he knew – if he knew – he didn't tell me. Why fight over it? Why not explain?'

'I assume,' said Henry, 'he didn't know you knew. Would he shame his dead wife by telling you?'

Servais clutched at his hair. 'I never thought – Not for a moment.'

'There is more to think,' said Henry sadly.

'What?'

'One might wonder how Bailey came to disappear, if your partner knew the tale. One might wonder if Bailey is alive. Is it not conceivable that Mr Kaufman, placing all the blame on the other man, confronted his wife to tell her he had driven her lover away, even killed him, perhaps, and asked her to come back to him – and the response was suicide?'

'No,' said Servais. 'That is impossible.'

'It would be best, then, to find Mr Bailey and make sure he is alive. It is the one way of proving your partner's innocence. It may be a task for the police.'

Servais had turned very pale. 'I can't go to the police with a story like that.'

'If you do not,' said Henry, 'it may be that your partner, brooding over what he has done – if indeed he has done it – will eventually take justice into his own hands.'

'You mean kill himself?' whispered Servais. 'Is that the choice you are facing me with: accuse him to the police or wait for him to kill himself?'

'Or both,' said Henry. 'Life is cruel.'

I have also been writing mystery stories for the junior high school age level at the instigation, originally, of an editor at Boys' Life. *Naturally, I made a junior high school boy the detective, and when I had written five of them, I put them together as a collection entitled* The Key Word and Other Mysteries *(Book 190). It was published by Walker and Company in 1977.*

The story I choose for inclusion here was rejected by Boy's Life *but was snapped up at once by EQMM. I can't explain these things.*

'The Thirteenth Day of Christmas' *(1977)*

This was one year we were *glad* when Christmas Day was over.

It had been a grim Christmas Eve and I had stayed awake as long as I could, half listening for bombs. And Mom and I stayed up until midnight on Christmas *Day*, too. Then Dad called and said, 'Okay, it's over. Nothing's happened. I'll be home as soon as I can.'

Mom and I danced around as if Santa Claus had just come and then, after about an hour, Dad came home and I went to bed and slept fine.

You see, it's special in our house. Dad's a detective on the force and these days, with terrorists and bombings, it can get pretty hairy. So, when on December 20, warnings reached headquarters that there would be a Christmas Day bombing at the Soviet offices in the United Nations, it had to be taken seriously.

The entire force was put on the alert and the FBI came in, too. The Soviets had their own security, I guess, but none of it satisfied Dad.

The day before Christmas was the worst.

'If someone is crazy enough to want to plant a bomb and if he's not too worried about getting caught afterwards, he's likely to be able to do it no matter what precautions we take.' Dad's voice had a grimness we rarely heard.

'I suppose there's no way of knowing who it is,' Mom said.

Dad shook his head. 'Letters from newspapers pasted on paper; no fingerprints; only smudges. Common stuff we can't trace and a threat that it would be the only warning we'd get. What can we do?'

'Well, it must be someone who doesn't like the Russians, I guess,' Mom said.

Dad said, 'That doesn't narrow it much. Of course, the Soviets say it's a Zionist threat, and we've got to keep an eye on the Jewish Defence League.'

'Gee, Dad,' I said. 'That doesn't make much sense. The Jewish people wouldn't pick Christmas to do it, would they? It doesn't mean anything to them; and it doesn't mean anything to the Soviet Union, either. They're officially atheistic.'

'You can't reason that out with the Russians,' Dad said. 'Now why don't you turn in, because tomorrow may be a bad day all round, Christmas or not.'

Then he left. He was out all Christmas, and it was pretty rotten. We didn't even open any presents – just sat listening to the radio, which was tuned to the news station.

Then at midnight when Dad called and nothing had happened, we could breathe again, but I still forgot to open my presents.

That didn't come till the morning of the twenty-sixth. We made *that* day Christmas. Dad had a day off and Mom baked the turkey a day late. It wasn't till after dinner that we talked about it at all.

Mom said, 'I suppose the person, whoever it was, couldn't find any way of planting the bomb once the Department drew the security strings tight.'

Dad smiled, as if he appreciated Mom's loyalty. 'I don't think you can make security that tight,' he said, 'but what's the difference? There was no bomb. Maybe it was a bluff. After all, it did disrupt the city a bit and it gave the Soviet people at the United Nations some sleepless nights, I'll bet. That might have been almost as good for the bomber as letting the bomb go off.'

'If he couldn't do it on Christmas,' I said, 'maybe he'll do it another time. Maybe he just said Christmas to get everyone keyed up and then, after they relax, he'll . . .'

Dad gave me one of his little pushes on the side of my head. 'You're a cheerful one, Larry . . . No, I don't think so. Real bombers value the sense of power. When they say something is going up at a certain time, it's got to be that time or it's no fun for them.'

I was still suspicious, but the days passed and there was no bombing and the Department gradually went back to normal. The FBI left and even the Soviet people seemed to forget about it, according to Dad.

On January 2, the Christmas–New Year's vacation was over and I went back to school. We started rehearsing our Christmas pageant. We didn't call it that, of course, because we're not supposed to have religious celebrations at school, what with the separation of church and state. We just made an elaborate show out of the song 'The Twelve Days of Christmas', which doesn't have any religion to it – just presents.

There were twelve of us kids, each one singing a particular line every time it came up and then coming in all together on the partridge in a pear tree. I was number five, singing 'five gold rings' because I was still a boy soprano and I could hit that high note pretty nicely, if I do say so myself.

Some kids didn't know why Christmas had twelve days, but I explained that if we count Christmas Day as one, the twelfth day after is January 6, when the Three Wise Men arrived with gifts for the Christ child. Naturally, it was on January 6 that we put on the show in the auditorium, with as many parents there as wanted to come.

Dad got a few hours off and was sitting in the audience

with Mom. I could see him getting set to hear his son's high note for the last time because by next year my voice would have changed.

Did you ever get an idea in the middle of a stage show and have to continue, no matter what?

We were only on the second day with its 'two turtle-doves' when I thought, 'Oh my, it's the *thirteenth* day of Christmas.' The whole world was shaking about me and I couldn't do a thing but stay on the stage and sing about five gold rings.

I didn't think they'd ever get to those stupid 'twelve drummers drumming'. It was like having itching powder on instead of underwear. I couldn't stand still. Then, when the last note was out, while they were still applauding, I broke away, went jumping down the steps from the plat-form and up the aisle calling, 'Dad!'

He looked startled, but I grabbed him, and I think I was babbling so fast, he could hardly understand.

I said, 'Dad, Christmas isn't the same day everywhere. It could be one of the Soviet's own people. They're officially atheist, but maybe one of them is religious and he wants to place the bomb for that reason. Only he would be a member of the Russian Orthodox Church. They don't go by our calendar.'

'What?' said Dad, looking as if he didn't understand a word I was saying.

'It's *so*, Dad. I read about it. The Russian Orthodox Church is still on the Julian calendar, which the West gave up for the Gregorian calendar centuries ago. The Julian calendar is thirteen days behind ours. The Orthodox Christmas is on *their* December 25, which is *our* January 7. It's *tomorrow*.'

He didn't believe me just like that. He looked it up in the almanac; then he called up someone in the Department who was Russian Orthodox.

He was able to get the Department moving again. They talked to the Soviets, and once the Soviets stopped talking about Zionists and looked at themselves, they got the man.

I don't know what they did with him, but there was no bombing on the thirteenth day of Christmas, either.

The Department wanted to give me a new bicycle for Christmas after that, but I turned it down. I was just doing my duty.

Which brings me to my favourite book of all two hundred I have written so far.

In April 1975, Larry Ashmead, then at Doubleday, suggested I attend the seventy-fifth annual meeting of the American Booksellers Association (ABA), which was to be held in New York over the Memorial Day weekend. I said I had to be there in any case since I had agreed to autograph books there for Fawcett Books.

Larry said he wanted me to attend all the sessions so that I might gather background information for a mystery he wanted me to write that was to be entitled Murder at the ABA.

I attended, and when it was over, Larry asked me if I could write the book. I said, yes, I already had a plot in mind.

'Good,' said Larry. 'We need it by next year's convention.'

'You'll have the manuscript by then,' I said.

'Not the manuscript,' he said. 'The finished book.'

I said, horrified, 'Then when do you want the manuscript?'

'By August.'

'But it's June 1 already.'

'By early August, if possible.'

Fortunately, the book went with incredible ease and rapidity and I finished it on August 3. It was published in 1976 as Book 172.

One of the reasons I loved the book was this: Though it was told in the first person by my character Darius Just (based distantly on my good friend Harlan Ellison), I introduced myself as a character in the third person, de-

*scribing myself quite accurately, I think, through the not
entirely sympathetic eyes of Darius (pronounced 'duh-RY-
us').*

Here is how I enter the story:

from MURDER AT THE ABA *(1976)*

I found myself a table that had not yet collected anyone
at any of its four chairs and sat down with a little sigh.
If I were left alone, if I were allowed to eat in peace, I
might yet brush away all the implacably humiliating events
of the day. Some people dissolve their woes in wine; I'm
quite likely to assuage my sadness in spiced sausage.

It wasn't to be. Nothing broke right that Sunday. I
hadn't completed my first mouthful when a cheerful voice
boomed out, 'Good old Darius Dust. Mind if I join you?'

I've got to explain about the name Darius. It was wished
upon me by a self-educated father. You can't trust self-
education – it goes too far, gets too bloated, knows no
moderation. My father's name was Alexander and he knew
that Alexander the Great had defeated Darius III of
Persia, and that was it. Perhaps he had the feeling that
even though he would see to it I had a thorough education
(he did) I would never be able to surpass *him*. Since he
was five feet ten, I guess I never did.

My mother, a very little woman whose genes, in that
respect, I inherited, went along with it. She had no choice.
No one ever had a choice within hearing distance of my
father.

To be the smallest kid in class is not exactly a passport
to happiness. To be any kid named Darius, surrounded by
Jims, Toms, and Bills, produces little joy. To be the
smallest kid in class and named Darius, too, is something
like sitting under a neon sign that flashes on and off with
the message, 'Kick me!'

It wasn't until I was in college that my name stopped
serving as an insult to everyone my age I ever met, an

insult to be personally avenged at once.

I hated that name at first, but held on to it with a wretched obstinacy. No one was going to force me out of it. By the time I acquired a coterie of friends old enough and sophisticated enough to be able to pronounce it and feel at home with it, I began to like it.

Correct pronunciation helps. Even among relatively sophisticated adults, it isn't a familiar name. Outside Herodotus, one is only likely to come across it in an old chestnut of a poem called 'Darius Green and His Flying Machine', by John Townsend Trowbridge, written a little over a hundred years ago. I hated that poem. Naturally the only Darius in popular literature was served up as comic relief.

I'm not sure what proportion of the general population knows how to pronounce the name, but even in the rarefied circles within which I have my being (God help me), I hear it more often mispronounced than pronounced. The first impulse is to pronounce the name so as to rhyme it with 'various', but that's not right. The accent is on the second syllable, with a long *i*, so that it rhymes with 'pious' and 'bias'.

That has its disadvantages, too, for once you learn to say Darius properly, you are bound to notice that it sounds something like 'dry as'. Then, if you have a particularly feeble mind, it occurs to you that if you change Just to Dust, the name becomes 'Dry as Dust', which is not exactly ideal for a writer.

Actually, only one person I know has the kind of perverted sense of humour that thinks this is funny. When I heard someone say 'Good old Dry as Dust. Mind if I join you?' I knew, without looking up, that it was Isaac Asimov. Word play is his idea of the empyrean heights of wisdom.

I didn't let it bother me. I just said, 'Hello, Ikey. Of course I mind having you join me, but sit down anyway.'

As it happens, there's nothing that Asimov can possibly call me that I would hate as much as he hates being called key. So one of these times, when it finally dawns on him that every 'Dry as Dust' will elicit an 'Ikey' without fail, he will quit. Anyone else would quit after two tries. I give Asimov twenty years.

Since this book is rather in the nature of a collaboration, with his name on it as sole author, however, I had better be particular about describing him.

He's five feet nine inches tall, rather fat, and more than rather grinning. He wears his hair long, and it's clear he does it out of laziness rather than out of any desire for a splendid leonine effect (which is how I've heard him describe it), because it never seems more than sketchily combed. The hair is somewhat grey and the sideburns, which run down to the angle of his jaw and which have been aptly described as looking like Brillo, are nearly white. He's got a bulbous nose, blue eyes, a bolo tic, and glasses with black frames. He has to remove his glasses to read or eat because he won't admit his age long enough to get bifocals.

He's like me in some respects. He doesn't smoke or drink any more than I do. Like me, he also likes to eat, but I don't get fat on it and he does. He thinks the difference is metabolism, which is funny for a guy who claims to be a biochemist. I know the difference is exercise. I work out in a gym nearly every day – but once Asimov has managed to lift himself out of bed in the morning, that is his exercise for the day. Except for typing, of course. His fingers are in good shape.

He had his plate heaped much higher than mine, but he couldn't stop himself from glancing anxiously at what I had retrieved, as though I might perhaps have found a goodie he had overlooked.

'What's the score now, Isaac?' No use calling him Ikey except under provocation.

He knew what I meant. 'A hundred sixty-three at the moment,' he said with his mouth full, 'but who's counting?'

'You are,' I said.

He swallowed and said in an aggrieved tone, 'I *have* t
That's my shtick. Everyone wants to know how ma
books I've published, and if I don't tell them they're di
appointed. What's more, if they ask me the question
two successive months and the figure doesn't go up by
least one, they feel cheated. Look, there's no need for yc
to be resentful. You've had a movie made out of one
your books. I haven't.'

I winced. The matter had been profitable, but it w
easily the worst movie ever made by the worst set
idiots you could find even in Hollywood. I kept hopir
no one would see it.

A hundred sixty-three books is no record, of cours
but I never met anyone for whom writing is as painless
it is for Asimov. And he's aware of it, and his pleasu
over it can be rather disgusting to see.

Once he crossed the room at a book-and-auth
luncheon, and someone muttered in my ear, 'There go
Asimov pushing his self-assurance ahead of him like
wheelbarrow.' (The same might be said of his abdome
of course.) Someone else once said that Asimov walke
as though he expected the air to part in front of him.

Actually, my own theory is that he lives so much of t
time inside his own head that he is unaware of the outsi
world. So when he seems to be utterly self-possessed, it
just that he's unaware that there's anything to be disturbe
about.

I said to him, 'What are you doing here, Isaac? Wl
aren't you home writing a book?'

He groaned. 'In a way that's what I'm doing her
Doubleday wants me to write a mystery novel entitle
Murder at the ABA. I don't know what I was thinking
when I signed up.'

'Why did you sign?'

'What did you expect me to do? I've signed so mar
contracts, it's a reflex action with me. And they want
completed manuscript by August. I've got three montl
at the outside.'

'That's all right. It will only take you a weekend, won't it?'

Asimov made himself a cold-cut sandwich on a giant scale and demolished half of it at a bite. With most of the bite gone, he said, 'The worst of all my literary troubles is the fact that I'm not allowed to have any literary troubles. If you said you had to do a book faster than you could do it, everyone would soak your jacket with sympathetic tears. When I say it, I get cheap jokes. The same cheap joke every time, I might add.'

This from a man who thinks Darius Dust is epigrammatic wit.

I didn't break down in tears. 'Just the same you'll do it. You've done mysteries before, haven't you?'

It was a pretty safe assumption. The man has written on every subject imaginable and if ever anyone didn't look it, it's Asimov. He looks stupid at first sight. And when you hear him tell endless jokes, hug every girl in reach, and never by any chance say anything thoughtful, you're convinced of it. It take considerable time before you find out that the man is so secure in his intelligence that he never troubles to display it.

Which annoys the hell out of me, actually.

'Of course I've done mysteries before,' he said indignantly. 'I've written straight mysteries and science fiction mysteries; novels and short stories; for adults, for teenagers, and for grade-schoolers.'

'Then what's the trouble?'

'I've got to give this local colour. I've got to hang around here for four days and see what's happening.'

'You're doing it, aren't you?'

'But I *can't* see what's happening. In my whole life, I've never seen anything that goes on around me.'

'Then how have you written a hundred sixty-three books.'

'*Published*,' he said. 'I have eleven in press . . . Because my books are without description. I have an unornamented style.'

'In that case, get someone to help you.'

It was odd that I should say that, for at that moment I couldn't possibly have supposed that matters would end up in such a way that *I* would help him.

After all, he *did* manage to do the book in time. You're reading it – *Murder at the ABA*, by Isaac Asimov.

It's just that it's *my* story and *I* am first-person while he is third-person. And since I've left the writing entirely in his hands and don't entirely trust him, the agreement is that I am to be allowed to add any comments of my own (within reason) in the form of footnotes where I consider him too far off base.*

He had finished his platter, and by that time the room was considerably more crowded than it had been when we had entered. It was quite hopeless to expect to see Giles in that mess. The noise level had become uncomfortable and the filth of cigarette smoke hung in the air. There was still time to leave, and then Asimov would have had to make up his own story – but I didn't budge because I hadn't had my coffee yet. There was always something to prevent the evasion of fate.

I said, 'Do you want some coffee, Isaac?'

'Sure, but let me go get it. I need the exercise.'

That wasn't it at all, of course. He came back with coffee for both of us and five assorted cookies for himself. At least he didn't offer me any of them.

---

* For instance, I can point out that while Asimov is sticking to the outline, he's dramatizing me into total distortion. I am five feet five and not five feet two. The subtle (or not so subtle) saturation of the story with my supposed pygmy complex is just designed to make him shine by contrast. — *D. J.*

Just is five feet five if you count his platform shoes! I'm not supposed to be literal here anyway. This is a work of fiction and I will take any liberties I choose with the facts. And as for making myself shine, I ask anyone who knows me to read these last few pages, in which I figure, and testify that I am sticking to Just's ridiculous attitudes *vis-à-vis* myself at some considerable cost to my self-respect. — *I. A.*

He dipped the chocolate-covered one in the coffee, transferred it expertly to his mouth without losing a drop, and said, 'And what are you doing here, Darius? You don't look particularly ecstatic.'

'I've no reason to look ecstatic,' I said. 'I've had a hell of a day and I don't intend to go into details.'

'Considering that you have no family responsibilities at all and write only one book every three years, what can possibly give you a hell of a day?'

I could almost believe he was serious in that question, but I ignored it anyway and said, 'You haven't by any chance seen Giles Devore at the convention?'

'Yes, I have.'

I was astonished. I was not expecting that answer. 'In here?'

'No, at the registration booth. He's autographing books tomorrow morning. At the same time as I, in fact.'

'I know he's autographing books,' I said. I swear I said it in the flattest possible way, without any hint of hidden meanings. In fact, I was cooling down and – who knows? – everything might have come to nothing, when Asimov stirred up my resentment against Giles for no reason I could see except to amuse himself, and laid *his* flagstone.

His blue eyes glittered and his eyebrows lifted and fell rapidly. (For someone who claims to see nothing of the world outside himself, he can have an unerring touch for the sore spot on the soul.)

He said, 'I'm glad he's your protégé and not mine. I don't know about you, but I would find it sickening to have a protégé zoom past me.'

'He's not my protégé,' I said.

'Listen, that first book of his was written out of your vest pocket. Everyone knows it – and the more fool, you.'

'Why? For helping?'

'No, of course not. For expecting gratitude.'

I shrugged but, inside, where he couldn't see, I burned. Damn it, I *had* expected gratitude, and whether that made me a fool or not, the lack of it made me furious.

I said, lying through my teeth, 'I never expected anything.'

But Asimov's eyes were no longer on me. They were straining across the room and I didn't have to follow them to know he was looking at a girl. I forgot to say that despite his general inability to see anything in the outside world, he has an odd capacity to see every girl within two hundred feet.

PART 15

Autobiography

The longer I kept writing books, and the more books I published, the more the publishers were willing to let me do as I pleased, even when what I pleased was unorthodox.

It has always pleased me to talk about myself, and little by little I let that creep into my books – and my publishers permitted it.

To begin with, my F & SF essays grew more and more highly personal, and eventually I took to beginning each with an autobiographical essay. Then I began to be highly personal in my introductions to stories in the anthologies I edited, then in the collections of my own stories.

Inevitably, I thought of doing a collection of my early stories against an autobiographical background of my life in those years. Doubleday published it as The Early Asimov *(Book 125) in 1972.*

When that did well, I was simply confirmed in this tendency of mine and had Doubleday publish Before the Golden Age *(Book 151) in 1974. This was a long book of nearly half a million words in which I anthologized my favourite stories from the 1930s against an autobiographical background of my life before I became a writer.*

And, just to show you that this tendency towards auto-biography is no recent phenomenon, let me quote a passage from Before the Golden Age, *in which I managed to find and reprint my* first *published production – and it was auto-biographical.*

from BEFORE THE GOLDEN AGE *(1974)*

In February 1934, I entered 'sixth term' at Boys' High. As a startling innovation, the school offered a special course in creative writing for those who chose to take it, and I jumped at the chance. I had been writing, on and off, ever since I had worked on the Greenville Chums. I don't remember any of the details at all, except that I remember being occasionally driven to attempt to write poetry.

Now there seemed a chance for me to demonstrate my literary prowess. (Somehow I saw the class only as a chance to shine. It never occurred to me that I might learn something. I felt I already *knew* how to write.)

The result was a fiasco. Surely few young men have had so marvellous a chance to make fools of themselves and then took advantage of the chance as liberally as I did. Everything I wrote was laughable, and it was all laughed at thoroughly, both by the teacher and by the other students.

I mentioned this in *The Early Asimov* and mentioned further that the one useful result of the course was that I wrote a humorous essay entitled 'Little Brothers', which was published in the Boys' High School literary semi-annual.

Until I mentioned the essay, I had never thought of it particularly, but once *The Early Asimov* appeared, I began to wonder if I ought to try to get a copy. In February 1973, I gave a talk to a group of librarians from the New York metropolitan area, and attending was the present librarian of Boys' High School. When she introduced herself, I asked at once if there was any chance she might perhaps locate a copy of the literary semi-annual in some of the dusty storage bins of the school.

In June 1973, she succeeded, and sent me a copy. This book had already been put together but was still in an early stage of production, so I could make the necessary revision.

When the magazine came – its name was *Boy's High Recorder*, incidentally, and the issue was spring 1934 – I turned to 'Little Brothers' at once and read it eagerly. I was sure I would find in it the clear signs of writing talent.

Alas, I didn't. It sounds exactly as any essay would that was written by a precocious fourteen-year-old. How disappointing! And yet, in order to keep the record complete and to prevent myself from receiving a horde of letters demanding to see it (presumably in order that all my readers have the same chance to laugh at me as the members of the damnable writing class did), here it is:

Little Brothers

My mission in life right now is to express the venomous feelings that we 'big' brothers have for the bane of our lives, the 'little' brothers.

When I first received the news that I had a little brother, on July 25, 1929, I felt slightly uncomfortable. As for myself, I knew nothing about brothers, but many of my friends had related at great length the inconveniences (to say the least) of attending babies.

On August 3, my little brother came home. All I could see was a little bundle of pink flesh, with apparently no ability to do the slightest mischief.

That night, I suddenly sprang out of bed with goose flesh all over me and my hair on end. I had heard a shriek apparently made by no earthly being. In response to my frenzied questions, my mother informed me in a commonplace manner that it was just the baby. Just the baby! I was almost knocked unconscious. A puny, nine-pound baby, ten days old, to make such a scream! Why, I was convinced that no less than three men together could have strained their vocal cords to such an extent.

But this was only the beginning. When he began teething, the real torture came. I did not sleep a wink for two months. I only existed by sleeping with my eyes open in school.

And still it wasn't all. Easter was coming, and I was feeling joyous at the prospect of a trip to Rhode Island, when that kid brother of mine got the measles and everything went up in smoke.

Soon he reached the age when his teeth had cut, and I hoped to obtain a little peace, but no, that could not be. I had yet to learn that when a child learns to walk, and talk baby-language, he is rather more of an inconvenience than a cyclone, with a hurricane thrown in for good measure.

His favourite recreation was that of falling down the stairs, hitting each step with a resounding bump. This occurred on the average of once every other minute and always brought on a scolding from my mother (not for him, but for me for not taking care of him).

This 'taking care' of him is not as easy as it sounds. The baby usually shows his devotion by grabbing generous fistfuls of hair and pulling with a strength that you would never have thought possible in a one-year-old. When, after a few minutes of excruciating torture, you persuade him to let go, he seeks diversion in hitting your shins with a heavy piece of iron, preferably a sharp or pointed one.

Not only is a baby a pest when awake; it is doubly so when taking its daily nap.

This is a typical scene. I am sitting in a chair next to the carriage, deeply immersed in *The Three Musketeers*, and my little brother is apparently sleeping peacefully; but he really isn't. With an uncanny instinct, in spite of his closed eyes and inability to read, he knows exactly when I reach an exciting point and with a malicious grin selects that very moment to awake. With a groan I leave my book and rock him till my arms feel as if they will fall off any minute. By the time he does go back to sleep, I have lost interest in the famous trio and my day is ruined.

Now my little brother is four and a half years old and most of these aggravating habits have disappeared, but I feel in my bones that there is more to come. I shudder to think of the day when he'll enter school and place a new burden upon my shoulders. I feel absolutely sure that not only will I be afflicted with the homework that my hard-hearted teachers will give me, but I will also be responsible for my little brother's.

I wish I were dead!

Needless to say, this essay is completely fictional except that the dates of my little brother's birth and his arrival home are correct. Actually, my brother Stan was a model child, who gave me very little trouble. I did wheel him about in his carriage an awful lot, but that was always with a book open on the handlebar, so it didn't matter to me. I also sat by the carriage when he was sleeping, but again I invariably read – and he rarely disturbed me. What's more, he always did his own homework when it came time for that.

One final comment concerning this tendency of mine.

As the time approached for my two hundredth book to appear, Doubleday let me know they would like to do it. I explained that this was impossible since Houghton Mifflin, having done Opus 100, was sure to feel condemned to do Opus 200 as well.

Doubleday, which understands the warmth of my feeling for Houghton Mifflin (as Houghton Mifflin understands the warmth of my feeling for Doubleday), argued no further but cast about for some other project to mark this milestone.

We agreed that I would write an autobiography, a formal autobiography of all aspects of my life and not only of my literary productions. I pointed out that nothing much had ever happened to me, but they said they didn't care.

So I sat down, and between March 9 and December 31, 1977, I turned out 640,000 words of autobiography. Poor Cathleen Jordan, who is now my editor at Doubleday, turned pale when I brought in the manuscript and muttered something about how much I might have written if something ever had *happened to me. The only conclusion possible was to put it out in two volumes.*

The first volume is coming out simultaneously with this book. I wouldn't dream of putting pressure on any of my gentle readers, but if you would like to buy my autobiography and read it, you have my permission to do so.

Indeed, if this book has so fascinated you with its samplings that you feel the urge to go out and buy all two hundred books – do so with my blessings.

APPENDIX

My Second Hundred Books

NOTE All dates are those of original American publication. Where
books have been separately published and are still in print in
Britain the name of the British publisher is given, preceded by the
abbreviation Br. In all other cases the publisher given is the original
American publisher.

	TITLE	PUBLISHER	DATE
101	ABC's of Space	Walker	1969
102	Great Ideas of Science	Houghton Mifflin	1969
103	The Solar System and Back	Doubleday	1970
104	Asimov's Guide to Shakespeare, Volume 1	Doubleday	1970
105	Asimov's Guide to Shakespeare, Volume 2	Doubleday	1970
106	Constantinople	Houghton Mifflin	1970
107	ABC's of the Ocean	Walker	1970
108	Light	Follett	1970
109	The Stars in Their Courses	Br. Panther	1971
110	Where Do We Go from Here?	Br. Sphere	1971
111	What Makes the Sun Shine?	Little, Brown	1971
112	The Sensuous Dirty Old Man	Walker	1971
113	The Best New Thing	World	1971
114	Isaac Asimov's Treasury of Humor	Br. Woburn Press	1971
115	The Hugo Winners, Volume 2	Doubleday	1971
116	The Land of Canaan	Houghton Mifflin	1971
117	ABC's of the Earth	Walker	1971
118	Asimov's Biographical Encyclopedia of Science and Technology (revised)	Br. Pan	1972
119	The Left Hand of the Electron	Br. Panther	1972
120	Asimov's Guide to Science	Br. Penguin	1972
121	The Gods Themselves	Br. Gollancz	1972
122	More Words of Science	Houghton Mifflin	1972

Acknowledgments

OPUS 100

The author wishes to thank the following for permission to quote all or part of the works listed:

Abelard-Schuman Limited: *Only a Trillion. The Chemicals of Life.* Copyright 1954 by Isaac Asimov. *The Wellsprings of Life.* © 1960 by Isaac Asimov.

American Institute of Physics: 'An Uncompromising View', book review from February 1969 issue of *The Physics Teacher.* Copyright © 1968 American Association of Physics Teachers.

Analog Science Fact-Fiction: 'Thiotimoline and the Space Age'. Copyright © 1960 by Street & Smith Publications, Inc.

Astonishing Stories: 'The Calistan Menace'. Copyright 1940 by Fictioneers, Inc. Copyright © renewed 1967 by Isaac Asimov. 'Superneutron'. Copyright 1941 by Fictioneers, Inc. Copyright © renewed 1968 by Isaac Asimov.

Astounding Science Fiction: 'Liar!' Copyright 1941 by Street & Smith Publications, Inc. Copyright © renewed 1968 by Isaac Asimov. 'Runaround'. Copyright 1942 by Street & Smith Publications, Inc. 'The Dead Hand'. Copyright 1945 by Street & Smith Publications, Inc. 'The Sound of Panting'. Copyright 1955 by Street & Smith Publications, Inc.

Basic Books, Inc., Publishers: *Photosynthesis.* © 1968 by Isaac Asimov. *The Intelligent Man's Guide to Science.* © 1960 by Basic Books, Inc. *The Noble Gases.* © 1966 by Isaac Asimov.

Dell Publishing Co., Inc.: 'On Prediction' from *Future Tense*, edited by Richard Curtis. Copyright © 1968 by Richard A. Curtis.

Doubleday & Company, Inc.: *Lucky Starr and the Oceans of Venus.* Copyright © 1954 by Doubleday & Company, Inc. *Lucky Starr and the Moons of Jupiter.* Copyright © 1957 by Doubleday & Company, Inc. *Asimov's Biographical Encyclopedia of Science and Technology.* Copyright © 1964 by Isaac Asimov. *The Neutrino.* Copyright © 1966 by Isaac Asimov. *Asimov's Guide to the Bible.* Copyright © 1968 by Isaac Asimov.

Follett Publishing Company: *Galaxies.* Copyright © 1968 by Follett Publishing Company.

Galaxy Science Fiction: 'The Martian Way'. Copyright 1952 by Galaxy Publishing Corporation.

Gnome Press: *I, Robot.* Copyright 1950 by Isaac Asimov.

Houghton Mifflin Company: *Realm of Numbers.* Copyright © 1959 by Isaac Asimov. *Words of Science.* Copyright © 1959 by Isaac Asimov. *Words on the Map.* Copyright © 1962 by Isaac

OPUS 200

By Jupiter and Other Stories. Copyright © 1973 by Saturday Evening Post Company. *Of Matters Great and Small.* Copyright © 1974 by Mercury Press Inc. *The Bicentennial Man and Other Stories.* Copyright © 1976 by Random House, Inc. *More Tales of the Black Widowers.* Copyright © 1976 by Isaac Asimov. *Murder at the ABA.* Copyright © 1976 by Isaac Asimov. *The Beginning and the End.* Copyright © 1974 by Triangle Publications, Inc. *Familiar Poems Annotated.* Copyright © 1977 by Isaac Asimov.

Follett Publishing Company: *Comets and Meteors.* Text Copyright © 1972 by Isaac Asimov.. *Light* Text Copyright © 1970 by Isaac Asimov. Used by permission of Follett Publishing Co., division of Follett Corporation.

Houghton Mifflin Company: *Isaac Asimov's Treasury of Humor.* Copyright © 1971 by Isaac Asimov. *The Land of Canaan.* Copyright © 1971 by Isaac Asimov. *More Words of Science.* Copyright © 1972 by Isaac Asimov. *The Shaping of France.* Copyright © 1972 by Isaac Asimov. *Please Explain.* Copyright © 1966, 1969, 1972 by the Hearst Corporation. *Eyes on the Universe.* Copyright © 1975 by Isaac Asimov. *The Golden Door.* Copyright © 1977 by Isaac Asimov. Reprinted by permission.

David McKay Company, Inc.: *The Ends of the Earth.* Copyright © 1975 by Isaac Asimov. Reprinted by permission of the David McKay Company, Inc.

William Morrow & Company, Inc.: *Alpha Centauri, the Nearest Star.* Copyright © Isaac Asimov. Reprinted by permission of William Morrow & Company, Inc.

Mysterious Press: *Asimov's Sherlockian Limericks:* Copyright © 1978 by Isaac Asimov.

The Saturday Evening Post Company: 'The Dream'; 'Benjamin's Dream'; and 'Benjamin's Bicentennial Blast'. Copyright © 1976 by the Saturday Evening Post Company. Reprinted by permission of the Saturday Evening Post Company.

Walker and Company: *ABC's of Space.* Copyright © 1969 by Isaac Asimov. *The Sensuous Dirty Old Man.* Copyright © 1971 by Isaac Asimov. *How Did We Find Out About Numbers?* Copyright © 1973 by Isaac Asimov. *How Did We Find Out About Germs?* Copyright © 1974 by Isaac Asimov. *How Did We Find Out About Comets?* Copyright © 1975 by Isaac Asimov. *Lecherous Limericks.* Copyright © 1975 by Isaac Asimov. *More Lecherous Limericks.* Copyright © 1976 by Isaac Asimov. *Still More Lecherous Limericks.* Copyright © 1977 by Isaac Asimov. 'The Thirteenth Day of Christmas'. First published in *Ellery Queen's Mystery Magazine* and reprinted from *The Key Word and Other Mysteries* by Isaac Asimov, published by Walker and Company, 1977. Copyright © 1977 by Isaac Asimov.